THE SHORT STORY

Classic & Contemporary

EDITED BY R. W. LID

J. B. LIPPINCOTT COMPANY

Philadelphia • New York • Toronto

Dedicated to the five who talked

THE LIPPINCOTT COLLEGE ENGLISH SERIES
Under the Editorship of
Albert J. Guerard, Stanford University

Third Printing

Library of Congress Catalog Card Number: 66-19069
Printed in the United States of America

Preface to the Teacher

IN ONE of the Oz books there is a group called the "flutterbudgets," little people who go about asking, "What might happen if . . . ?"

Question: What might happen if a teacher were given the opportunity to put together an ideal anthology of shorter fiction for college students?

Answer: . . . Well, in my case at least, that ideal anthology would not differ substantially from the book you see here. It would simply be thicker—thousands and thousands of pages thicker; for anyone who sets out to edit an anthology of shorter fiction is faced with an embarrassment of riches.

To compromise with the ideal in this instance is to be forced to reveal taste and some prejudice and also various assumptions—about what constitutes the good, and also the great, in fiction; about form and language and their arrangements in fiction; about the nature of the teaching of fiction.

The stories included in this collection were selected first of all because they are examples of good, and sometimes great, shorter fiction. I have not included any mediocre story because it teaches well or provides a means of illuminating other, better stories. All of the stories in *The Short Story: Classic and Contemporary* are in my eyes first-rate stories. Some of them are widely known. Some have seldom been anthologized; a few, never. I have included works in translation because it seems wrong to me to exclude such stories, which number among them some of the greatest ever written, simply because of a supposed language barrier. In each case I have provided the best translation available.

The editorial apparatus of this volume consists of (1) brief introductions to ten stories, here called "contexts," since the intention in each instance has been to suggest, in four brief paragraphs, without jargon or special patois, something of the author's background, his art and his achievement, while leaving the stories intact for the teacher; (2) a series of questions for each of the ten stories; (3) an appendix which contains Nelson Algren's "A Bottle of Milk for Mother," with an extended commentary on the story by me; (4) an appendix which contains Ernest Hemingway's "Old Man at the Bridge" and the transcript of a taped discussion of the story by some students and myself. As far as I know this is the first time the transcript of an actual discussion has been included in an anthology of this kind. Neither the discussion of Hemingway nor the commentary on Algren is intended to be in any way prescriptive, though they do suggest the kinds of consideration that were involved in selecting the classics and contemporaries of shorter fiction which make up this volume.

I have enjoyed teaching these stories. I hope you do too.

January, 1966 R. W. LID

Contents

Stories in Context

THERE ARE TWO questions which can be asked about any work of fiction:

(1) Why does the author say one thing instead of another?

(2) Why does he say it in one way instead of another?

With these two questions you can approach any story in this anthology.

Fiction, then, is a far simpler matter than some of you are going to want to make it. But it is also a far more difficult matter, for to answer these two questions to any degree of satisfaction means asking a great many other questions—about the author's subject matter, about the form of the work; ultimately, about the relationship between structure and significance. And there is no easy place to begin the asking, no set of simple questions that will do the trick for you.

Nor can a teacher tell you exactly what you are supposed to have learned from reading a short story. There is no easy measure of awareness and understanding. What you discover will have to be your own discovery, for this is the only way fiction becomes meaningful.

But teachers may help you to learn how to read fiction. They can show you what questions to ask and when to ask them. Indeed, they will ask many more than they answer. When you begin to see the "why" behind their questions, you will know that you are beginning to read fiction as it should be read.

Most serious writers of shorter fiction leave a considerable body of work behind them, and all of them leave their signatures on their pages. It is impossible for the knowledgeable reader not to recognize a story by Chekhov or Faulkner or Hemingway. Some of his pleasure, and a good deal of his insight, comes from this recognition.

While there is no easy substitute for such knowledge, the brief introductions to the stories which follow are designed to provide each story with a literary context for the reader short of his having read other stories by the same author. They give, in other words, one set of clues on how to read the author at hand. Another set is given in the brief questions which follow each story.

THE AMERICAN SCENE

F. Scott Fitzgerald

Winter Dreams

LIKE THE HERO of his novel THE GREAT GATSBY, *F. Scott Fitzgerald had a "heightened sensitivity to the promises of life." This "romantic readiness," as Fitzgerald spoke of it, is reflected in his best fiction, which deals with American youth and its dreams of success.*

Dexter Green of "Winter Dreams" is one such youth. He is middle-class, ambitious, hard-working—but his dreams, which Fitzgerald invests with some of the import of the great American dream, are romantic dreams, elusive and, perhaps, illusory. Something of Dexter's personal passion can be seen in the way these dreams are embodied for him in a beautiful woman, Judy Jones, who comes early in his life to stand for all he desires.

In the particular coming together of youth, money, gentility, and beauty which makes up "Winter Dreams" we have the major configuration of Fitzgerald's fictional world. That Dexter's life ends in personal tragedy, as does that of Jay Gatsby, suggests that, while Fitzgerald shared the hopes and aspirations he ascribed to his figures, he was not blinded by their dreams. "The test of a first-rate intelligence," he once remarked, "is the ability to hold two opposed ideas in the mind at the same time, and still retain the ability to function." It could be said that a somewhat similar self-test occurs for the author in most of his fiction. That is, Fitzgerald's heightened aware-

ness that his vision was partial, incomplete, uncertain, tentative, led him to use character and fable to test a series of passionately held hypotheses about life.

One sign of the critical intelligence which lies behind Fitzgerald's narrative imagination is the author's attempt to achieve an objectivity about the events he relates. This can be seen in "Winter Dreams" in his use of a narrative voice, which dominates the story throughout, though it is perhaps most obvious in the ending of the story.

SOME OF the caddies were poor as sin and lived in one-room houses with a neurasthenic cow in the front yard, but Dexter Green's father owned the second best grocery-store in Black Bear—the best one was "The Hub," patronized by the wealthy people from Sherry Island—and Dexter caddied only for pocket-money.

In the fall when the days became crisp and gray, and the long Minnesota winter shut down like the white lid of a box, Dexter's skis moved over the snow that hid the fairways of the golf course. At these times the country gave him a feeling of profound melancholy—it offended him that the links should lie in enforced fallowness, haunted by ragged sparrows for the long season. It was dreary, too, that on the tees where the gay colors fluttered in summer there were now only the desolate sand-boxes knee-deep in crusted ice. When he crossed the hills the wind blew cold as misery, and if the sun was out he tramped with his eyes squinted up against the hard dimensionless glare.

In April the winter ceased abruptly. The snow ran down into Black Bear Lake scarcely tarrying for the early golfers to brave the season with red and black balls. Without elation, without an interval of moist glory, the cold was gone.

Dexter knew that there was something dismal about this Northern spring, just as he knew there was something gorgeous about the fall. Fall made him clinch his hands and tremble and repeat idiotic sentences to himself, and make brisk abrupt gestures of command to imaginary audiences and armies. October filled him with hope which November raised to a sort of ecstatic triumph, and in this mood the fleeting brilliant impressions of the summer at Sherry Island were ready grist to his mill. He became a golf champion and defeated Mr. T. A. Hedrick in a marvellous match played a hundred times over the fairways of his imagination, a match each detail of which he changed about untiringly—sometimes he won with almost laughable ease, sometimes he came up magnificently from behind. Again, stepping from a Pierce-Arrow automobile, like Mr. Mortimer Jones, he strolled frigidly into the lounge of the Sherry Island Golf Club—or perhaps, surrounded by an admiring crowd, he gave an exhibition of fancy diving from the spring-board of the club raft. . . . Among those who watched him in open-mouthed wonder was Mr. Mortimer Jones.

And one day it came to pass that Mr. Jones—himself and not his ghost—came up to Dexter with tears in his eyes and said that Dexter was the— —best caddy in the club, and wouldn't he decide not to quit if Mr. Jones made it worth his while, because every other— —caddy in the club lost one ball a hole for him—regularly——

"No, sir," said Dexter decisively, "I don't want to caddy any more." Then, after a pause: "I'm too old."

"You're not more than fourteen. Why the devil did you decide just this morning that you wanted to quit? You promised that next week you'd go over to the state tournament with me."

"I decided I was too old."

Dexter handed in his "A Class" badge, collected what money was due him from the caddy master, and walked home to Black Bear Village.

"The best— —caddy I ever saw," shouted Mr. Mortimer Jones over a drink that afternoon. "Never lost a ball! Willing! Intelligent! Quiet! Honest! Grateful!"

The little girl who had done this was eleven—beautifully ugly as little girls are apt to be who are destined after a few years to be inexpressibly lovely and bring no end of misery to a great number of men. The spark, however, was perceptible. There was a general ungodliness in the way her lips twisted down at the corners when she smiled, and in the—Heaven help us!—in the almost passionate quality of her eyes. Vitality is born in such women. It was utterly in evidence now, shining through her thin frame in a sort of glow.

She had come eagerly out on to the course at nine o'clock with a white linen nurse and five small new golf-clubs in a white canvas bag which the nurse was carrying. When Dexter first saw her she was standing by the caddy house, rather ill at ease and trying to conceal the fact by engaging her nurse in an obviously unnatural conversation graced by startling and irrelevant grimaces from herself.

"Well, it's certainly a nice day, Hilda," Dexter heard her say. She drew down the corners of her mouth, smiled, and glanced furtively around, her eyes in transit falling for an instant on Dexter.

Then to the nurse:

"Well, I guess there aren't very many people out here this morning, are there?"

The smile again—radiant, blatantly artificial—convincing.

"I don't know what we're supposed to do now," said the nurse, looking nowhere in particular.

"Oh, that's all right. I'll fix it up."

Dexter stood perfectly still, his mouth slightly ajar. He knew that if he moved forward a step his stare would be in her line of vision—if he moved backward he would lose his full view of her face. For a moment he had not realized how young she was. Now he remembered having seen her several times the year before—in bloomers.

Suddenly, involuntarily, he laughed, a short abrupt laugh—then, startled by himself, he turned and began to walk quickly away.

"Boy!"

Dexter stopped.

"Boy——"

Beyond question he was addressed. Not only that, but he was treated to that absurd smile, that preposterous smile—the memory of which at least a dozen men were to carry into middle age.

"Boy, do you know where the golf teacher is?"

"He's giving a lesson."

"Well, do you know where the caddy-master is?"

"He isn't here yet this morning."

"Oh." For a moment this baffled her. She stood alternately on her right and left foot.

"We'd like to get a caddy," said the nurse. "Mrs. Mortimer Jones sent us out to play golf and we don't know how without we get a caddy."

Here she was stopped by an ominous glance from Miss Jones, followed immediately by the smile.

"There aren't any caddies here except me," said Dexter to the nurse, "and I got to stay here in charge until the caddy-master gets here."

"Oh."

Miss Jones and her retinue now withdrew, and at a proper distance from Dexter became involved in a heated conversation, which was concluded by Miss Jones taking one of the clubs and hitting it on the ground with violence. For further emphasis she raised it again and was about to bring it down smartly upon the nurse's bosom, when the nurse seized the club and twisted it from her hands.

"You damn little mean old *thing!*" cried Miss Jones wildly.

Another argument ensued. Realizing that the elements of the comedy were implied in the scene, Dexter several times began to laugh, but each time restrained the laugh before it reached audibility. He could not resist the monstrous conviction that the little girl was justified in beating the nurse.

The situation was resolved by the fortuitous appearance of the caddy-master, who was appealed to immediately by the nurse.

"Miss Jones is to have a little caddy, and this one says he can't go."

"Mr. McKenna said I was to wait here till you came," said Dexter quickly.

"Well, he's here now." Miss Jones smiled cheerfully at the caddy-master. Then she dropped her bag and set off at a haughty mince toward the first tee.

"Well?" The caddy-master turned to Dexter. "What you standing there like a dummy for? Go pick up the young lady's clubs."

"I don't think I'll go out to-day," said Dexter.

"You don't——"

"I think I'll quit."

The enormity of his decision frightened him. He was a favorite caddy, and the thirty dollars a month he earned through the summer were not to be made elsewhere around the lake. But he had received a strong emotional shock, and his perturbation required a violent and immediate outlet.

It is not so simple as that, either. As so frequently would be the case in the future, Dexter was unconsciously dictated to by his winter dreams.

II

Now, of course, the quality and the seasonability of these winter dreams varied, but the stuff of them remained. They persuaded Dexter several years later to pass up a business course at the State university—his father, prospering now, would have paid his way—for the precarious advantage of attending an older and more famous university in the East, where he was bothered by his scanty funds. But do not get the impression, because his winter dreams happened to be concerned at first with musings on the rich, that there was anything merely snobbish in the boy. He wanted not association with glittering things and glittering people—he wanted the glittering things themselves. Often he reached out for the best without knowing why he wanted it—and sometimes he ran up against the mysterious denials and prohibitions in which life indulges. It is with one of those denials and not with his career as a whole that this story deals.

He made money. It was rather amazing. After college he went to the city from which Black Bear Lake draws its wealthy patrons. When he was only twenty-three and had been there not quite two years, there were already people who liked to say: "Now *there's* a boy—" All about him rich men's sons were peddling bonds precariously, or investing patrimonies precariously, or plodding through the two dozen volumes of the "George Washington Commercial Course," but Dexter borrowed a thousand dollars on his college degree and his confident mouth, and bought a partnership in a laundry.

It was a small laundry when he went into it, but Dexter made a specialty of learning how the English washed fine woolen golf-stockings without shrinking them, and within a year he was catering to the trade that wore knickerbockers. Men were insisting that their Shetland hose and sweaters go to his laundry, just as they had insisted on a caddy who could find golf-balls. A little later he was doing their wives' lingerie as well—and running five branches in different parts of the city. Before he was twenty-seven he owned the largest string of laundries in his section of the country. It was then that he sold out and went to New York. But the part of his story that concerns us goes back to the days when he was making his first big success.

When he was twenty-three Mr. Hart—one of the gray-haired men who like to say "Now there's a boy"—gave him a guest card to the Sherry Island Golf Club for a week-end. So he signed his name one day on the register, and that afternoon played golf in a foursome with Mr. Hart and Mr. Sandwood and Mr. T. A. Hedrick. He did not consider it necessary to remark that he had once carried Mr. Hart's bag over these same links, and that he knew every trap and gully with his eyes shut—but he found himself glancing at the four caddies who trailed them, trying to catch a gleam or gesture that would remind him of himself, that would lessen the gap which lay between his present and his past.

It was a curious day, slashed abruptly with fleeting, familiar impressions. One minute he had the sense of being a trespasser—in the next he was impressed by the tremendous superiority he felt toward Mr. T. A. Hedrick, who was a bore and not even a good golfer any more.

Then, because of a ball Mr. Hart lost near the fifteenth green, an enormous thing happened. While they were searching the stiff grasses of the rough there was a clear call of "Fore!" from behind a hill in their rear. And as they all turned abruptly from their search a bright new ball sliced abruptly over the hill and caught Mr. T. A. Hedrick in the abdomen.

"By Gad!" cried Mr. T. A. Hedrick, "they ought to put some of these crazy women off the course. It's getting to be outrageous."

A head and a voice came up together over the hill:

"Do you mind if we go through?"

"You hit me in the stomach!" declared Mr. Hedrick wildly.

"Did I?" The girl approached the group of men. "I'm sorry. I yelled 'Fore!' "

Her glance fell casually on each of the men—then scanned the fairway for her ball.

"Did I bounce into the rough?"

It was impossible to determine whether this question was ingenuous or malicious. In a moment, however, she left no doubt, for as her partner came up over the hill she called cheerfully:

"Here I am! I'd have gone on the green except that I hit something."

As she took her stance for a short mashie shot, Dexter looked at her closely. She wore a blue gingham dress, rimmed at throat and shoulders with a white edging that accentuated her tan. The quality of exaggeration, of thinness, which had made her passionate eyes and down-turning mouth absurd at eleven, was gone now. She was arrestingly beautiful. The color in her cheeks was centered like the color in a picture—it was not a "high" color, but a sort of fluctuating and feverish warmth, so shaded that it seemed at any moment it would recede and disappear. This color and the mobility of her mouth gave a continual impression of flux, of intense life, of passionate vitality—balanced only partially by the sad luxury of her eyes.

She swung her mashie impatiently and without interest, pitching the ball into a sand-pit on the other side of the green. With a quick, insincere smile and a careless "Thank you!" she went on after it.

"That Judy Jones!" remarked Mr. Hedrick on the next tee, as they waited—some moments—for her to play on ahead. "All she needs is to be turned up and spanked for six months and then to be married off to an old-fashioned cavalry captain."

"My God, she's good-looking!" said Mr. Sandwood, who was just over thirty.

"Good-looking!" cried Mr. Hedrick contemptuously. "She always looks as if she wanted to be kissed! Turning those big cow-eyes on every calf in town!"

It was doubtful if Mr. Hedrick intended a reference to the maternal instinct.

"She'd play pretty good golf if she'd try," said Mr. Sandwood.

"She has no form," said Mr. Hedrick solemnly.

"She has a nice figure," said Mr. Sandwood.

"Better thank the Lord she doesn't drive a swifter ball," said Mr. Hart, winking at Dexter.

Later in the afternoon the sun went down with a riotous swirl of gold and varying blues and scarlets, and left the dry, rustling night of Western summer. Dexter watched from the veranda of the Golf Club, watched the even overlap of the waters in the little wind, silver molasses under the harvest-moon. Then the moon held a finger to her lips and the lake became a clear pool, pale and quiet. Dexter put on his bathing-suit and swam out to the farthest raft, where he stretched dripping on the wet canvas of the springboard.

There was a fish jumping and a star shining and the lights around the lake were gleaming. Over on a dark peninsula a piano was playing the songs of last summer and of summers before that—songs from "Chin-Chin" and "The Count of Luxemburg" and "The Chocolate Soldier"—and because the sound of a piano over a stretch of water had always seemed beautiful to Dexter he lay perfectly quiet and listened.

The tune the piano was playing at that moment had been gay and new five years before when Dexter was a sophomore at college. They had played it at a prom once when he could not afford the luxury of proms, and he had stood outside the gymnasium and listened. The sound of the tune precipitated in him a sort of ecstasy and it was with that ecstasy he viewed what happened to him now. It was a mood of intense appreciation, a sense that, for once, he was magnificently attune to life and that everything about him was radiating a brightness and a glamour he might never know again.

A low, pale oblong detached itself suddenly from the darkness of the Island, spitting forth the reverberate sound of a racing motorboat. Two white streamers of cleft water rolled themselves out behind it and almost immediately the boat was beside him, drowning out the hot tinkle of the piano in the drone of its spray. Dexter raising himself on his arms was aware of a figure standing at the wheel, of two dark eyes regarding him over the lengthening space of water—then the boat had gone by and was sweeping in an immense and purposeless circle of spray round and round in the middle of the lake. With equal eccentricity one of the circles flattened out and headed back toward the raft.

"Who's that?" she called, shutting off her motor. She was so near now that Dexter could see her bathing-suit, which consisted apparently of pink rompers.

The nose of the boat bumped the raft, and as the latter tilted rakishly he was precipitated toward her. With different degrees of interest they recognize each other.

"Aren't you one of those men we played through this afternoon?" she demanded.

He was.

"Well, do you know how to drive a motor-boat? Because if you do I wish you'd drive this one so I can ride on the surf-board behind. My name is Judy Jones"—she favored him with an absurd smirk—rather, what tried to be a smirk, for, twist her mouth as she might, it was not grotesque, it was merely beautiful—"and I live in a house over there on the Island, and in that house there is a man waiting for me. When he drove up at the door I drove out of the dock because he says I'm his ideal."

There was a fish jumping and a star shining and the lights around the lake were gleaming. Dexter sat beside Judy Jones and she explained how her boat was driven. Then she was in the water, swimming to the floating surf-board with a sinuous crawl. Watching her was without effort to the eyes, watching a branch waving or a sea-gull flying. Her arms, burned to butternut, moved sinuously among the dull platinum ripples, elbow appearing first, casting the forearm back with a cadence of falling water, then reaching out and down, stabbing a path ahead.

They moved out into the lake; turning, Dexter saw that she was kneeling on the low rear of the now uptilted surf-board.

"Go faster," she called, "fast as it'll go."

Obediently he jammed the lever forward and the white spray mounted at the bow. When he looked around again the girl was standing up on the rushing board, her arms spread wide, her eyes lifted toward the moon.

"It's awful cold," she shouted. "What's your name?"

He told her.

"Well, why don't you come to dinner to-morrow night?"

His heart turned over like the fly-wheel of the boat, and, for the second time, her casual whim gave a new direction to his life.

III

Next evening while he waited for her to come down-stairs, Dexter peopled the soft deep summer room and the sun-porch that opened from it with the men who had already loved Judy Jones. He knew the sort of men they were—the men who when he first went to college had entered from the great prep schools with graceful clothes and the deep tan of healthy summers. He had seen that, in one sense, he was better than these men. He was newer and stronger. Yet in acknowledging to himself that he wished his children to be like them he was admitting that he was but the rough, strong stuff from which they eternally sprang.

When the time had come for him to wear good clothes, he had known who were the best tailors in America, and the best tailors in America had made him the suit he wore this evening. He had acquired that particular reserve peculiar to his university, that set it off from other universities. He recognized the value to him of such a mannerism and he had adopted it; he knew that to be careless in dress and manner required more confidence than to be careful. But carelessness was for his children. His mother's name had been Krimslich. She was a Bohemian of the peasant class and she had talked broken English to the end of her days. Her son must keep to the set patterns.

At a little after seven Judy Jones came down-stairs. She wore a blue silk afternoon dress, and he was disappointed at first that she had not put on something more elaborate. This feeling was accentuated when, after a brief greeting, she went to the door of a butler's pantry and pushing it open called: "You can serve dinner, Martha." He had rather expected that a butler would announce dinner, that there would be a cocktail. Then he put these thoughts behind him as they sat down side by side on a lounge and looked at each other.

"Father and mother won't be here," she said thoughtfully.

He remembered the last time he had seen her father, and he was glad the parents were not to be here to-night—they might wonder who he was. He had been born in Keeble, a Minnesota village fifty miles farther north, and he always gave Keeble as his home instead of Black Bear Village. Country towns were well enough to come from if they weren't inconveniently in sight and used as footstools by fashionable lakes.

They talked of his university, which she had visited frequently during the past two years, and of the near-by city which supplied Sherry Island with its patrons, and whither Dexter would return next day to his prospering laundries.

During dinner she slipped into a moody depression which gave Dexter a feeling of uneasiness. Whatever petulance she uttered in her throaty voice worried him. Whatever she smiled at—at him, at a chicken liver, at nothing—it disturbed him that her smile could have no root in mirth, or even in amusement. When the scarlet corners of her lips curved down, it was less a smile than an invitation to a kiss.

Then, after dinner, she led him out on the dark sun-porch and deliberately changed the atmosphere.

"Do you mind if I weep a little?" she said.

"I'm afraid I'm boring you," he responded quickly.

"You're not. I like you. But I've just had a terrible afternoon. There was a man I cared about, and this afternoon he told me out of a clear sky that he was poor as a church-mouse. He'd never even hinted it before. Does this sound horribly mundane?"

"Perhaps he was afraid to tell you."

"Suppose he was," she answered. "He didn't start right. You see, if I'd thought of him as poor—well, I've been mad about loads of poor men, and fully intended to marry them all. But in this case, I hadn't thought of him that way, and my interest in him wasn't strong enough to survive the shock. As if a girl calmly informed her fiancé that she was a widow. He might not object to widows, but—

"Let's start right," she interrupted herself suddenly. "Who are you, anyhow?"

For a moment Dexter hesitated. Then:

"I'm nobody," he announced. "My career is largely a matter of futures."

"Are you poor?"

"No," he said frankly, "I'm probably making more money than any man my age in the Northwest. I know that's an obnoxious remark, but you advised me to start right."

There was a pause. Then she smiled and the corners of her mouth drooped and an almost imperceptible sway brought her closer to him, looking up into his eyes. A lump rose in Dexter's throat, and he waited breathless for the experiment, facing the unpredictable compound that would form mysteriously from the elements of their lips. Then he saw—she communicated her excitement to him, lavishly, deeply, with kisses that were not a promise but a fulfilment. They aroused in him not hunger demanding renewal but surfeit that would demand more surfeit . . . kisses that were like charity, creating want by holding back nothing at all.

It did not take him many hours to decide that he had wanted Judy Jones ever since he was a proud, desirous little boy.

IV

It began like that—and continued, with varying shades of intensity, on such a note right up to the dénouement. Dexter surrendered a part of himself to the most direct and unprincipled personality with which he had ever come in contact. Whatever Judy wanted, she went after with the full pressure of her charm. There was no divergence of method, no jockeying for position or premeditation of effects—there was a very little mental side to any of her affairs. She simply made men conscious to the highest degree of her physical loveliness. Dexter had no desire to change her. Her deficiencies were knit up with a passionate energy that transcended and justified them.

When, as Judy's head lay against his shoulder that first night, she whispered, "I don't know what's the matter with me. Last night I thought I was in love with a man and to-night I think I'm in love with you——" —it seemed to him a beautiful and romantic thing to say. It was the exquisite excitability that for the moment he controlled and owned. But a week later he was compelled to view this same quality in a different light. She took him in her roadster to a picnic supper, and after supper she disappeared, likewise in her roadster, with another man. Dexter became enormously upset and was scarcely able to be decently civil to the other people present. When she assured him that she had not kissed the other man, he knew she was lying—yet he was glad that she had taken the trouble to lie to him.

He was, as he found before the summer ended, one of a varying dozen who circulated about her. Each of them had at one time been favored above all others—about half of them still basked in the solace of occasional sentimental revivals. Whenever one showed signs of dropping out through long neglect, she granted him a brief honeyed hour, which encouraged him to tag along for a year or so longer. Judy made these forays upon the helpless and defeated without malice, indeed half unconscious that there was anything mischievous in what she did.

When a new man came to town every one dropped out—dates were automatically cancelled.

The helpless part of trying to do anything about it was that she did it all herself. She was not a girl who could be "won" in the kinetic sense—she was proof against cleverness, she was proof against charm; if any of these assailed her too strongly she would immediately resolve the affair to a physical basis, and under the magic of her physical splendor the strong as well as the brilliant played her game and not their own. She was entertained only by the gratification of her desires and by the direct exercise of her own charm. Perhaps from so much youthful love, so many youthful lovers, she had come, in self-defense, to nourish herself wholly from within.

Succeeding Dexter's first exhilaration came restlessness and dissatisfaction. The helpless ecstasy of losing himself in her was opiate rather than tonic. It was fortunate for his work during the winter that those moments of ecstasy came infrequently. Early in their acquaintance it had seemed for a while that there was a deep and spontaneous mutual attraction—that first August, for example—three days of long evenings on her dusky veranda, of strange wan kisses through the late afternoon, in shadowy alcoves or behind the protecting trellises of the garden arbors, of mornings when she was fresh as a dream and almost shy at meeting him in the clarity of the rising day. There was all the ecstasy of an engagement about it, sharpened by his realization that there was no engagement. It was during those three days that, for the first time, he had asked her to marry him. She said "maybe some day," she said "kiss me," she said "I'd like to marry you," she said "I love you"—she said—nothing.

The three days were interrupted by the arrival of a New York man who visited at her house for half September. To Dexter's agony, rumor engaged them. The man was the son of the president of a great trust company. But at the end of a month it was reported that Judy was yawning. At a dance one night she sat all evening in a motor-boat with a local beau, while the New Yorker searched the club for her frantically. She told the local beau that she was bored with her visitor, and two days later he left. She was seen with him at the station, and it was reported that he looked very mournful indeed.

On this note the summer ended. Dexter was twenty-four, and he found himself increasingly in a position to do as he wished. He joined two clubs in the city and lived at one of them. Though he was by no means an integral part of the stag-lines at these clubs, he managed to be on hand at dances where Judy Jones was likely to appear. He could have gone out socially as much as he liked—he was an eligible young man, now, and popular with down-town fathers. His confessed devotion to Judy Jones had rather solidified his position. But he had no social aspirations and rather despised the dancing men who were always on tap for the Thursday or Saturday parties and who filled in at dinners with the younger married set. Already he was playing with the idea of going East to New York. He wanted to take Judy Jones with him. No disillusion as to the world in which she had grown up could cure his illusion as to her desirability.

Remember that—for only in the light of it can what he did for her be understood.

Eighteen months after he first met Judy Jones he became engaged to another girl. Her name was Irene Scheerer, and her father was one of the men who had always believed in Dexter. Irene was light-haired and sweet and honorable, and a little stout, and she had two suitors whom she pleasantly relinquished when Dexter formally asked her to marry him.

Summer, fall, winter, spring, another summer, another fall—so much he had given of his active life to the incorrigible lips of Judy Jones. She had treated him with interest, with encouragement, with malice, with indifference, with contempt. She had inflicted on him the innumerable little slights and indignities possible in such a case—as if in revenge for having ever cared for him at all. She had beckoned him and yawned at him and beckoned him again and he had responded often with bitterness and narrowed eyes. She had brought him ecstatic happiness and intolerable agony of spirit. She had caused him untold inconvenience and not a little trouble. She had insulted him, and she had ridden over him, and she had played his interest in her against his interest in his work—for fun. She had done everything to him except to criticise him—this she had not done—it seemed to him only because it might have sullied the utter indifference she manifested and sincerely felt toward him.

When autumn had come and gone again it occurred to him that he could not have Judy Jones. He had to beat this into his mind but he convinced himself at last. He lay awake at night for a while and argued it over. He told himself the trouble and the pain she had caused him, he enumerated her glaring deficiencies as a wife. Then he said to himself that he loved her, and after a while he fell asleep. For a week, lest he imagined her husky voice over the telephone or her eyes opposite him at lunch, he worked hard and late, and at night he went to his office and plotted out his years.

At the end of a week he went to a dance and cut in on her once. For almost the first time since they had met he did not ask her to sit out with him or tell her that she was lovely. It hurt him that she did not miss these things—that was all. He was not jealous when he saw that there was a new man to-night. He had been hardened against jealousy long before.

He stayed late at the dance. He sat for an hour with Irene Scheerer and talked about books and about music. He knew very little about either. But he was beginning to be master of his own time now, and he had a rather priggish notion that he—the young and already fabulously successful Dexter Green—should know more about such things.

That was in October, when he was twenty-five. In January, Dexter and Irene became engaged. It was to be announced in June, and they were to be married three months later.

The Minnesota winter prolonged itself interminably, and it was almost May when the winds came soft and the snow ran down into Black Bear Lake at last. For the first time in over a year Dexter was enjoying a certain tranquillity of spirit. Judy Jones had been in Florida, and afterward in Hot Springs, and somewhere she had been engaged, and somewhere she had broken it off. At first, when Dexter had definitely given her up, it had made him sad that people still linked them together and asked for news of her, but when he began to be placed at dinner next to Irene Scheerer people didn't ask him about her any more—they told him about her. He ceased to be an authority on her.

May at last. Dexter walked the streets at night when the darkness was damp as rain, wondering that so soon, with so little done, so much of ecstasy had gone from him. May one year back had been marked by Judy's poignant, unforgivable, yet forgiven turbulence—it had been one of those rare times when he fancied she had grown to care for him. That old penny's worth of happiness he had spent for this bushel of content. He knew that Irene would be no more than a curtain spread behind him, a hand moving among gleaming teacups, a voice calling to children . . . fire and loveliness were gone, the magic of nights and the wonder of the varying hours and seasons . . . slender lips, down-turning, dropping to his lips and bearing him up into a heaven of eyes. . . . The thing was deep in him. He was too strong and alive for it to die lightly.

In the middle of May when the weather balanced for a few days on the thin bridge that led to deep summer he turned in one night at Irene's house. Their engagement was to be announced in a week now—no one would be surprised at it. And to-night they would sit together on the lounge at the University Club and look on for an hour at the dances. It gave him a sense of solidity to go with her—she was so sturdily popular, so intensely "great."

He mounted the steps of the brownstone house and stepped inside.

"Irene," he called.

Mrs. Scheerer came out of the living-room to meet him.

"Dexter," she said, "Irene's gone up-stairs with a splitting headache. She wanted to go with you but I made her go to bed."

"Nothing serious, I——"

"Oh, no. She's going to play golf with you in the morning. You can spare her for just one night, can't you, Dexter?"

Her smile was kind. She and Dexter liked each other. In the living-room he talked for a moment before he said good-night.

Returning to the University Club, where he had rooms, he stood in the doorway for a moment and watched the dancers. He leaned against the door-post, nodded at a man or two—yawned.

"Hello, darling."

The familiar voice at his elbow startled him. Judy Jones had left a man and crossed the room to him—Judy Jones, a slender enamelled doll in cloth of gold: gold in a band at her head, gold in two slipper points at her dress's hem. The fragile glow of her face seemed to blossom as she smiled at him. A breeze of warmth and light blew through the room. His hands in the pockets of his dinner-jacket tightened spasmodically. He was filled with a sudden excitement.

"When did you get back?" he asked casually.

"Come here and I'll tell you about it."

She turned and he followed her. She had been away—he could have wept at the wonder of her return. She had passed through enchanted streets, doing things that were like provocative music. All mysterious happenings, all fresh and quickening hopes, had gone away with her, come back with her now.

She turned in the doorway.

"Have you a car here? If you haven't, I have."

"I have a coupé."

In then, with a rustle of golden cloth. He slammed the door. Into so many cars she had stepped—like this—like that—her back against the leather, so—her elbow resting on the door—waiting. She would have been soiled long since had there been anything to soil her—except herself—but this was her own self outpouring.

With an effort he forced himself to start the car and back into the street. This was nothing, he must remember. She had done this before, and he had put her behind him, as he would have crossed a bad account from his books.

He drove slowly down-town and, affecting abstraction, traversed the deserted streets of the business section, peopled here and there where a movie was giving out its crowd or where consumptive or pugilistic youth lounged in front of pool halls. The clink of glasses and the slap of hands on the bars issued from saloons, cloisters of glazed glass and dirty yellow light.

She was watching him closely and the silence was embarrassing, yet in this crisis he could find no casual word with which to profane the hour. At a convenient turning he began to zigzag back toward the University Club.

"Have you missed me?" she asked suddenly.

"Everybody missed you."

He wondered if she knew of Irene Scheerer. She had been back only a day—her absence had been almost contemporaneous with his engagement.

"What a remark!" Judy laughed sadly—without sadness. She looked at him searchingly. He became absorbed in the dashboard.

"You're handsomer than you used to be," she said thoughtfully. "Dexter, you have the most rememberable eyes."

He could have laughed at this, but he did not laugh. It was the sort of thing that was said to sophomores. Yet it stabbed at him.

"I'm awfully tired of everything, darling." She called every one darling, endowing the endearment with careless, individual camaraderie. "I wish you'd marry me."

The directness of this confused him. He should have told her now that he was going to marry another girl, but he could not tell her. He could as easily have sworn that he had never loved her.

"I think we'd get along," she continued, on the same note, "unless probably you've forgotten me and fallen in love with another girl."

Her confidence was obviously enormous. She had said, in effect, that she found such a thing impossible to believe, that if it were true he had merely committed a childish indiscretion—and probably to show off. She would forgive him, because it was not a matter of any moment but rather something to be brushed aside lightly.

"Of course you could never love anybody but me," she continued, "I like the way you love me. Oh, Dexter, have you forgotten last year?"

"No, I haven't forgotten."

"Neither have I!"

Was she sincerely moved—or was she carried along by the wave of her own acting?

"I wish we could be like that again," she said, and he forced himself to answer:

"I don't think we can."

"I suppose not. . . . I hear you're giving Irene Scheerer a violent rush."

There was not the faintest emphasis on the name, yet Dexter was suddenly ashamed.

"Oh, take me home," cried Judy suddenly; "I don't want to go back to that idiotic dance—with those children."

Then, as he turned up the street that led to the residence district, Judy began to cry quietly to herself. He had never seen her cry before.

The dark street lightened, the dwellings of the rich loomed up around them, he stopped his coupé in front of the great white bulk of the Mortimer Joneses' house, somnolent, gorgeous, drenched with the splendor of the damp moonlight. Its solidity startled him. The strong walls, the steel of the girders, the breadth and beam and pomp of it were there only to bring out the contrast with the young beauty beside him. It was sturdy to accentuate her slightness—as if to show what a breeze could be generated by a butterfly's wing.

He sat perfectly quiet, his nerves in wild clamor, afraid that if he moved he would find her irresistibly in his arms. Two tears had rolled down her wet face and trembled on her upper lip.

"I'm more beautiful than anybody else," she said brokenly, "why can't I be happy?" Her moist eyes tore at his stability—her mouth turned slowly downward with an exquisite sadness: "I'd like to marry you if you'll have me, Dexter. I suppose you think I'm not worth having, but I'll be so beautiful for you, Dexter."

A million phrases of anger, pride, passion, hatred, tenderness fought on his lips. Then a perfect wave of emotion washed over him, carrying off with it a sediment of wisdom, of convention, of doubt, of honor. This was his girl who was speaking, his own, his beautiful, his pride.

"Won't you come in?" He heard her draw in her breath sharply.

Waiting.

"All right," his voice was trembling, "I'll come in."

V

It was strange that neither when it was over nor a long time afterward did he regret that night. Looking at it from the perspective of ten years, the fact that Judy's flare for him endured just one month seemed of little importance. Nor did it matter that by his yielding he subjected himself to a deeper agony in the end and gave serious hurt to Irene Scheerer and to Irene's parents, who had befriended him. There was nothing sufficiently pictorial about Irene's grief to stamp itself on his mind.

Dexter was at bottom hard-minded. The attitude of the city on his action was of no importance to him, not because he was going to leave the city, but because any outside attitude on the situation seemed superficial. He was completely indifferent to popular opinion. Nor, when he had seen that it was no use, that he did not possess in himself the power to move fundamentally or to hold Judy Jones, did he bear any malice toward her. He loved her, and he would love her until the day he was too old for loving—but he could not have her. So he tasted the deep pain that is reserved only for the strong, just as he had tasted for a little while the deep happiness.

Even the ultimate falsity of the grounds upon which Judy terminated the engagement that she did not want to "take him away" from Irene—Judy who had wanted nothing else—did not revolt him. He was beyond any revulsion or any amusement.

He went East in February with the intention of selling out his laundries and settling in New York—but the war came to America in March and changed his plans. He returned to the West, handed over the management of the business to his partner, and went into the first officers' training-camp in late April. He was one of those young thousands who greeted the war with a certain amount of relief, welcoming the liberation from webs of tangled emotion.

VI

This story is not his biography, remember, although things creep into it which have nothing to do with those dreams he had when he was young. We are almost done with them and with him now. There is only one more incident to be related here, and it happens seven years farther on.

It took place in New York, where he had done well—so well

that there were no barriers too high for him. He was thirty-two years old, and, except for one flying trip immediately after the war, he had not been West in seven years. A man named Devlin from Detroit came into his office to see him in a business way, and then and there this incident occurred, and closed out, so to speak, this particular side of his life.

"So you're from the Middle West," said the man Devlin with careless curiosity. "That's funny—I thought men like you were probably born and raised on Wall Street. You know—wife of one of my best friends in Detroit came from your city. I was an usher at the wedding."

Dexter waited with no apprehension of what was coming.

"Judy Simms," said Devlin with no particular interest; "Judy Jones she was once."

"Yes, I knew her." A dull impatience spread over him. He had heard, of course, that she was married—perhaps deliberately he had heard no more.

"Awfully nice girl," brooded Devlin meaninglessly, "I'm sort of sorry for her."

"Why?" Something in Dexter was alert, receptive, at once.

"Oh, Lud Simms has gone to pieces in a way. I don't mean he ill-uses her, but he drinks and runs around——"

"Doesn't she run around?"

"No. Stays at home with her kids."

"Oh."

"She's a little too old for him," said Devlin.

"Too old!" cried Dexter. "Why, man, she's only twenty-seven."

He was possessed with a wild notion of rushing out into the streets and taking a train to Detroit. He rose to his feet spasmodically.

"I guess you're busy," Devlin apologized quickly. "I didn't realize——"

"No, I'm not busy," said Dexter, steadying his voice. "I'm not busy at all. Not busy at all. Did you say she was—twenty-seven? No, I said she was twenty-seven."

"Yes, you did," agreed Devlin dryly.

"Go on, then. Go on."

"What do you mean?"

"About Judy Jones."

Devlin looked at him helplessly.

"Well, that's—I told you all there is to it. He treats her like the devil. Oh, they're not going to get divorced or anything. When he's particularly outrageous she forgives him. In fact, I'm inclined to think she loves him. She was a pretty girl when she first came to Detroit."

A pretty girl! The phrase struck Dexter as ludicrous.

"Isn't she—a pretty girl, any more?"

"Oh, she's all right."

"Look here," said Dexter, sitting down suddenly. "I don't understand. You say she was a 'pretty girl' and now you say she's 'all right.' I don't understand what you mean—Judy Jones wasn't a pretty girl, at all. She was a great beauty. Why, I knew her, I knew her. She was——"

Devlin laughed pleasantly.

"I'm not trying to start a row," he said. "I think Judy's a nice girl and I like her. I can't understand how a man like Lud Simms could fall madly in love with her, but he did." Then he added: "Most of the women like her."

Dexter looked closely at Devlin, thinking wildly that there must be a reason for this, some insensitivity in the man or some private malice.

"Lots of women fade just like *that,*" Devlin snapped his fingers. "You must have seen it happen. Perhaps I've forgotten how pretty she was at her wedding. I've seen her so much since then, you see. She has nice eyes."

A sort of dullness settled down upon Dexter. For the first time in his life he felt like getting very drunk. He knew that he was laughing loudly at something Devlin had said, but he did not know what it was or why it was funny. When, in a few minutes, Devlin went he lay down on his lounge and looked out the window at the New York skyline into which the sun was sinking in dull lovely shades of pink and gold.

He had thought that having nothing else to lose he was invulnerable at last—but he knew that he had just lost something more, as surely as if he had married Judy Jones and seen her fade away before his eyes.

The dream was gone. Something had been taken from him. In a sort of panic he pushed the palms of his hands into his eyes and tried to bring up a picture of the waters lapping on Sherry Island and the moonlit veranda, and gingham on the golf-links and the dry sun and the gold color of her neck's soft down. And her mouth damp to his kisses and her eyes plaintive with melancholy and her freshness like new fine linen in the morning. Why, these things were no longer in the world! They had existed and they existed no longer.

For the first time in years the tears were streaming down his face. But they were for himself now. He did not care about mouth and eyes and moving hands. He wanted to care, and he could not care. For he had gone away and he could never go back any more. The gates were closed, the sun was gone down, and there was no beauty but the gray beauty of steel that withstands all time. Even the grief he could have borne was left behind in the country of illusion, of youth, of the richness of life, where his winter dreams had flourished.

"Long ago," he said, "long ago, there was something in me, but now that thing is gone. Now that thing is gone, that thing is gone. I cannot cry. I cannot care. That thing will come back no more."

Questions

1. **The last section of the story is cast in another locale, set seven years forward in time, and introduces an outsider, ironically named Devlin, who serves as *deus ex machina*. What do you make of this—in terms of structure? In terms of meaning? Is there anything in the last section which suggests that Fitzgerald did not achieve full objectivity about the events he relates?**
2. **Judy Jones serves as both character and commentary. In what ways is this dual function useful to the author?**

3. Examine Dexter's conduct in the light of Fitzgerald's own standard for a first-rate intelligence.
4. At the beginning of the last section, the narrator remarks: "This story is not his biography, remember, although things creep into it which have nothing to do with those dreams he had when he was young." What does he mean by this statement?
5. Consider the following interchange:

   Fitzgerald: "The rich are different from us."

   Hemingway: "Yes, they have more money."

   In what ways are the statements of Fitzgerald and Hemingway applicable to this story?

Allan Seager

This Town and Salamanca

LIKE F. Scott Fitzgerald, Allan Seager has carried on a long romance with his country, though both his perspective and the world he writes about are uniquely his own.

The Seager milieu is the rural America of the Middle West, rich farming country, dotted with small towns. Main Street is a patchwork quilt of brick and concrete with the tracks of long-defunct trolley lines embedded in the pavement, a stoplight interrupting the flow of through-automobiles, going Somewhere from Somewhere. Like that flow of traffic, life seemingly passes by the people in the small factories and the houses on the surrounding streets and blocks. It is in the limitations of such a view that Allan Seager finds his major subject matter.

The study of provincial manners, Flaubert taught and Seager believes, calls for modes of knowing that are neither sentimental nor simple. In such serious and finely wrought novels as AMOS BERRY, *as well as in his shorter fiction, Seager has explored, at various levels of consciousness, something approximating the psyche of midland America, its sense of a corporate fate. It could be said that he is writing a version of cultural history, subtle and sophisticated and marked by an intellectual honesty which refuses completely to accept or fully to reject what lies before him in the American scene. One re-*

flection of this honesty is the narrative voice which speaks in "This Town and Salamanca."

"This Town and Salamanca" is an early Seager story, yet it presents, at least in part, the major concerns of his fiction, particularly in his figures' sense of entrapment as they search for cultural figments that are seemingly absent from American life. Klug and Gordon, for example, both successful members of the town's community, invest the travels of John Baldwin to far-distant places with a romance which, the narrator suggests, they do not possess.

SO WHEN he returned, we asked him why he had gone to live there and he said he'd just heard of it and thought it might be a nice place to live in for a while. He had lived in an old house built around a court. The walls were four feet thick and the windows were larger on the outside than they were on the inside; the sills slanted. They kept goats' milk there on the window sills because the stone made the air cool. You could see the sticks of a hawk's nest hanging over one corner of the roof, and Jesus, the landlady's son—he looked up here to see if we thought it was funny that a man should be named Jesus, but none of us said anything. We read a great deal—he often whistled to it evenings. Yes, the food was good. They had a sausage with tomatoes in it that was very good and the wine was not like French wine, it was heavier and sweeter. And there were no fireplaces for heating but things they called *braseros*. They were big pans like that with his arms stretched and on cold mornings they set it alight and covered the flame with ashes. They would put the *brasero* under a big table. The table had a sort of plush cover to it that hung down to the floor with slits in it. You put your feet through the slits and wrapped the cover around your waist. Then although your feet roasted, you

From *The Old Man of the Mountain* by Allan Seager, Simon and Schuster, Inc., New York, 1950.

could still see your breath and you couldn't stay in the room long because of the fumes, and sitting by the *brasero* gave you chilblains but they were a common thing and no one minded. Klug asked him about the women. Were they—you know? The women were all right, he said. The peasant girls were very pretty but they faded early and got fat. Yes, but, Klug said impatiently, but he was talking then about the riots, how they used beer bottles full of black powder for bombs and when they bombed the convent, the nuns all ran out crying and waving their arms after the explosion and some fell on their knees and prayed in the midst of the rioters but the bomb had not even chipped the wall, it was four feet thick. All the houses were like that with big thick walls and the streets were narrow and the town was quiet. They could not hang the washing in the courtyards because it was too cool for it to dry, so they spread it on rocks beside the river when they finished. It was a very old town and they lived in the same way year after year. Gordon asked him about the spiritual remnants of medievalism. He answered that the people were very pious and went to the cathedral to pray for everything, even lost articles. The cathedral had small windows and the light was yellow inside, not like the gray light inside the cathedrals in Île de France.

Well, I thought, as they talked on into the evening, it is not anything like that here. You see I remember this particular evening very clearly and all that we said because it was the last time John had anything new to tell us, and from that time on, he has lived here with us in this town. We never thought he would settle here. It is a good enough town but nothing to the places he has seen, not even the kind of place you would close your book to watch if you went through on the train. First there are the ball-bearing factory and the electric bell factory, with the other factories hidden behind them; then there are trees hiding the houses with their backs turned toward you; and then you would see the spire, not of a cathedral, but of the Methodist church, and the town would soon dwindle away into the cornfields and just after that you could look at your watch to see how long before Chicago. It is not like Salamanca, but the four of us were born and grew up here and only John had gone away. And when he came home to see his mother, he would tell us these things that made us seem fools to ourselves for having stayed but we were busy with our work and could not follow him. There are maple trees on both sides of the streets and in summer it is like driving through a tunnel of green leaves.

You see he never answered Gordon's intelligent questions and he always disappointed Klug, who thinks that all the women in foreign countries wait on street corners after dark winking and motioning yonder with their heads. John seldom was an actor in his own play—he merely looked, it seemed, and told us what he saw. It was the best way, keeping himself out, but they would not admit it, so they kept on with the questions. They admitted it to themselves though. Klug said he thought of the peasant girls with their ankles shining under their tucked-up skirts doing the washing by the riverbank when he was scrubbing his hands after taking the cancer out of Mrs. Gira, the Polish washwoman, and the nurse was counting the used wet sponges and the hospital smell made his stomach turn. And when the aldermen brought the plans of the new railroad station back to Gordon and sat down to talk and object for hours, he saw the smoke drifting from where the bomb exploded and the nuns praying in the confusion and one of the aldermen had spots on his waistcoat that he kept picking at. Though we had nothing but questions when he came, we all knew that the questions were merely little signs to show that we too might very well have been there and seen these things, and that it was nothing more important than chance that we had stayed here. He talked late and I remember there was a bat lurching to and fro under a light down the street.

Mrs. Gira got well though and it is a fine new railroad station.

II

He was in an old boathouse whistling. We heard him when we came down the path. The boathouse was so old the shingles curled and weeds grew on the roof, and we used to tell him that some day the whole shebang would give way with him in it and he would have to swim out with the rafters round his neck. He had borrowed the use of it from Old Man Suggs, who hadn't kept a boat in years. When we were kids I remember seeing it when we went to the riverflats to look for dog-tooth violets. It was a motor launch and he sold it when the tomato cannery started up. Every summer the river is full of blobs of red tomato pulp and no one wants to go out in a boat then. But John was building a sailboat. It was May then and he had worked all his spare time on it since the August before; every Saturday afternoon, and nights after supper he would go down and work by the light of three oil lamps he got from his mother. That was the winter we played so much poker and sometimes we would go to the boathouse at midnight and ask John to take a hand. He was always pleasant about it, without any scruples against gambling, but he never stopped working and we would shout above the hammer blows, "Where do you think you're going in this boat when it's finished? Going to haul tomatoes for the cannery?" He would laugh and say that a good many waters would wet this hull before she was much older. We would laugh because we knew he had got the phrase out of some book, and we would start up the path. The ripples on the water always shone in the lamplight and we could hear his hammer as far as the dirt road where we turned to Klug's house. Often we played till midnight. I won a lot of money that winter.

When we entered the boathouse we could see it was nearly finished. It looked very big and white and seemed not too much to have put a winter's work into. He was planing some teak for the deck, and when we came near there was the acrid leathery odor of the fresh shavings. We had seen pictures of yachts, and once or twice the ore boats on the big lakes, but the things we saw every day, the houses, trees, and grain elevators, went straight up from the ground. They had roots. If they had not, as they seemed, been always in one place, they always would be. John's boat was a strange shape, curved for the water. Even in the dim boathouse, propped up with blocks, she seemed ready for movement. I looked at John with the handle of the plane easy in his hand, and we were going to be "professional" men, and I knew he would go away. The boat had sprung from some matrix within him that we would never understand, just as he was puzzled when Gordon asked how long she was and how many tons' weight as if she were a heifer fattened for market. When we went out of the boathouse, Klug said, "So long, skipper."

He went away in the boat as I thought he would and after this he never came back for long at a time. God knows how he got the blocks from under her without any help, but one afternoon he launched her all by himself, and in ten days he had her rigged and the galley full of stores. He sailed away without saying anything to anyone, down our little river into the Ohio and then into the Mississippi and out into the Gulf below New Orleans. He was gone all summer into October. I saw him on the street when he returned. He was tanned almost black. We shook hands and I said "Where did you go? Did you have a good trip?"

He looked at me a moment before answering. "Trip" means a journey you take in a car during your two-weeks' vacation in the summer, maybe to Yellowstone or the Grand Canyon or Niagara. It is a relaxation from your work. I could see as I said it that "trip" was the wrong word, but just how far wrong, it took me years to find out and then I never was certain. I thought of his boat, a strange and unfamiliar shape, and how he, whom we had seen unsuspectingly every day through his boyhood, had made it.

"Yes, I had a good time."

"Where did you go?"

"Well, down into the Gulf and around."

"Cuba?"

"Yes, I put in at Havana," and then as if he had at last found something he could tell me, "you know, Klug would like that place—they've got a park there where you can get free beer. It's owned by a brewing company and you can go there and drink all you want, free."

"Where else did you go?"

"Oh, the Tortugas, Haiti, Veracruz."

He showed me a gold piece he had got off a pawnbroker in Port-au-Prince. He said it was a moidore. He was nineteen then.

III

When he returned next time, he was less reticent. It was not because he was proud of being a traveler but more, I think, that he saw we really wanted to hear about the distant places he had been. When his ship was coming into the harbor of Singapore, he said you could see the junks waiting with their crinkled sails. And when the ship came near, they sailed right in front of the bow as close as they could. Sometimes they didn't make it and they all smashed up and drowned. He said they did it to cut off the devils following behind. The day after he told us that Gordon asked Tom Sing, who runs the chop suey joint, if he believed in devils but Tom only grinned. Gordon said it was the oriental inscrutability. Gordon is quite serious.

During the next ten years John did all the things we said we'd do that time in the apple orchard. He joined the Army to fly and left the Army after a time and went to Italy. I went to his house from the office the day he got home. He was dressed in white, lunging at himself in a long mirror with a foil in his hand. The French held their foils this way with the thumb so, but the Italians that way. After that he was a sailor again on one of the crack clippers that still bring the wheat up from Australia, and from Liverpool I had a postcard with a picture of Aintree racecourse on the back. It said, "Give Gordon my congratulations." Gordon had been elected mayor and we were very proud of him. How John heard of it we couldn't figure out.

One time there was a card from Aden and another from Helsinki. You can see he traveled. No one in the town had ever gone so far and people used to stop his mother on the street to ask where he was then, not that they really cared but because the thread that tied them to him as a local boy tied them also to the strange name his mother answered when they asked.

When he was a sailor in the Pacific, spinal meningitis broke out on board. Eighteen people died and they put the bodies down in the hold. The ship's doctor examined all the crew and said John was the healthiest and the captain ordered him to go below and sew up the bodies in shrouds and heave them overboard.

John got a roll of canvas, a reel of packthread, a leather palm-guard and a needle and went down into the hold. He rigged up an electric light in a wire cage and swung it from a hook over his head. The eighteen lay there in a row. They were quite stiff, and when the ship rolled, sometimes an arm would come up and pause until the ship rolled back. But they were in the shadow and he did not watch them much because the sewing was hard work, about an hour to each one. He jabbed his finger with the needle three or four times and that made it harder. When he got one ready, he would put it over his shoulder and stagger up the companionway to the deck.

High up above him beside the funnel, to escape the risk of infection, stood an Anglican parson, one of the passengers. He had an open prayer book and said the service very quickly, the leaves fluttering in the wind. Then John would pick up the corpse again and heave it over the side. Sometimes a shark would rip the shroud almost as it hit the water; others he could see jerked from the ring of foam of their impact and carried quickly below. There were at least a dozen sharks and John said he knew his work was useless and he took bigger and bigger stitches in the canvas. There was quite a wind and John could never hear the whole service because the wind blew the words away but a few snatches would come down to him. He and the parson were all alone, the other people having hidden from fear; and they did not speak to each other. When John brought up the last corpse, it had been a Portuguese merchant from Manila on his way to Goa to see his daughter, the wind stopped suddenly and there was a moment of calm. ". . . to the deep to be turned into corruption," the parson said. John picked up the merchant, balanced him on the rail, shoved him over, and the sharks came.

IV

"And Eloise said it was when she was getting the coffee after dinner. Mr. and Mrs. Booth were setting in the parlor and Mr. Booth was drinking brandy like he always does and the both of them quiet as mutes at a funeral when all at once the door bell rang and Eloise answered it and there stood John Baldwin. My, I think he's handsome. Oh, he's much better-looking than him. And he asked could he see Mr. Booth and Eloise said he could; he was right in the parlor. So Mr. Baldwin come in but he wouldn't give Eloise his hat. He kep' it and said he was only staying a minute. Well, Eloise said she went to the kitchen to get another cup naturally expecting Mr. Baldwin would have some coffee and when she come back through the diningroom she was so surprised she nearly dropped it.

"She said Mr. Baldwin was standing right in front of Mr. Booth and he says, 'Dennis, I've come for your wife.' Just like that. And Mr. Booth says, 'What do you mean—you've come for my wife?' Eloise said she got behind the window drapes so they wouldn't see her and Mr. Baldwin says, 'Frances loves me. I want you to divorce her.' Mr. Booth was drunk on all that brandy and he jumped up and began to shout that it was damned cool and a lot of things about throwing Mr. Baldwin out of the house only Eloise don't think for a minute he could have even if he was sober. Why, John Baldwin's way over six feet and a sailor and always fighting with them little swords and all, but Mr. Booth got white he was so mad, and Mrs. Booth she didn't say anything. She just sat there and looked at them and Eloise said it was like Mr. Baldwin didn't hear a word Mr. Booth said because he was looking at Mrs. Booth all the time and when Mr. Booth stopped talking Mr. Baldwin looked up at him quick like you do when a clock stops. Then he just says, 'Well, Dennis,' and Mr. Booth began to swear something terrible but he didn't try to throw him out, he didn't even come close to him. Then Mr. Baldwin looked at Mrs. Booth and smiled and says, 'Come along, Frances,' and Mrs. Booth smiled back and they walked right out of the house without her even packing any clothes. And that's all there was to it. Eloise says Mrs. Booth walked right out of her house into a new life, never to return. And they say Mrs. Booth has gone to Paris, France, to get a divorce from Mr. Booth. Well, all I got to say is, it serves him right—he was always running around after them dirty little factory girls. Certainly he was. Everybody knows it. Why you know that little Muller girl, the one with the fox fur. Why Eloise says that . . ."

I stopped listening then. I always liked to look at the Italian flags on bottles of olive oil when I was a kid. I had the same feeling then: no one does things like that here, walking into a man's house and taking his wife. If you want a man's wife, you meet her by chance in Chicago and she goes on being his wife afterwards. Or maybe it was like the boat. We hadn't lived with him. He was only the things he had done and those at a distance. Now that he had begun his marriage this way I did not think he would change the pattern, but that was before I knew he intended to settle here.

He was, I thought then, rootless and invincible. He didn't seem to want what we had, what we had remained here and worked for. Which comes down to this, I suppose, and little more: the same trees every day when you go to work, in summer hanging over the lawns beside the walks, and bare with snow at the forks of the limbs and the sound of snow shovels scraping the walks; and when you look up, the line of the roof of the house next door against the sky. You could call it peace. It is just peace with no brilliance. I remembered how bright the gold piece was in his hand.

But he didn't go away again. He settled here very quietly and took a nice little house. He and Frances were very happy, and we all used to say how glad we were that they were so happy. We used to say it very loudly to ourselves and sometimes to him, and we put ourselves out to help him meet people. He had been away so long that he had forgot or never had known them. We got him into the golf club the first week he was in the bank. Everything we could show him about the town we did gladly.

After he had been married a year, we all came to Gordon's one night to drink beer. Most of the evening we taught John poker, and after that we just sat around and talked. John said, "You know Roy Curtis from out Fruit Ridge way? He came in today and he wanted to borrow the money to buy another hundred acres. That piece by the bridge there. Belongs to Dick Sheppard."

"He'll raise wheat. No money in wheat now."

"That's what I told him but he wants to have a shot at it just the same. Offered to mortgage his place. I don't know, though. What do you think?"

Without saying that we didn't ordinarily do a banker's thinking for him publicly, we told him Roy Curtis was a fool if he thought he could make money in wheat at fifty-six cents a bushel.

"He's got a combine, you know. He says he'll have two hundred acres in wheat and he and his boy can work it all by themselves."

We remembered when he had bought the combine. Two hundred acres is too small for one of those big combines. This isn't Dakota.

"You wouldn't lend him the money, then? He's coming in Thursday. It's good security, a mortgage on his place."

We told him we wouldn't lend the money, but John had drunk a lot of beer. He kept on talking about it.

"He's a smart farmer, Roy. Look at that house he's got there. It's a fine place, as good as any of these here in town. Got a Packard and a big radio. Why, he said he got Rome on that radio the other night. He didn't make his money doing foolish things. I don't know about the loan."

Roy's aunt had left him the money, but that was while John was away. We didn't tell him.

I said: "Do you fence any now, John?"

He got up laughing and went out into the hall and got a mashie out of Gordon's golf bag and came in with it. He began, standing with a bent leg and one hand flung up behind him. He went through the lunges and parries laughing.

"Getting fat," he said, "I can't do 'em any more."

I had to leave then because I had to be at the office early next day. John was still talking about the loan when I left. It had been raining and the wind had blown down leaves from the maples. The evening had been unsatisfactory and I thought about it as I walked along. I was in sight of my house before I thought why, and I stopped to pick off the red leaves stuck to my shoes.

I remembered him in white with his face grave. "You see, the French hold a foil this way. It's not like the Italians. I learned in Marseille." That was the way he used to talk. We knew all about loans; we knew all about him now. Of course I could never do more than just remind him of these things because he was so happy. But I did not think he would ever go away again to return and tell us these things, because of his happiness. Suddenly I felt old. It was as if we had trusted him to keep our youth for us and he had let it go. But our youth only.

Questions

1. **Characterize Gordon and Klug. How do they function in the story? Characterize John Baldwin. Is he in any way an enigmatic figure? If so, explain.**
2. **A large element in the story's success is the narrative voice. Why is the narrator nameless? What sort of a person is he? The tone in which he speaks is partly a reflection of Seager's prose style. How would you characterize that style?**
3. **The use of detail is an important aspect of Seager's style. In what ways is this apparent in "This Town and Salamanca"?**
4. **Seager has broken his story into rather small sections. Why has he done this? Are events related in chronological order? If not, precisely what is the order?**
5. **Juxtaposition, the meaningful putting together of different things, plays a major role in "This Town and Salamanca." What is the effect of setting side-by-side such sentences as the following? "And when he came home to see his mother, he would tell us these things that made us seem fools to ourselves for having stayed but we were busy with our work and could not follow him. There are maple trees on both sides of the streets and in summer it is like driving through a tunnel of green leaves."**

John Cheever

The Enormous Radio

THE WORLD of John Cheever's short stories is largely high-rise Manhattan and the status suburbs which lie within easy distance of it. The people in this world are apartment dwellers and commuters, businessmen and their families, and those who serve them—maids, elevator boys, doormen, building custodians.

By and large Cheever's people are members of the affluent society, and a good deal of their time and energy is given over to maintaining a position in this society. They worry about taxes, bills, their children's education, their jobs. Heartbreak is real in Cheever's world, and tragedy, if personal and muted, not uncommon. Many of his stories have dealt with what he has called "that enormous stratum of the middle class that is distinguished by its ability to recall better times."

One mark of Cheever's fiction is its urbanity and reasonableness, traits which the author shares with other NEW YORKER *writers such as William Maxwell and John Updike. Yet Cheever has always been aware of the dark pit; for him it is the gaping hole in the surface of events which his figures, unlike their creator, would prefer not to see.*

Cheever is more concerned with the shortcomings and limitations of a class than with individuals. As often as not, his people are designed to be typical and representative. In "The Enormous Radio," for example, Jim and Irene Westcott are described as differing from their friends and classmates and neighbors only in the interest they share in serious music. In the course of the story they are momentarily allowed a privileged glimpse into the daily disasters which surround the lives of their neighbors—illness, debt, wife-beating, deceit, dishonesty. Irene, upset by what she has learned, finds life "too terrible, too sordid and awful." She and Jim, she feels, don't live like that. "We're not hypercritical or worried about money or dishonest, are we?" she asks her husband. The concluding section of the story suggests, ironically, that she and Jim have more in common with their neighbors than she thought.

JIM AND IRENE WESTCOTT were the kind of people who seem to strike that satisfactory average of income, endeavor, and respectability that is reached by the statistical reports in college alumni bulletins. They were the parents of two young children, they had been married nine years, they lived on the twelfth floor of an apartment house near Sutton Place, they went to the theatre on an average of 10.3 times a year, and they hoped someday to live in Westchester. Irene Westcott was a pleasant, rather plain girl with soft brown hair and a wide, fine forehead upon which nothing at all had been written, and in the cold weather she wore a coat of fitch skins dyed to resemble mink. You could not say that Jim Westcott looked younger than he was, but you could at least say of him that he seemed to feel younger. He wore his graying hair cut very short, he dressed in the kind of clothes his class had worn at Andover, and his manner was earnest, vehement, and intentionally naïve. The Westcotts differed from their friends, their classmates, and their neighbors only in an interest they shared in serious music. They went to a great many concerts—although they seldom mentioned this to anyone—and they spent a good deal of time listening to music on the radio.

Their radio was an old instrument, sensitive, unpredictable, and beyond repair. Neither of them understood the mechanics of radio—or of any of the other appliances that surrounded them—and when the instrument faltered, Jim would strike the side of the cabinet with his hand. This sometimes helped. One Sunday afternoon, in the middle of a Schubert quartet, the music faded away altogether. Jim struck the cabinet repeatedly, but there was no response; the Schubert was lost to them forever. He promised to buy Irene a new radio, and on Monday when he came home from work he told her that he had got one. He refused to describe it, and said it would be a surprise for her when it came.

The radio was delivered at the kitchen door the following afternoon, and with the assistance of her maid and the handyman Irene uncrated it and brought it into the living room. She was struck at once with the physical ugliness of the large gumwood cabinet. Irene was proud of her living room, she had chosen its furnishings and colors as carefully as she chose her clothes, and now it seemed to her that the new radio stood among her intimate possessions like an aggressive intruder. She was confounded by the number of dials and switches on the instrument panel, and she studied them thoroughly before she put the plug into a wall socket and turned the radio on. The dials flooded with a malevolent green light, and in the distance she heard the music of a piano quintet. The quintet was in the distance for only an instant; it bore down upon her with a speed greater than light and filled the apartment with the noise of music amplified so mightily that it knocked a china ornament from a table to the floor. She rushed to the instrument and reduced the volume. The violent forces that were snared in the ugly gumwood cabinet made her uneasy. Her children came home from school then, and she took them to the Park. It was not until later in the afternoon that she was able to return to the radio.

The maid had given the children their suppers and was supervising their baths when Irene turned on the radio, reduced the volume, and sat down to listen to a Mozart quintet that she knew and enjoyed. The music came through clearly. The new instrument had a much purer tone, she thought, than the old one. She decided that tone was most important and that she could conceal the cabinet behind a sofa. But as soon as she had made her peace with the radio, the interference began. A crackling sound like the noise of a burning powder fuse began to accompany the singing of the strings. Beyond the music there was a rustling that reminded Irene unpleasantly of the sea, and as the quintet progressed, these noises were joined by many others. She tried all the dials and switches but nothing dimmed the interference, and she sat down, disappointed and bewildered, and tried to trace the flight of the melody. The elevator shaft in her building ran beside the living-room wall, and it was the noise of the elevator that gave her a clue to the character of the static. The rattling of the elevator cables and the opening and closing of the elevator doors were reproduced in her loudspeaker, and, realizing that the radio was sensitive to electrical currents of all sorts, she began to discern through the Mozart the ringing of telephone bells, the dialing of phones, and the lamentation of a vacuum cleaner. By listening more carefully, she was able to distinguish doorbells, elevator bells, electric razors, and Waring mixers, whose sounds had been picked up from the apartments that surrounded hers and transmitted through her loudspeaker. The powerful and ugly instrument, with its mistaken sensitivity to discord, was more than she could hope to master, so she turned the thing off and went into the nursery to see her children.

When Jim Westcott came home that night, he went to the radio confidently and worked the controls. He had the same sort of experience Irene had had. A man was speaking on the station Jim had chosen, and his voice swung instantly from the distance into a force so powerful that it shook the apartment. Jim turned the volume control and reduced the voice. Then, a minute or two later, the interference began. The ringing of telephones and doorbells set in, joined by the rasp of elevator doors and the whir of cooking appliances. The character of the noise had changed since Irene had tried the radio earlier; the last of the electric razors was being unplugged, the vacuum cleaners had all been returned to their closets, and the static reflected that change in pace that overtakes the city after the sun goes down. He fiddled with the knobs but couldn't get rid of the noises, so he turned the radio off and told Irene that in the morning he'd call the people who had sold it to him and give them hell.

The following afternoon, when Irene returned to the apartment from a luncheon date, the maid told her that a man had come and fixed the radio. Irene went into the living room before she took off her hat or her furs and tried the instrument. From the loudspeaker came a recording of the "Missouri Waltz." It reminded her of the thin, scratchy music from an old-fashioned phonograph that she sometimes heard across the lake where she spent her summers. She waited until the waltz had finished, expecting an explanation of the recording, but there was none. The music was followed by silence, and then the plaintive and scratchy record was repeated. She turned the dial and got a satisfactory burst of Caucasian music—the thump of bare feet in the dust and the rattle of coin jewelry—but in the background she could hear the ringing of bells and a confusion of voices. Her children came home from school then, and she turned off the radio and went to the nursery.

When Jim came home that night, he was tired, and he took a bath and changed his clothes. Then he joined Irene in the living room. He had just turned on the radio when the maid announced dinner, so he left it on, and he and Irene went to the table.

Jim was too tired to make even a pretense of sociability, and there was nothing about the dinner to hold Irene's interest, so her attention wandered from the food to the deposits of silver polish on the candlesticks and from there to the music in the other room. She listened for a few moments to a Chopin prelude and then was surprised to hear a man's voice break in. "For Christ's sake, Kathy," he said, "do you always have to play the piano when I get home?" The music stopped abruptly. "It's the only chance I have," a woman said. "I'm at the office all day." "So am I," the man said. He added something obscene about an upright piano, and slammed the door. The passionate and melancholy music began.

"Did you hear that?" Irene asked.

"What?" Jim was eating his dessert.

"The radio. A man said something while the music was still going on—something dirty."

"It's probably a play."

"I don't think it *is* a play," Irene said.

They left the table and took their coffee into the living room. Irene asked Jim to try another station. He turned the knob. "Have you seen my garters?" a man asked. "Button me up," a woman said. "Have you seen my garters?" the man said again. "Just button me up and I'll find your garters," the woman said. Jim shifted to another station. "I wish you wouldn't leave apple cores in the ashtrays," a man said. "I hate the smell."

"This is strange," Jim said.

"Isn't it?" Irene said.

Jim turned the knob again. " 'On the coast of Coromandel where the early pumpkins blow,' " a woman with a pronounced English accent said, " 'in the middle of the woods lived the Yonghy-Bonghy-Bo. Two old chairs, and half a candle, one old jug without a handle . . .' "

"My God!" Irene cried. "That's the Sweeneys' nurse."

" 'These were all his worldly goods,' " the British voice continued.

"Turn that thing off," Irene said. "Maybe they can hear *us.*" Jim switched the radio off. "That was Miss Armstrong, the Sweeneys' nurse," Irene said. "She must be reading to the little girl. They live in 17-B. I've talked with Miss Armstrong in the Park. I know her voice very well. We must be getting other people's apartments."

"That's impossible," Jim said.

"Well, that was the Sweeneys' nurse," Irene said hotly. "I know her voice. I know it very well. I'm wondering if they can hear us."

Jim turned the switch. First from a distance and then nearer, nearer, as if borne on the wind, came the pure accents of the Sweeneys' nurse again: *" 'Lady Jingly! Lady Jingly!' "* she said, *" 'Sitting where the pumpkins blow, will you come and be my wife,* said the Yonghy-Bonghy-Bo. . . .' "

Jim went over to the radio and said "Hello" loudly into the speaker.

" 'I am tired of living singly,' " the nurse went on, *" 'on this coast so wild and shingly, I'm a-weary of my life; if you'll come and be my wife, quite serene would by my life . . .' "*

"I guess she can't hear us," Irene said. "Try something else."

Jim turned to another station, and the living room was filled with the uproar of a cocktail party that had overshot its mark. Someone was playing the piano and singing the Whiffenpoof Song, and the voices that surrounded the piano were vehement and happy. "Eat some more sandwiches," a woman shrieked. There were screams of laughter and a dish of some sort crashed to the floor.

"Those must be the Fullers, in 11-E," Irene said. "I knew they were giving a party this afternoon. I saw her in the liquor store. Isn't this too divine? Try something else. See if you can get those people in 18-C."

The Westcotts overheard that evening a monologue on salmon fishing in Canada, a bridge game, running comments on home movies of what had apparently been a fortnight at Sea Island, and a bitter family quarrel about an overdraft at the bank. They turned off their radio at midnight and went to bed, weak with laughter. Sometime in the night, their son began to call for a glass of water and Irene got one and took it to his room. It was very early. All the lights in the neighborhood were extinguished, and from the boy's window she could see the empty street. She went into the living room and tried the radio. There was some faint coughing, a moan, and then a man spoke. "Are you all right, darling?" he asked. "Yes," a woman said wearily. "Yes, I'm all right, I guess," and then she added with great feeling, "but, you know, Charlie, I don't feel like myself any more. Sometimes there are about fifteen or twenty minutes in the week when I feel like myself. I don't like to go to another doctor, because the doctor's bills are so awful already, but I just don't feel like myself, Charlie. I just never feel like myself." They were not young, Irene thought. She guessed from the timbre of their voices that they were middle-aged. The restrained melancholy of the dialogue and the draft from the bedroom window made her shiver, and she went back to bed.

The following morning, Irene cooked breakfast for the family—the maid didn't come up from her room in the basement until ten—braided her daughter's hair, and waited at the door until her children and her husband had been carried away in the elevator. Then she went into the living room and tried the radio. "I don't want to go to school," a child screamed. "I hate school. I won't go to school. I hate school." "You will go to school," an enraged woman said. "We paid eight hundred dollars to get you into that school and you'll go if it kills you." The next number on the dial produced the worn record of the "Missouri Waltz." Irene shifted the control and invaded the privacy of several breakfast tables. She overheard demonstrations of indigestion, carnal love, abysmal vanity, faith, and despair. Irene's life was nearly as simple and sheltered as it appeared to be, and the forthright and sometimes brutal language that came from the loudspeaker that morning astonished and troubled her. She continued to listen until her maid came in. Then she turned off the radio quickly, since this insight, she realized, was a furtive one.

Irene had a luncheon date with a friend that day, and she left her apartment at a little after twelve. There were a number of women in the elevator when it stopped at her floor. She stared at their handsome and impassive faces, their furs, and the cloth flowers in their hats. Which one of them had been to Sea Island, she wondered. Which one had overdrawn her bank account? The elevator stopped at the tenth floor and a woman with a pair of Skye terriers joined them. Her hair was rigged high on her head and she wore a mink cape. She was humming the "Missouri Waltz."

Irene had two Martinis at lunch, and she looked searchingly at her friend and wondered what her secrets were. They had intended to go shopping after lunch, but Irene excused herself and went home. She told the maid that she was not to be disturbed; then she went into the living room, closed the doors, and switched on the radio. She heard, in the course of the afternoon, the halting conversation of a woman entertaining her aunt, the hysterical conclusion of a luncheon party, and a hostess briefing her maid about some cocktail guests. "Don't give the best Scotch to anyone who hasn't white hair," the hostess said. "See if you can get rid of that liver paste before you pass those hot things, and could you lend me five dollars? I want to tip the elevator man."

As the afternoon waned, the conversations increased in intensity. From where Irene sat, she could see the open sky above the East River. There were hundreds of clouds in the sky, as though the south wind had broken the winter into pieces and were blowing it north, and on her radio she could hear the arrival of cocktail guests and the return of children and businessmen from their schools and offices. "I found a good-sized diamond on the bathroom floor this morning," a woman said. "It must have fallen out of that bracelet Mrs. Dunston was wearing last night." "We'll sell it," a man said. "Take it down to the jeweller on Madison Avenue and sell it. Mrs. Dunston won't know the difference, and we could use a couple of hundred bucks . . ."

" 'Oranges and lemons, say the bells of St. Clement's,' " the Sweeneys' nurse sang. " 'Half-pence and far-things, say the bells of St. Martin's. When will you pay me? say the bells at old Bailey . . .' " "It's not a hat," a woman cried, and at her back roared a cocktail party. "It's not a hat, it's a love affair. That's what Walter Florell said. He said it's not a hat, it's a love affair," and then, in a lower voice, the same woman added, "Talk to somebody, for Christ's sake, honey, talk to somebody. If she catches you standing here not talking to anybody, she'll take us off her invitation list, and I love these parties."

The Westcotts were going out for dinner that night, and when Jim came home, Irene was dressing. She seemed sad and vague, and he brought her a drink. They were dining with friends in the neighborhood, and they walked to where they were going. The sky was broad and filled with light. It was one of those splendid spring evenings that excite memory and desire, and the air that touched their hands and faces felt very soft. A Salvation Army band was on the corner playing "Jesus Is Sweeter." Irene drew on her husband's arm and held him there for a minute, to hear the music. "They're really such nice people, aren't they?" she said. "They have such nice faces. Actually, they're so much nicer than a lot of the people we know." She took a bill from her purse and walked over and dropped it into the tambourine. There was in her face, when she returned to her husband, a look of radiant melancholy that he was not familiar with. And her conduct at the dinner party that night seemed strange to him, too. She interrupted her hostess rudely and stared at the people across the table from her with an intensity for which she would have punished her children.

It was still mild when they walked home from the party, and Irene looked up at the spring stars. " 'How far that little candle throws its beams,' " she exclaimed. " 'So shines a good deed in a naughty world.' " She waited that night until Jim had fallen asleep, and then went into the living room and turned on the radio.

Jim came home at about six the next night. Emma, the maid, let him in, and had taken off his hat and was taking off his coat when Irene ran into the hall. Her face was shining with tears and her hair was disordered. "Go up to 16-C, Jim!" she screamed. "Don't take off your coat. Go up to 16-C. Mr. Osborn's beating his wife. They've been quarrelling since four o'clock, and now he's hitting her. Go up there and stop him."

From the radio in the living room, Jim heard screams, obscenities, and thuds. "You know you don't have to listen to this sort of thing," he said. He strode into the living room and turned the switch. "It's indecent," he said. "It's like looking in windows. You know you don't have to listen to this sort of thing. You can turn it off."

"Oh, it's so horrible, it's so dreadful," Irene was sobbing. "I've been listening all day, and it's so depressing."

"Well, if it's so depressing, why do you listen to it? I bought this damned radio to give you some pleasure," he said. "I paid a great deal of money for it. I thought it might make you happy. I wanted to make you happy."

"Don't, don't, don't, don't quarrel with me," she moaned, and laid her head on his shoulder. "All the others have been quarrelling all day. Everybody's been quarrelling. They're all worried about money.

Mrs. Hutchinson's mother is dying of cancer in Florida and they don't have enough money to send her to the Mayo Clinic. At least, Mr. Hutchinson says they don't have enough money. And some woman in this building is having an affair with the handyman—with that hideous handyman. It's too disgusting. And Mrs. Melville has heart trouble and Mr. Hendricks is going to lose his job in April and Mrs. Hendricks is horrid about the whole thing and that girl who plays the 'Missouri Waltz' is a whore, a common whore, and the elevator man has tuberculosis and Mr. Osborn has been beating Mrs. Osborn." She wailed, she trembled with grief and checked the stream of tears down her face with the heel of her palm.

"Well, why do you have to listen?" Jim asked again. "Why do you have to listen to this stuff if it makes you so miserable?"

"Oh, don't, don't, don't," she cried. "Life is too terrible, too sordid and awful. But we've never been like that, have we, darling? Have we? I mean we've always been good and decent and loving to one another, haven't we? And we have two children, two beautiful children. Our lives aren't sordid, are they, darling? Are they?" She flung her arms around his neck and drew his face down to hers. "We're happy, aren't we, darling? We are happy, aren't we?"

"Of course we're happy," he said tiredly. He began to surrender his resentment. "Of course we're happy. I'll have that damned radio fixed or taken away tomorrow." He stroked her soft hair. "My poor girl," he said.

"You love me, don't you?" she asked. "And we're not hypercritical or worried about money or dishonest, are we?"

"No, darling," he said.

A man came in the morning and fixed the radio. Irene turned it on cautiously and was happy to hear a California-wine commercial and a recording of Beethoven's Ninth Symphony, including Schiller's "Ode to Joy." She kept the radio on all day and nothing untoward came from the speaker.

A Spanish suite was being played when Jim came home. "Is everything all right?" he asked. His face was pale, she thought. They had some cocktails and went in to dinner to the "Anvil Chorus" from "Il Trovatore." This was followed by Debussy's "La Mer."

"I paid the bill for the radio today," Jim said. "It cost four hundred dollars. I hope you'll get some enjoyment out of it."

"Oh, I'm sure I will," Irene said.

"Four hundred dollars is a good deal more than I can afford," he went on. "I wanted to get something that you'd enjoy. It's the last extravagance we'll be able to indulge in this year. I see that you haven't paid your clothing bills yet. I saw them on your dressing table." He looked directly at her. "Why did you tell me you'd paid them? Why did you lie to me?"

"I just didn't want you to worry, Jim," she said. She drank some water. "I'll be able to pay my bills out of this month's allowance. There were the slipcovers last month, and that party."

"You've got to learn to handle the money I give you a little more intelligently, Irene," he said. "You've got to understand that we won't have as much money this year as we had last. I had a very sobering talk with Mitchell today. No one is buying anything. We're spending all our time promoting new issues, and you know how long that takes. I'm not getting any younger, you know. I'm thirty-seven. My hair will be gray next year. I haven't done as well as I'd hoped to. And I don't suppose things will get any better."

"Yes, dear," she said.

"We've got to start cutting down," Jim said. "We've got to think of the children. To be perfectly frank with you, I worry about money a great deal. I'm not at all sure of the future. No one is. If anything should happen to me, there's the insurance, but that wouldn't go very far today. I've worked awfully hard to give you and the children a comfortable life," he said bitterly. "I don't like to see all of my energies, all of my youth, wasted in fur coats and radios and slipcovers and—"

"Please, Jim," she said. "Please. They'll hear us."

"Who'll hear us? Emma can't hear us."

"The radio."

"Oh, I'm sick!" he shouted. "I'm sick to death of your apprehensiveness. The radio can't hear us. Nobody can hear us. And what if they can hear us? Who cares?"

Irene got up from the table and went into the living room. Jim went to the door and shouted at her from there. "Why are you so Christly all of a sudden? What's turned you overnight into a convent girl? You stole your mother's jewelry before they probated her will. You never gave your sister a cent of that money that was intended for her—not even when she needed it. You made Grace Howland's life miserable, and where was all your piety and your virtue when you went to that abortionist? I'll never forget how cool you were. You packed your bag and went off to have that child murdered as if you were going to Nassau. If you'd had any reasons, if you'd had any good reasons—"

Irene stood for a minute before the hideous cabinet, disgraced and sickened, but she held her hand on the switch before she extinguished the music and the voices, hoping that the instrument might speak to her kindly, that she might hear the Sweeneys' nurse. Jim continued to shout at her from the door. The voice on the radio was suave and noncommital. "An early-morning railroad disaster in Tokyo," the loudspeaker said, "killed twenty-nine people. A fire in a Catholic hospital near Buffalo for the care of blind children was extinguished early this morning by nuns. The temperature is forty-seven. The humidity is eighty-nine."

Questions

1. The new radio is described as seeming to Irene "like an aggressive intruder." Its dials flood "with malevolent light." Violent forces are "snared in the ugly gumwood cabinet." What is the effect of such statements? At one point early in the story "the powerful and ugly instrument, with its mistaken sensitivity to discord," is said to be more than Irene "could hope to master," and she turns it off. Does this in any way foreshadow events to come?

2. The device of a radio which can be tuned in on other apart-

ments is basically a trick, a gimmick. How does Cheever make the radio's strange powers plausible? What does the radio come to stand for in the course of the story?

3. **The weight of events falls on Irene, not her husband. Is he anything more than a device? Why didn't Cheever develop his involvement more fully?**
4. **What is the function of the last section? Why isn't it longer?**
5. **Why does Cheever close his story with a brief news report by a radio commentator? How are the news events relevant to the story? Is there any irony involved?**

CONTINENTAL CLASSICS

Ivan Turgenev

Bezhin Meadow

HENRY JAMES once called Turgenev "the novelist's novelist." It would be equally appropriate to call him the storyteller's storyteller, for Turgenev was the supreme professional; his art was to conceal the art behind his stories.

Nothing is more natural than a Turgenev story. It appears to have written itself. A series of events, apparently taken directly from life, are set down, apparently as they occurred. The whole art would seem to lie in the recording. *"Bezhin Meadow," for example, which is one of a series of tales which make up* THE HUNTING SKETCHES, *would appear to be simply a retelling of how the sportsman, after a day of shooting, lost his way home at dusk, wandered into Bezhin Meadow, and spent the night beside a campfire listening to the talk of five peasant boys who were watching over a herd of horses.*

The art behind such apparently simple telling lies in construction and in the selection of detail. For one thing, the story of the sportsman losing his way is calculated to prepare the reader for the story of the boys, which is Turgenev's true subject matter. And what follows is not merely a record of what the boys talked about around the fire; the entire night's events are viewed through the eyes of the sophisticated narrator, who gives them a form, and even a climax.

Turgenev believed that a true creative writer thinks in images. He once said, speaking of his own method of writing fiction, that he "never started from ideas *but always from* characters." *One of the achievements of Turgenev's stories is that ideas are so embodied in character and event that it is impossible to distinguish them from the stories which embody them.*

It was a splendid day in July, one of those days which occur only during a long spell of good weather. Since earliest morning the sky is clear; the dawn glow does not flare like a conflagration—it diffuses itself like a gentle blush. The sun is not fire, is not incandescent, as it is during a sultry drought, nor is it a dull purple, as before a storm, but bright and affably radiant; it floats upward peacefully from under a narrow and lengthy cloud, sends its fresh radiance through it, and then plunges into its lilac haze. The thin upper rim of the distended cloudlet begins to coruscate with little snakes of light: their gleam is like the gleam of wrought silver. But now the playful beams have again gushed forth—and blithely and majestically, as if it were winging upward, the mighty luminary comes up.

About noontime a host of round, lofty clouds appears, aureately gray, rimmed with soft whiteness. Like islands scattered over a river in infinite flood that runs around them in deeply transparent channels, they hardly budge; farther on, toward the sky's rim, they move near to one another, they huddle; there is no longer any blue to be seen between them, but they themselves are of the same azure as the sky; all of them are shot through and through with light and warmth. The hue of the horizon, ethereal, pale lilac, does not change throughout the day and is uniform all around; nowhere is there a thunderstorm darkling, gathering, save that here and there streaks of pale blue may extend downward: a barely noticeable drizzle, this, being sown upon the earth. Toward evening these clouds vanish; the last of them, rather black and of indeterminate form, like smoke, lie down in roseate swirls against the setting sun; at the spot where it has set, as calmly as it had risen in the sky, a ruby-red aura lingers for a brief while over the darkened earth and, gently flickering, like a candle solicitously borne along, the evening star will come to a soft glow against it.

On such days all pigments are softened, they are bright yet not vivid; an impress of some touching mildness lies upon all things. On such days the heat can, at times, be quite intense—occasionally it even steams along the slopes of the fields; but the wind scatters, sunders the accumulated sultriness, and whirlwinds (an indubitable sign of a long spell of good weather) wander in towering white pillars on their rounds over the roads, across plowed land. The dry and pure air is filled with the odors of wormwood, of reaped rye, of buckwheat; even at the hour before nightfall you feel no dampness. It is weather such as this that the husbandman longs for to gather in his grain.

It was on just such a day that I happened to be hunting grouse in the Chernov district of the Tula province. I had come across and had shot quite a lot of game; the full gamebag was cutting into my shoulder mercilessly; but it was only when the evening glow had already died out and the chill shadows were already beginning to grow denser and to spread through the air, which was still full of light although no longer lit by the rays of the set sun, that I at last decided to turn homeward. With long strides I traversed an extensive stretch of brushwood, clambered up on a knoll—and, instead of the familiar plain I expected, with a small oak grove to the right and a squat little church in the distance, beheld an altogether different locality which was unknown to me. A narrow dale stretched away at my feet; directly opposite me a thick copse of aspens rose in a steep wall. I halted in perplexity and looked about me.

"Eh!" I reflected. "I haven't hit on the right spot at all—I've gone too far to the right." And, wondering at my own mistake, I quickly descended the knoll. An unpleasant, stagnant dampness enveloped me at once, just as though I had stepped into a cellar; wet grass, thick and high, looked as white and even as a tablecloth at the bottom of the dale; one felt somehow creepy walking on it. I clambered out as quickly as I could on the other side and went on, heading to the left along the copse of aspens. Bats, mysteriously circling and quivering against the dimly clear sky, were already flitting over the slumbering treetops; a young hawk, belated, flew past, hastening to its nest.

"There," I kept thinking, "as soon as I come out at that end I'll hit on the road at once. But, just the same, I must have gone almost a mile out of my way!"

I finally managed to reach the end of the woods, but there was no road of any sort there: some kind of untouched low bushes spread far and wide before me, while beyond them, ever so far off, one could glimpse a desertlike field. I stopped again.

"What is all this! Come, where am I, after all?"

I started in recalling which way I had been going and where I had been during the course of the day.

"Why, this is the Parahin stretch of brushwood!" I exclaimed at last. "Sure enough—that must be the Sindeiev copse over there. Yes, but how did I ever get here, as far as all this? That's odd! Now I'll have to turn to the right."

I started off toward the right, through the bushes. In the meanwhile the night was nearing and spreading, like a thundercloud; darkness seemed to be rising everywhere with the evening vapors, and even pouring down from on high. I came across a little-used, grass-grown path; I set out along it, peering ahead. Everything around me was darkling fast and quieting down; the quail alone were calling out at infrequent intervals. Some small night bird, darting low and without a sound of its soft wings, almost flew against me and then swooped to one side in fright. I came out on the edge of the brushwood and walked along the boundary line between two fields. By now I could make out objects in the distance only with difficulty: the field was glimmering whitely all around; beyond it, advancing with every moment in enormous swirls, somber murk was rising fast. My steps echoed dully in the congealing air. The sky, which had grown wan, had again begun to turn blue—but now it was the blue of night. The little stars had started twinkling, had started stirring in it.

That which I had taken for a copse turned out to be a dark and rounded mound. "Come, where am I, after all?" I repeated aloud, stopped for the third time, and looked questioningly at my yellow-spotted bitch Dianka, who was of an English breed, absolutely the cleverest of all four-legged creatures. But the cleverest of all four-legged creatures merely kept wagging her bit of a tail, blinked her tired little eyes dismally, and offered me no sound advice whatsoever. I became ashamed before her and desperately hastened onward, as though I had suddenly conjectured which way I ought to go, skirted the mound, and discovered I was in a shallow valley that had been plowed everywhere. At once a strange feeling took possession of me. This valley looked almost like a regular caldron with sloping sides; at its bottom several huge white stones were standing up on end—it seemed as if they had crept together there for a secret council—and so voiceless and forsaken was everything in that valley, and so flat, and so despondently did the sky hang over it, that my heart shrank within me. Some tiny beast emitted a faint and plaintive squeak among the stones. I lost no time in clambering back up on the mound. Up to now I still hadn't abandoned hope of finding the way home, but at this point I became definitely convinced that I had gone completely astray and, no longer making the least attempt to recognize my surroundings, by now almost sunk in gloom, I went straight ahead, following the stars—and trusting to luck.

For something like half an hour did I walk thus, shifting my feet with difficulty. It seemed to me as if I had never been in such a deserted locality in all my born days: not a light, no matter how small, glimmered anywhere, nor was there a sound of any sort to be heard. One sloping knoll succeeded another, field stretched endlessly after field, the bushes seemed to spring up unexpectedly out of the ground before my very nose. I kept on walking, and was just about to lie down somewhere until morning when I suddenly found myself above a frightful chasm.

I quickly drew my lifted foot back and, through the barely transparent dusk of night, saw an enormous plain far below me. A broad river curved around it, receding from me in a semicircle; steely reflections on the water, glimmering indistinctly and intermittently, marked its current. The knoll on which I found myself went down in an abrupt, almost perpendicular precipice; its enormous outlines stood out darkly from the bluish ethereal void and, directly beneath me, in the angle formed by that precipice and the plain, near the river which at that spot, under the steepest part of the knoll, was an unmoving dark mirror, two small fires were flaming redly and smoking close to each other. People were bustling and shadows were swaying around them; now and then the forepart of some small curly head would become vividly lit.

I recognized, at last, the place I had come to. This meadow is celebrated throughout our parts under the name of Bezhin Meadow. However, there was no possibility whatsoever of turning homeward then, especially in the nighttime; my legs were caving in under me from fatigue. I decided to walk over to the fires and to bide the coming of the dawn in the company of those people, whom I took to be drovers. I came down safely, but hardly had I let go of the last branch I had seized when two great, white shaggy dogs suddenly threw themselves upon me with vicious barking. Children's voices were raised around the fires; two or three boys quickly got up from the ground. I answered their hails. They ran up, immediately called off their dogs, who had been particularly overcome when my Dianka had put in her appearance, and I came over to them.

I had erred in taking those sitting around the fires for drovers. They were simply peasant urchins from a village close by, tending a drove of horses. During the hot spells of summer the horses in our parts are driven out to graze at night; in the daytime the flies and gadflies would give them no rest. To bring out the drove toward evening and to bring it back at morning glow is a great and festal affair for peasant boys. Bareheaded, in old sheepskin jackets, astride the liveliest of the little nags, they race along with gay whoops and shouts, their arms and legs threshing about, their laughter ringing as they bounce high. The light dust rises and races along the road in a yellow pillar; the beat of hoofs pounding in unison spreads far and wide; the horses run with their ears cocked; at their very head, with his tail straight up and constantly changing stride, gallops some russet-colored shaggy stallion with cockleburs in his tangled mane.

I told the boys that I had lost my way and sat down near them. They asked me where I had come from, were silent for a while, and made room for me. We talked a little. I lay down under a small bush that had been nibbled clean and began looking about me. The picture was a wondrous one: a round, reddish reflection quivered near the fires and seemed to poise in midair, leaning against the darkness; the flames, flaring up, would cast occasional fleeting glints beyond the limits of that ringed reflection; a slender tongue of light would lick the bare boughs of the willow bushes and momentarily vanish; long, pointed shadows, impetuously intruding for an instant, in their turn darted up to the very embers: murk contending with light.

Now and then, when the flame burned fainter, and the ring of light contracted, out of the advancing darkness a horse's head would emerge suddenly—a sorrel head, with a winding scar, or one all white; it would regard you attentively and stolidly, champing the high grass in an expert fashion and, lowering itself again, would promptly disappear. All one could hear was its continued champing and its snorts. When one sits where it is light, it is hard to make out what is going on in the dark, and therefore everything near at hand seemed to have an almost black curtain drawn over it; but farther on, toward the horizon, one could glimpse the knolls and woods dimly, lying in long blotches. The dark clear sky in all its mysterious splendor was austere and unencompassably high above us. One's chest felt a delectable pressure as it breathed in that unique, stirring, and fresh fragrance—the fragrance of a Russian night in summer. All around us there was hardly a noise of any sort to be heard. Only at infrequent intervals, in the river close by, some large fish would plash with abrupt loudness, and the bankside reeds, barely stirred by some suddenly risen wave, would break into faint soughing. . . . All was quiet, save for the crackling, ever so low, of the small campfires.

The boys were sitting around them; here, too, squatted those dogs who had been so eager to devour me. For a long time they could not become reconciled to my presence and, drowsily puckering up their eyes against the fire and watching it askance, kept growling every so often with an extraordinary sense of their own dignity; they would growl at first, and then whine a little, as though regretting the impossibility of fulfilling their desire. There were five boys in all: Fedya, Pavlusha, Iliusha, Kostya, and Vanya. (I picked up their names from their conversations, and it is my intention to acquaint the reader with these boys right now.)

Fedya, the first and the oldest among them, one would judge to be fourteen. A well-built boy, this, with handsome and fine features, somewhat small, hair flaxen and curly, clear eyes and a steady smile, half merry, half absent-minded. By all the signs he belonged to a well-to-do family and had ridden out into the field not out of any necessity but just so, for the fun of the thing. He had on a shirt of brightly patterned calico, hemmed with yellow; his small, new overcoat, thrown over his narrow little shoulders, perched there precariously; a comb dangled from his belt of pale-blue leather. His boots, with low tops, were his own sure enough, and no hand-me-downs from his father.

Pavlusha, the second boy, had black tousled hair, gray eyes, broad cheekbones, a face pale, pockmarked, a mouth wide yet regular; his whole head was huge, big as a beer vat, as they say; his body was squat, unwieldy. None too good-looking a youngster—what's the use of talking!—but just the same I took a liking to him; his looks were very intelligent and forthright, and in his voice, too, there was the ring of strength. He could hardly have shown off with his clothes: they consisted, all in all, of a common linen shirt and much-patched breeches.

The face of the third, Iliusha, was rather insignificant: hump-nosed, long-drawn, purblind, it bore an expression of some dull, sickly care; his pursed lips did not move, his knit eyebrows did not relax—he seemed to be puckering his eyes from the firelight all the time. His yellow, almost white hair stuck out in pointed tufts like little pigtails from under his rather low, small felt cap, which he was forever shoving down over his ears with both hands. He had on new bast sandals and foot clouts; a stout rope, wound thrice about his waist, snugly girded his neat, black, short overcoat. Both he and Pavlusha looked no more than twelve.

The fourth, Kostya, a boy of ten, aroused my curiosity by his stare of melancholy and deep thought. His whole face was none too big; it was thin, sprinkled with freckles, sharply pointed toward the chin, like a squirrel's; one could barely make out his lips; but it was his eyes—big, dark, gleaming with a fluid gleam—which created a strange impression: they wanted to say something, it seemed, something for which language (his language, at least) had no words. He was short, of a puny build, and was dressed rather poorly.

The last, Vanya, I had at first actually failed to notice: he was lying on the ground, curled up ever so peacefully under stiff matting, and only at rare intervals did he thrust out his flaxen, curly head from under it. This boy was no more than seven.

And so, I was lying off to one side under a small bush and looking at the boys from time to time. A small kettle was hanging over one of the fires, with "spuds" cooking therein. Pavlusha was keeping an eye on them, standing on his knees and thrusting a piece of kindling wood into the water, which was coming to a boil. Fedya was lying propped up on one elbow and with the skirts of his overcoat spread out. Iliusha was sitting alongside of Kostya and puckering his eyes as intently as before. Kostya had let his head droop a little and was looking somewhere off into the distance. Vanya did not stir under his matting. I pretended to be asleep. Little by little the boys got to talking again.

At first they chatted a bit about this and that, about the work they would have to face on the morrow, about horses—when Fedya suddenly turned to Iliusha and, as though he were resuming an interrupted conversation, asked him:

"Well, now, and did you see the hobgoblin for fair?"

"No, see him I didn't, and besides you can't see him," Iliusha answered in a hoarse and weak voice, the sound of which could not possibly have been more in keeping with the expression on his face. "But I did hear him. And I weren't the only one that did."

"And whereabouts in your place does he keep himself?" asked Pavlusha.

"In the old rolling room."[1]

"Why, do you people go to the paper mill?"

"Sure, why not? My brother Avdiushka and me work there as glossers."[2]

"So that's how. You're factory hands!"

"Well, how come you to hear him?" asked Fedya.

"Why, this is how. It so happened that my brother Avdiushka and me, and Fedor Mihievsky, and Ivashka Kossoi, and also another Ivashka, the one from Red Knolls, and still another Ivashka, by the name of Suhorukii, and there was other lads there, too—there must have been ten boys of us altogether—the whole shift, for the matter of that—well, it so happened we had to pass the night in that rolling room; that is, we didn't really have to, only Nazarov, the overseer, forbade us to go home: 'What's the use of you boys traipsing home,' says he, 'there's a lot of work tomorrow, so don't you go home, lads.' So we stayed on there, and we was lying together, all of us, and Avdiushka he gets to talking: 'Well, now, lads, what if the hobgoblin was to come?' And hardly had he done saying this—Avdei, I mean—when all of a sudden somebody starts walking around over our heads; we was lying down below, see, but he starts walking around up there, near the wheel. We hear him walking around, the boards simply bending, simply cracking under him; there, he'd passed right over our heads—when all of a sudden the water starts making a noise, and what a noise! going over the wheel; the wheel begins knocking, knocking, and turning—and yet the gates to the castle,[3] now, was all lowered. So we wondered who could ever have raised them, so that

[1] The building where the paper is dipped up from the vats in a paper mill is called the rolling or dipping room. It is located near the very dam, under the wheel.—*Author.*

[2] The glossers calendar and pare the paper.—*Author.*

[3] A local name for the sluiceway bringing the water to the mill wheel. —*Author.*

the water had started flowing. However, that wheel turned and turned a while, and then stopped.

"Then he began walking about again, making for the door upstairs, and then he started down the stairs, and he was coming down them stairs like he weren't in no hurry at all; the steps was just simply groaning under him. Well, he walked right up to our door, hung around and hung around there for a bit—and then all of a sudden that door pops right open. All startled, we was; then we look—and there's nothing there. Suddenly, when we give another look, there was the form[4] at one of the vats moving, rising, dipping; it kept going like that for a while through the air, as if someone was rinsing it, and then got back to its place again. Then at another vat the hook took off of its nail and fell back on the nail again; after that it seemed like somebody had walked over toward the door, and all of a sudden he got such a coughing spell, such a sneezing fit, like a sheep or something, and that so loud and all. We just tumbled down in a heap, all of us, trying to crawl under one another. Lord, but we was plenty scared that time!"

"So that's how it was!" Pavel commented. "But what made him go off in a coughing spell like that?"

"Don't know; maybe it was the damp."

They were all silent for a space.

"Well, now, is them spuds cooked yet?" asked Fedya.

Pavlusha prodded them:

"No; they're still hard. Listen to that splash!" he added, turning his face toward the river. "Must be a pike. And look at that little star rolling down the sky—"

"Well, now, fellows, here's something I'm going to tell you," Kostya began in a piping voice. "You just listen to what my dad was telling us the other day, whilst I happened to be there—"

"All right, we're listening," said Fedya with a patronizing air.

"Guess you know Gavrila, the carpenter in that big village near town?"

"Well, yes, we know him."

[4] The wire cloth or apron for dipping up the paper.—*Author.*

"But do you know why he's always down in the mouth like that, never saying anything? Do you know why? Here's why he's such a glum fellow; he once went, says my dad—he once went, brothers of mine, into the forest, after nuts. Well, so he went into the forest, after nuts, and he ups and loses his way; he went ever so far out of his way—God knows how far out of his way he went. And he walked, and he walked, brothers of mine—but he couldn't find the right path, nohow! And it was already night out. So then he sat him down under a tree: 'There, now, let's wait for morning here'; he sat him down and dozed off. There, he'd dozed off, and all of a sudden he heard someone calling him. He looked—there was no one around. He dozed off again, and again he heard someone calling him. He looked and he looked—and right before him there was a nixie, perched on a bough; she was swinging there and calling him to come to her, whilst she herself was laughing, laughing fit to kill. And the moon, now—the moon was shining ever so bright, plain as plain; you could see everything, brothers of mine. There, she was calling him to come to her, and she herself, this water creature, was such a shining little thing, for all the world like she were some small dace, or a minnow—there's also a carp like that, all sort of white, silverlike. Gavrila the carpenter, he were plum scared to death, brothers of mine; but all she knew was to laugh out loud, and all the time she kept beckoning to him with her hand to come over to her—like this. Gavrila, he'd already gotten up on his feet, actually; he was all set by then to heed that water fairy, brothers of mine, but I guess the Lord Himself must have sent him some sense: he did contrive to make the sign of the cross over himself. And how hard it was for him by then to be making that sign, brothers of mine! 'My hand,' said he later, 'was like stone, for fair; couldn't even turn it. Ah, hang it all!'

"Well, soon as he'd made that sign, brothers of mine, that there little nixie she plumb stopped laughing—and all of a sudden started in to weep! My! She was weeping, brothers of mine, wiping her eyes with her hair—and her hair was all green, now, green as hemp. So Gavrila he looked and looked at her, and he started in for to question her: 'What are you weeping about, you evil forest creature?' But the nixie, she spoke up to him: 'You oughtn't to be crossing yourself,' said she, 'you that was born of woman, but ought to be living with me in blitheness to the end of your days; and the reason I'm weeping, killing myself for grief, is because you made the sign of the cross over yourself; however, I won't be the only one killing myself for grief: kill yourself with grief also, to the end of your days.' And right then and there, brothers of mine, she vanished; and as for Gavrila, everything at once became clear to him—how he was to get out of the forest, that is. Only thing is, since that time he walks about the way you see him, always down at the mouth."

"There!" Fedya got out after a brief silence. "But could such a foul forest creature ever spoil a human soul—after all, he had paid her no heed."

"And yet, there it is!" said Kostya. "And Gavrila was also telling us that her voice, now, was ever so high, ever so pitiful, like a toad's."

"Was it your old man himself who told this story?" Fedya persisted.

"He himself. I was lying on the ledge atop the oven; I heard everything."

"It sure is a queer business! Still, why should he be down at the mouth? Well, I guess he must have been to her liking, seeing as how she was calling him."

"Yes, was he to her liking?" Iliusha chimed in quickly.

"Guess again! She was after tickling him to death, that's what she was after. That's what they do, those nixies, now."

"Why, I guess there must be nixies right around here, too," Fedya remarked.

"No," answered Kostya, "this place is clean, right out in the open. The only thing is, the river is close by."

They all fell silent. Suddenly, somewhere in the distance, a long-drawn, ringing, almost moaning sound arose, one of those incomprehensible night sounds which sometimes spring up amid profound silence; they soar, linger in the air, and at last spread slowly, as if dying away. Hearken closely—and it is as though there were no sound, and yet there is a ringing in the air. It sounded as if someone had emitted a long, long cry, under the very rim of the sky, as if some other had responded in the forest with high-pitched, piercing laughter, and a faint, sibilant whistle had then sped over the river. The boys exchanged looks, shuddered. . . .

"The power of the Cross be with us!" Ilya got out in a whisper.

"Oh, you crows!" Pavel called out. "What did you get all up in the air about? Look, now, them spuds is all cooked." They all moved up to the small kettle and began eating the steaming potatoes; Vanya alone did not stir. "Say, what about you?" Pavel asked him, but Vanya did not crawl out from under his matting. It was not long before the kettle was empty.

"But have you heard, fellows," Iliusha spoke up, "about what happened the other day in our Varnavitzy?"

"On the dam, now?" Fedya wanted to know.

"Yes, yes, on the dam—the one that the water broke through. Now *there's* an unclean place that's really unclean, and ever so forsaken. There's all them ravines and gullies roundabout, and the gullies is all full of snakes."

"Well, what happened there? Go ahead and tell us."

"Why, here's what happened. Maybe you don't know it, Fedya, but we've got a drowned man buried there, and he drowned himself ever so long ago, when the millpond was still deep; however, you can still see his small grave, although you can hardly make it out, at that—it's just a little mound. Well, a few days ago our clerk calls Ermila, the kennel keeper: 'You go and fetch the mail, now, Ermil,' he tells him. Our Ermil always goes after the mail, for he'd done all his hounds to death—they don't live under his care, somehow, and they never did, if it comes to that, yet he's a good man with dogs, in all ways. So this Ermil, now, he started off on a horse for the mail, but he hung around a little too long in town, and when he was driving back he was already tipsy. And it was night by then, a light night—the moon was shining. Well, so there was Ermil, riding across the dam. That was the road he'd happened to take. So there he was, riding along like that, this Ermil the kennel keeper, and what does he see but a little woolly lamb on the drowned man's grave—a white little thing, its wool all curly—a pretty little thing, ambling about. So Ermil, he thought to himself: 'Might as well take it along—what's the use of its getting lost, all for nothing,' and he got off of his horse and took that little lamb in his arms. And the lamb, now, it don't mind at all. So then Ermil he goes toward his horse—but the horse backs away from him, breathing hard, tossing its head; just the same, he quieted it down, got up on it together with the lamb, and rode on, holding the lamb in front of him. He looks at it, and the lamb just stares him right in the eye. He felt uncanny, did this Ermil the kennel keeper. 'I disremember,' he kept thinking, 'about any rams staring anyone in the eye like that.' However, it weren't so bad; he fell to stroking its wool, like that, and talking to it: 'There, little lamby, there!' But that there little ram, it bares its teeth, all of a sudden, and comes right back at him: 'There, little lamb, there!' "

Hardly had the narrator uttered the last word when both dogs suddenly rose up as one, dashed away from the fire with convulsive barking, and vanished in the dark. All the boys were thoroughly frightened. Vanya jumped out from under his matting. Pavlusha, shouting, rushed off after the dogs. Their barking was rapidly receding. One could hear the uneasy trampling of the startled drove. "Here, Gray! Here, Beetle!" Pavlusha was loudly calling. In a few moments the barking quieted down; by now Pavel's voice was coming from afar. A little more time passed; the boys were looking at one another in perplexity, as though waiting for what would happen next. Suddenly there came the hoofbeats of a galloping horse; it stopped short near the fire, and holding tight to its mane, Pavlusha sprang down nimbly from its back. Both dogs in their turn leaped within the ring of light and immediately squatted on their haunches, letting their red tongues loll.

"What happened there? What's up?" asked the boys.

"Nothing," answered Pavel, taking a swipe at the horse. "The dogs must have scented something, that's all. I thought it might be a wolf," he added in an indifferent voice, breathing quickly with all his chest heaving.

I involuntarily took an admiring look at Pavlusha. He was very fine at that moment. His homely face, animated from the fast ride, glowed with derring-do and firm resolve. Without as much as a dry twig in his hand, at night, he had without the least hesitation dashed off against a wolf all by himself. "What a splendid boy!" I reflected as I looked at him.

"But has anybody seen them, now—the wolves, I mean?" asked Kostya, the little poltroon.

"There's always plenty of them around here," Pavel answered. "But it's only in winter that they're troublesome."

He again snuggled down before the fire. As he had been about to sit down on the ground he let his hand drop on the shaggy neck of one of the dogs, and the animal, thus gladdened, would not turn its head for a long time, glancing out of the corner of its eye at Pavlusha with appreciative pride.

Vanya again burrowed deep under his matting.

"My, Iliusha, what dreadful things you were telling us," began Fedya, upon whom, as the son of a well-to-do peasant, it devolved to start the talk going. (He himself spoke little, as though wary of lowering his dignity.) "Then, too, the Restless One had to egg on the dogs to start barking. But it's true enough—I've heard tell your place is haunted."

"The Varnavitzy? I should say so! And how! They've seen our old master there more than once. He walks about in a long-skirted coat, they say, and all the time he keeps oh'ing, like this, looking for something on the ground. Grandpa Trophimych met up with him once. 'What, now, may it be your pleasure to be seeking for on the ground, Ivan Ivanych, father of mine?' "

"He asked him that?" the astonished Fedya interrupted him.

"Yes, he did."

"Well, I must say Trophimych is a brave fellow after that. Well, and what did the other have to say?"

" 'It's loose-all grass I'm looking for,' said he. And he said it in such a stifled voice, ever so stifled. 'And what would you be wanting loose-all grass for, Ivan Ivanych, father of mine?'—'My grave is crushing me,' said the other, 'it's crushing me, Trophimych; I want to get out of it, I want to get out—' "

"So that's the sort he is!" remarked Fedya. "Guess he hadn't lived long enough."

"That sure is a great wonder!" Kostya commented. "I thought you can see the departed only on a Parental Sabbath."[5]

"You can see the departed at any time," Iliusha chimed in with assurance—he, as far as I could observe, knew all the local superstitions better than the others. "But then, on a Parental Sabbath you can see even the living departed—those whose turn has come to die that year, I mean. All you've got to do is to sit down on the church porch at night, and keep watching the road. And those people will start marching past you along the road—those, that is, who are to die that year. There was Uliana, now, one of our womenfolk—she went to the church porch at night last year."

"Well, and did she see anybody?" Kostya asked with curiosity.

"I should say so! First off, she sat there a long, long while, without seeing or hearing anybody—only all the time it sounded like there was a little dog starting in to bark, sort of, starting in to bark somewheres. All of a sudden she gives a look, and there's a little boy walking along the road, in nothing but a little shift. She looked more closely: it was Ivashka Theodosiev walking along—"

"The one that died this spring?" Fedya cut in.

"The very same. He was walking along, and didn't even raise his little head, but Uliana recognized him. And then she looked again, and there was a countrywoman coming along. Uliana, she looked more closely and—the Lord be with us!—if it weren't her own self walking along that road . . . Uliana, her own self."

"Her own self, for sure?" asked Fedya.

"Her own self, by God!"

"Well, what of it? For she hasn't died yet, has she?"

"Yes, but the year ain't over yet. Just the same, you take a look at her: it's a wonder how she keeps body and soul together."

[5] A day of prayers for the departed on their graves. There were three such Sabbaths on the Greek-Catholic calendar: Tuesday after Quasimodo, Whitsun Sabbath, and during the Feast of the Intercession of the Most Holy Virgin, which began October 1st (Old Style).—*Translator*.

They all fell silent again. Pavel threw a handful of dry branches into the fire. They showed sharply black against the instantaneous flare-up of the flames, began to crackle, to smoke, and then to buckle, lifting up their charred ends. The reflection of the light, fitfully quivering, spurted in all directions, especially upward. Suddenly, coming from none knows where, a white pigeon flew straight against this reflection, timorously circled a while in one spot, all bathed in the warm glow, and vanished, beating its wings resoundingly.

"Guess it's lost its way home," Pavel remarked. "Now it'll keep on flying until it strikes against something, and wherever it strikes, that's where it'll stay through the night until dawn."

"Well, now, Pavlusha," Kostya spoke up, "weren't that some righteous soul winging its way to heaven, eh?"

Pavel threw another handful of dead branches into the fire.

"Could be," he let drop at last.

"But tell me, Pavlusha, do," Fedya began, "were you Shalamovo folks, too, able to see the heavenly prevision?" That is what our muzhiks call a solar eclipse.

"You mean when you couldn't see the sun any more? I should say so!"

"Guess your folks got plenty scared, too?"

"Why, we wasn't the only ones. Our master, now, even though he made it clear to us beforehand, telling us: 'You're going to have a prevision,' got scared himself as pretty as you please, they say, soon as it turned dark. And in the servants' quarters, I heard tell, the old woman that does the cooking, soon as it started turning dark in the middle of the day, why, she took and smashed all the pots with an oven fork: 'Who'd be eating now,' said she, 'when the Day of Judgment is upon us!' There was rivers of cabbage soup all over the place. And, brother, what rumors there were going around in our village! That there would be white wolves, now running over the land, that they would be devouring folks, that there would be flights of birds of prey, and that folks might even behold Trishka[6] himself."

[6] The belief concerning Trishka is, probably, an echo of the tradition concerning Antichrist.—*Author.*

"What Trishka is that?" asked Kostya.

"Why, don't you know?" Iliusha chimed in ardently. "Why, brother, where do you come from that you don't know about Trishka? They sure must be a lot of sticks-in-the mud in your village, that's what, just sticks-in-the-mud! Trishka, he's a certain amazing man who will come, and he'll come, this amazing man, in such a way that you won't be able as much as to lay hands on him, and there's nary a thing you'll be able to do to him; that's the sort of amazing man he will be. Suppose, for instance, the peasants want to take him; they'll come out against him with oaken staves, and will throw a ring around him, but he'll just pull the wool over their eyes, in such a way that they themselves will beat up one another. They may put him in prison, for instance, so he'll beg for a drink of water out of a dipper; they'll bring him the dipper, but he'll dive right into it—and that's the last they'll ever see of him. They'll put him in chains, but he'll just clasp his hands together, and those chains will fall right off of him. Well, then, this Trishka will be going about through the hamlets and the towns, and this Trishka will be tempting Christian folks—and yet there'll be nary a thing you can do to him. For that's the sort of amazing, crafty man he will be."

"Well, yes," Pavel resumed after this interruption, "that's what he's like. The old folks was saying, now, that as soon as the heavenly prevision would begin, why, Trishka would come. And so the prevision began. All the folks poured out of doors, into the fields, waiting for what would come. And, as you know, our place is such that you can see everything—there's plenty of room. There they were, watching, when all of a sudden, coming down the hill from the big village near town, there's some sort of a man walking along, queer as can be, the head on him so amazing—they all just let out one yell: 'Oh, Trishka's coming! Oh, Trishka's coming!' and each one lit out for himself, every which way. Our elder, he crawled into a ditch; the elder's wife, she got stuck under a gate, screaming for all she was worth, scaring her own yard dog so that it tore loose off of its chain, and over the wattle fence it went, and kept on into the woods, whilst Dorotheich—Kuzka's father, that is—dived into a field of oats, squatted there, and started calling like a quail, figuring that, who knows, maybe the Enemy, the Destroyer of Souls, might spare a bird, at least. That's how upset they all was! But the man that was walking along, now, was none other than our own cooper, Vavila; he'd bought himself a new tub with handles, and had put that tub on his head, so's to carry it the better."

All the boys broke into laughter and again fell silent for a moment, as is so often the case when people are talking out of doors. I looked around me: night was all about us, silent and majestic; the damp freshness of late evening had been replaced by the crisp warmth of midnight, and for a long while yet was it to lie in a soft pall upon the fields that had fallen into slumber; still a long time remained to the first bird song, to the first dewdrops of dawn. There was no moon in the sky—at that period it rose late. The innumerable golden stars were trying to outtwinkle one another, were flowing along, it seemed, in the same direction as the Milky Way; and, watching them, you yourself seemed to feel vaguely the impetuous, never-ceasing course of the earth. . . . A strange, grating, pained scream broke out over the river, twice in succession, and a few seconds later was repeated, this time farther off.

Kostya shuddered: "What was that?"

"That's a crane calling," Pavel replied calmly.

"A crane," Kostya repeated. "But there was something I heard yesterday," he added after a short silence. "Maybe you know—"

"What was it you heard?"

"Well, here's what. I was walking from Stony Ridge to Shashkino, and at first I kept close to our hazel bushes, then started going along a little meadow—you know, there where it comes out at a sharp turn from the gully, there's a deep water hole left after the spring freshets, you must know it, why, it's even all grown over with reeds—well, then, I started going past this water hole, brothers of mine, when all of a sudden somebody in that there water hole starts in to moan—and that so pitifully, so pitifully: *Oo-oo . . . oo-oo . . . oo-oo!* What a scare came over me then, brothers of mine! The time was so late, and the voice was full of such pain. Why, you felt you'd be starting in to cry yourself right then and there. What might that have been? Eh?"

"Last year some thieves drowned Akim the forester in that water hole," Pavlusha remarked, "so maybe it were his soul, complaining, like."

"Well, come to think of it, brothers of mine, that may be the very thing," Kostya spoke up, opening wide his eyes, which were enormous enough even without that. "And I didn't even know that they'd drowned Akim in that water hole—if I had, I'd have been scared still worse!"

"Then, too, they say there's a kind of tiny frogs," Pavel went on, "that have a way of croaking so pitifully."

"Frogs? Well, no, that weren't no frogs; how could it have been—" At this point the crane again sent forth its call over the river. "Eh, damn her!" Kostya said involuntarily. "Screeching like a forest fiend!"

"A forest fiend don't screech—he's mute," Iliusha caught him up. "All he does is clap his hands and cackle—"

"Why, did you ever lay eyes on him, by any chance—on a forest fiend, that is?" Fedya cut him short mockingly.

"No, I never did, and may God save me from seeing him, but there's others as has. There, just the other day he got around one of our muzhiks; he led him about and about, through the woods, and kept him going in circles over a certain meadow. It was all he could do to reach home just as it was getting light."

"Well, and did he see the forest fiend?"

"He did that. Ever so big, he was, big as big, says he, all dark, muffled up, just like he was behind a tree or something—no making him out well, like he were hiding from the moon, and he stares and stares at you with those huge eyes of his, now, and he keeps on blinking them, and blinking them—"

"Oh, my!" Fedya cried out, with a slight shudder and his shoulders jerking, and spat in disgust.

"And why have these foul things come upon this world in such numbers?" Pavel remarked. "Really, now!"

"Stop calling names," Ilya remarked in his turn. "Watch out, he may hear you."

There was another silence.

"Just look, lads, just look!" Vanya's childish voice suddenly broke the silence. "Just look at God's little stars; they're swarming like bees!"

He thrust out his fresh little face from under the matting, propped his head on one tiny fist, and slowly raised his big, gentle eyes. The eyes of all the boys were raised toward the heavens, and it was some time before they lowered them again.

"Well, Vanya," Fedya began kindly, "how is your sister Aniutka? Is she all right?"

"She is," Vanya answered, lisping a little.

"You ask her, why don't she come to us?"

"I don't know."

"You tell her to come."

"I will."

"You tell her I'll give her a present."

"And will you give me one, too?"

"And you, too."

Vanya sighed. "Well, no, I don't need it. Better give it to her; our Aniutka is such a kind little thing."

And Vanya again laid his head on the ground. Pavel got up and picked up the small kettle, now empty.

"Where you going?" Fedya asked him.

"To the river, to dip up some water; I feel like having a drink."

The dogs got up and followed him.

"Watch out; don't fall into the river," Iliusha called after him.

"Why should he fall in?" asked Fedya. "He'll be careful."

"Yes, he'll be careful. But there's all sorts of things can happen. There, he may lean over, start dipping up the water—and the water fiend will grab a holt of his hand and begin pulling him in. Later on they'll be saying: 'The little boy tumbled into the water, now.' Tumbled, me eye! The-ere, he's climbed in amongst the reeds," he added, listening intently.

Sure enough: the reeds, as they parted, were rustling.

"But is it true," Kostya asked, "that Akulina has been a little innocent ever since that time she'd been under water?"

"From that very time. And what she looks like now! And yet they say she used to be a beauty. The water fiend ruined her. Guess he weren't expecting they would pull her out so soon. Well, it was he that ruined her there, in his place at the bottom of the river."

(I myself had more than once come across this Akulina. Covered with tatters, frightful, gaunt, with a face black as coal, with a bewildered gaze and her teeth perpetually bared, she would stomp for hours on the same spot, somewhere on the road, with her bony hands pressed hard to her breast, and slowly shifting from foot to foot, just like some wild beast in its cage. She understood nothing, no matter what you said to her, and merely laughed loudly and spasmodically every now and then.)

"Still, they do be saying," Kostya went on, "that Akulina threw herself into the river for no other reason than that her lover deceived her."

"That's the very reason."

"And do you remember Vassya?" Kostya added sadly.

"What Vassya is that?" asked Fedya.

"Why, the one that drowned in this very river," answered Kostya. "What a fine lad he was, what a lad! His mother, Theklista, now—oh, how she loved him, how she loved this Vassya! And it was as though she felt, this Theklista, now, that he would come to his end because of water. Whenever that same Vassya would go with us in the summertime to swim in the river—why, she'd get all in a fluster. The other womenfolk, going by with their washtubs, waddling along, why, they don't pay no mind to their children; but Theklista, she'd put down her tub on the ground and start calling him: 'Come back, now, my little sun! Oh, come back, my young falcon!' And the Lord only knows how he come to drown! He was playing on the bank, and his mother was right there, raking the hay, when all of a sudden she hears a sound like someone was letting bubbles in the water. She looks, and there's nothing there but Vassya's little cap floating on the water. And it's from that very time that Theklista ain't in her right mind; she'll come and lie down at the spot where he drowned; she'll lie down, brothers of mine, and start singing a long-drawn little song—you remember, Vassya, now, always used to sing a song like that;

well, that's the very song she'll start singing, and she'll cry, and cry, complaining bitterly to God—"

"There, Pavlusha is coming," Fedya remarked.

Pavel walked up to the fire, lugging the filled kettle.

"Well, lads," he began after a short silence, "it's a bad business."

"Why, what's up?" Kostya asked hastily.

"I heard Vassya's voice."

All of them plainly shuddered.

"What are you saying, what are you saying?" babbled Kostya.

"I did hear it, by God! No sooner did I start bending over the water when all of a sudden I heard someone calling me, like it was in Vassya's little voice, and just as if it was coming from under the water: 'Pavlusha, oh, Pavlusha—come here.' I walked a little ways off. I did draw some water, though."

"Oh, Lordy! Oh, Lordy!" the boys managed to say, crossing themselves.

"Why, that was a water fiend calling you, Pavel," Fedya added. "And we was just talking about him—about Vassya, that is—"

"Ah, that is a bad sign," Iliusha uttered, stopping at every word.

"Well, it don't matter—let come what may!" Pavel declared resolutely and resumed his seat. "No man can get around his fate."

The boys quieted down. It was evident that Pavel's words had made a deep impression on them. They began bedding down before the fire, as if preparing for sleep.

"What's that?" Kostya asked abruptly, raising his head.

Pavel listened attentively. "Those are snipe, calling as they fly."

"But where are they flying to?"

"Why, to the place where there's no winter, they say."

"And is there such a land?"

"There is."

"Far away?"

"Far, far away, beyond the warm seas."

Kostya sighed and closed his eyes.

More than three hours had passed since I had joined the boys. The crescent moon rose at last; I did not notice it at once, so small was it and so slender. This practically moonless night was, it seemed, still as magnificent as before. But many stars that only a short while ago had been high in heaven had already inclined to the earth's dark rim; all about us everything had become perfectly stilled, as it usually does only toward morning; everything was sleeping the unbroken, motionless sleep that comes before dawn. The air was no longer so fraught with night odors; dampness seemed to be spreading through it anew. Not long do the nights of summer last! The talk of the boys was dying down together with the fires. Even the dogs were dozing; the horses, as far as I could make out in the barely glimmering, faintly flowing light of the stars, were also lying down, with their heads drooping. A slight drowsiness overcame me; it passed into dozing.

A stream of fresh air sped across my face. I opened my eyes: morning was being engendered. As yet the flush of the dawn glow was nowhere to be seen, but already something was showing white in the east. Everything had become visible, even though only dimly visible, all about me. The pale-gray sky was growing light, chill, blue; the stars now twinkled with a faint light, now vanished; the earth had had its fill of dampness, the leaves had broken into a sweat, living sounds began to spring up here and there, and voices, and the tenuous early breeze was already wandering and fluttering over the earth. My body responded to it by a light, joyous shiver. I got up quickly enough and went over toward the boys. They were all sleeping as if they had been slain; Pavel alone raised himself halfway and looked at me intently. I nodded to him and went my way along the river, now smoky with mist.

I had hardly gone a little over a mile when torrents of young, hot light came pouring down all around me—over the far-spreading wet meadow, and ahead of me, over the now newly green knolls, from forest to forest, and behind me, over the long, dusty road, over the sparkling, encrimsoned bushes, and over the river, diffidently showing its blue from under its now thinning mist—torrents of light, at first ruby-red, then red, and golden. . . . Everything began to stir, everything awoke, broke into song, into sound. Everywhere, in rayey gems, great drops of dew burst into glow; pure and clear, as though they too had been laved by the morning coolness, the peals of bells came floating toward me, and suddenly, urged on by the boys whom I now knew, the rested drove of horses raced by. . . .

I must add, to my regret, that in the same year Pavel was no longer among the living. He did not drown; he was killed in a fall off a horse. A pity; he was a fine lad!

Questions

1. How does Turgenev use the first part of the story as preparation for the second part? Why is the first part so long?
2. Each of the five boys is carefully described by Turgenev. Why does he do this? How does he use these descriptions?
3. The setting plays an important part in the story. How is it related to the subject matter of the boys' talk? Describe the talk.
4. Describe Pavel. Why does the narrator admire him so?
5. What do you make of the ending of the story? What is Turgenev saying?

Gustave Flaubert

A Simple Heart

I

WHEN Gustave Flaubert published his novel MADAME BOVARY *in 1857 he irrevocably set the course of modern fiction. After Flaubert writers saw more clearly how to use the lives of ordinary people, rather than the adventures of romantic heroes and heroines, as the raw stuff of their stories. And from that time on, under his influence, writers became more concerned with the question of how something is said in narrative.*

Flaubert's own method is justifiably famous. One technical advance Flaubert made was consciously to suppress the author from the pages of the book. He no longer made comments in his own person. The author became impartial, impersonal, objective. Events and people were seen largely through the eyes of the characters themselves, though, it should be pointed out, the concealed author selected and organized what was seen into effective patterns.

With such a method, things*—what people see and touch—become increasingly important. They are no longer merely the ingredients of inert descriptive passages. Often they take on symbolic significance. In "A Simple Heart," for example, the parrot functions in a number of ways besides that of a pet to occupy the simple Félicité's lonely moments.*

Part of Flaubert's method, then, resides in the selection of detail, concrete particulars. Another part lies in the language used, in the selection of the right word, or le mot juste. *A third part lies in the careful juxtaposition of character to character, scene to scene, event to event. In "A Simple Heart" the death of Victor, the nephew of Félicité, is set without comment beside the death of Virginie, the daughter of Félicité's employer. The one is comment on the other, and both are comment on the simple life of this simple heart.*

I

FOR half a century the womenfolk of Pont-l'Evêque begrudged Mme. Aubain her servant, Félicité.

For one hundred francs a year she cooked and did the housework, sewed, washed, ironed, and knew how to bridle a horse, how to "fatten" the chickens, how to make butter, and she remained loyal to her mistress who, it must be noted, was not a very easy person to get along with.

Mme. Aubain had married a handsome fellow, without means, who had died at the beginning of the year 1809, leaving her with two very young children and many debts. At that time she sold what landed property she possessed, except two farms, one at Toucques and another at Geffosses, the income of which brought her, at most, five thousand francs a year; and she gave up her house at Saint Melaine to move into another less costly to maintain—a house that had belonged to her ancestors and that was situated behind the market square.

This house, with its slate roof, stood between an alley and a little street that led to the river. Inside it had different levels which caused one to stumble. A narrow vestibule separated the kitchen from the parlor where Mme. Aubain, seated near the casement window in her wicker chair, spent the entire day. Against the wainscoting, painted white, were aligned eight mahogany chairs. A pyramid of wooden boxes and pasteboard cartons were piled up on an old piano, underneath a barometer. Two small stuffed armchairs flanked the yellow marble fireplace, in the style of Louis XV. The clock in the center depicted a temple of Vesta—the whole room smelled slightly musty, because the floor was on a level lower than the garden.

On the first floor, there was first Madame's bedroom, very large, papered in a pale flower design, with a portrait of "Monsieur" in a foppish costume on the wall. A smaller room in which were to be seen two children's beds, without mattresses, adjoined hers. Next came the salon, always kept locked, and cluttered with furniture covered over with sheets. Then a corridor led to the study; books and miscellaneous papers filled the shelves of a bookcase, the three sections of which surrounded a large desk made of black wood. The two panels in the corner were almost completely covered with pen sketches, water colors, and engravings by Audran—souvenirs of better times and vanished luxury. A dormer window on the second floor lighted Félicité's room, which overlooked the fields.

Félicité rose at daybreak so as not to miss mass, and she worked till evening without interruption; then, when dinner was over, the dishes done, the door bolted, she would smother the burning log in the ashes and fall asleep before the hearth, her rosary beads still in her hand. No one was better at stubborn bargaining in the marketplace than she. As for cleanliness, the shine on her pots and pans was the despair of the other servants. Very thrifty, she ate slowly and gathered together with her finger the bread crumbs on the table—her bread, which weighed twelve pounds, was especially baked for her, and lasted twenty days.

During all seasons she wore a calico neckerchief over her shoulders, pinned at the back, a bonnet hiding her hair, gray stockings, a red petticoat, and over her bodice an apron like those worn by hospital nurses.

Her face was thin and her voice sharp. At twenty-five, people took her to be forty. After she reached fifty, she showed no age at all; and always taciturn, with her erect posture and measured movements, she seemed like a woman made of wood, performing like an automaton.

II

Like any other, Félicité had had her love story.

Her father, a stonemason, had been killed by a fall from a scaffold. Then her mother died, her sisters wandered away, a farmer took her in and employed her, while still very young, to watch over his cows in the pasture. She shivered in her thin rags; drank water, lying on her stomach, from ponds; for no reason received whippings, and finally was sent away because of a theft of thirty sous—a crime she had not committed. She went to another farm, tended the poultry yard, and because she pleased her employers the other servants became jealous of her.

One evening in August (she was then eighteen) she was taken to a party at Colleville. Immediately she was bewildered, dazzled by the noise of the fiddlers, the lights hanging from the trees, the medley of costumes, the laces, the gold crosses, the immense crowd of people all bustling about. She was standing modestly aside, when a young, well-dressed man, smoking a pipe while resting his elbows on the shaft of a cart, came over and asked her to dance. He bought her cider, coffee and cakes, and a silk scarf, and, imagining that she guessed what he was thinking about, offered to take her home. On their way past a field of oats, he threw her backward very roughly. She was frightened and began to scream. He ran off.

Another evening, on the road to Beaumont, she wanted to pass a large wagon of hay that was going along slowly, and brushing against the wheels, she recognized Théodore.

He addressed her calmly, saying that she must forgive him everything, since it was "the fault of the drink."

She did not know what to say; and she wanted to run away.

Immediately he began to speak about the harvesting and the important people of the commune, for his father had left Colleville and had taken over the farm at Écots, so that now they were neighbors. "Oh!" she said. He went on to say that they wanted him to settle down. However, he was in no hurry, and was going to wait till he found a wife to his taste. She lowered her head. Then he asked her had she thought of marriage. She replied, smiling, that it wasn't nice to make fun of her.

"But I'm not making fun of you, I swear!" said he, putting his left arm around her waist. She walked along leaning on him. They slowed their pace. The wind was gentle, stars were shining; in front of them the huge hay wagon swayed from side to side; the four horses, dragging their hoofs, were stirring up dust. Then suddenly the horses veered to the right. He kissed her once more. She disappeared into the darkness.

The following week, Théodore had several meetings with her.

They met in remote farmyards, behind walls, or under some isolated tree. She was not innocent like well-bred young ladies—she had learned from being around animals; but reason and her self-esteem kept her from giving in. Her resistance exasperated Théodore's passion, so much so that to satisfy it (or perhaps naïvely) he proposed marriage to her. At first she doubted his sincerity, but he made strong vows of love.

Soon afterward, he confessed to her a troublesome bit of news: his parents, the year before, had bought him a substitute for the army, but any day now he could be drafted again; the idea of military service frightened him. Félicité interpreted this cowardice as proof of his affection, and it redoubled hers. She stole away at night to meet him, and while they were together Théodore tortured her with his problems and entreaties.

At last, he declared that he would go himself to the prefecture for information, and that he would inform her of what he found out on the following Sunday, between eleven o'clock and midnight.

When the moment arrived she hastened to her lover.

In his stead, she found one of his friends.

He told her that she was never to see Théodore again. To prevent himself from being drafted, Théodore had married a very rich *old* lady, Mme. Lehoussais of Toucques.

Félicité, beside herself with grief, threw herself to the ground, uttering cries, and calling upon the merciful God above. All alone she stayed there in the fields, and wept till morning. Then she went back to the farm and announced that she was leaving; and, at the end of the month, when she had received her wages, she bundled up her few little belongings in a handkerchief and went to Pont-l'Évêque.

In front of the inn, she made some inquiries of a woman wearing a widow's cap, and who, it just so happened, was looking for a cook. This young girl did not know much, but she seemed so willing and was asking for so little that Mme. Aubain ended by saying: "All right, I'll take you!"

Fifteen minutes later, Félicité was settled in her new house.

At first, she lived there in a sort of fear and trembling caused by "the tone of the house" and by the vivid memory of "Monsieur" which hovered over everything! Madame's children, Paul and Virginie, one seven and the other four, respectively, seemed to her to be made of some rare substance; she liked to carry them piggyback. But Mme. Aubain forbade her to kiss them too often, which mortified Félicité. However, she was happy. The gentleness of her surroundings had softened her grief.

Every Thursday, the close friends of Mme. Aubain used to come for a game of "Boston." Félicité had to get the cards and foot warmers ready in advance. They always arrived precisely at eight and left before the clock struck eleven.

Every Monday morning, the junk dealer who lived on the same street used to spread out his wares on the ground. Then the whole town was filled with the hum of many voices—together with the neighing of horses, the bleating of sheep, the grunting of pigs, and the rattle of carts down the street. About noon, when market time reached its peak, a tall, old peasant with a hooked nose, wearing his cap on the back of his head, would appear and stand in the doorway—this was Robelin, a farmer of Geffosses. A little while later, Liébard, a farmer from Toucques, short, ruddy, corpulent, wearing a gray coat and spurs, appeared in the same place.

Both brought chickens and cheeses to their landlady, Mme. Aubain. Invariably Félicité would cunningly outwit them, and they would go away with more respect for her shrewdness.

At various times, the Marquis of Gremanville, one of Mme. Aubain's uncles, used to visit her. He had ruined himself by debauchery and was now living in Falaise on his last bit of farmland. He invariably came at lunch time, accompanied by a dreadful poodle that always dirtied the furniture with his paws. Despite his efforts to play the role of the gentleman (he would raise his hat every time he said, "my late father"), force of habit compelled him to drink one glass after another and to blurt out risqué stories. Félicité would politely usher him out the door, saying "You have had enough, Monsieur de Gremanville! Some other time!" And she would shut the door on him.

To M. Bourais, a retired lawyer, the door was invitingly opened. His white cravat, his bald head, his frilled shirt, his full-fitting brown frock coat, his way of flourishing his arm when he took snuff—his whole person produced in her a certain excitement such as we all experience at the sight of extraordinary men.

As he was the manager of Madame's properties, he spent hours with her in "Monsieur's" study, all the time fearful of compromising his position. He had great respect for the bench. Moreover, he had some pretensions to being a Latin scholar.

To make learning pleasant for the children, he gave them a geography book consisting of prints. There were representative scenes from all over the world: cannibals with feathered headdresses; a monkey carrying away a damsel; Bedouins in the desert; a whale being harpooned, and so on.

Paul explained these pictures to Félicité. And this was the extent of her literary education.

The children's education was in the hands of Guyot, a wretched individual working at the Town Hall, who was famous for his beautiful handwriting and for the way he sharpened his penknife on his boot.

When the weather was clear, they all used to start early for the Geffosses farm.

The farmyard is on the side of a slope, with the house in the middle; and the sea, from a distance, looks like a gray blot.

Félicité would take out slices of cold meat from her basket, and they all would eat in a room that adjoined the milk house. It was all that remained of a once elegant country house. Now the wallpaper hung like tattered ribbons, and rustled with the drafts from the window. Mme. Aubain would bow her head, weighed down by memories of the past; the children would no longer dare to speak. "Go out and play!" she would say to them; and off they would go.

Paul climbed up in the barn, caught birds, played ducks and drakes, or tapped with a stick the huge barrels that rumbled like drums.

Virginie fed the rabbits and scampered away to pick cornflowers, her legs moving so quickly that you could see her little lace-trimmed drawers.

One autumn evening they were returning through the fields.

The moon in its first quarter lit a segment of the sky, and a haze floated like a scarf over the winding Toucques river. Cattle, lying in the middle of the meadow, gazed contentedly at these four people. In the third pasture, some of the cows got up and circled them. "Don't be afraid!" said Félicité, and stroking the back of the one nearest to her, she murmured a sort of lament. It turned around and the others did the same. But, when they crossed the next field, they heard a loud bellow. It was a bull, hidden in the haze. He came toward the two women. Mme. Aubain was about to run. "No, no, not so fast!" Nevertheless, though they quickened their steps, they heard back of them the sound of snorting, coming closer and closer. His hoofs beat like hammer blows on the meadow grass. Now he was galloping toward them! Félicité turned around and, with both hands, snatched up clods of turf to throw into the bull's eyes. He lowered his head, shook his horns, and, trembling with fury, bellowed terribly. Mme. Aubain, at the end of the pasture with the two little ones, looked frantically for a way to get over the high bank. Félicité backed steadily away from the bull, throwing grass and dirt at him all the time, to blind him, while at the same time she shouted, "Hurry! Hurry!"

Mme. Aubain jumped into the ditch, pushing Virginie, then Paul, in front of her. She stumbled several times, struggling to climb the bank, and by sheer courage finally succeeded.

The bull had backed Félicité against a fence; his slaver spattered her face; a second more and he would have gored her. She just had time to crawl between two fence rails. The huge animal stopped, amazed.

At Pont-l'Évêque, they talked of this adventure for many years. However, Félicité was not proud of it, nor did she think that she had done anything heroic.

Virginie took up all her time—for, as a result of her fright, she had developed a nervous disorder, and M. Poupart, the physician, advised sea-baths for her at Trouville.

At that time not many people frequented Trouville. Mme. Aubain sought information about the place, consulted with Bourais, and made preparations as if embarking on a long voyage.

They sent off her baggage the day before, in Liébard's cart. The next day, he brought to the house two horses, one of which had a lady's saddle, with a velvet back; the other had a cloak rolled up like a seat on the crupper.

Mme. Aubain mounted her horse, behind Liébard. Félicité took charge of Virginie, and Paul rode M. Lechaptois' donkey, lent to him on condition that he take good care of it.

The road was so bad that it took two hours to go five miles. The horses sank into mud up to their pasterns, and had to make strenuous movements with their haunches to extricate themselves; they would sometimes stumble in ruts; other times they had to leap over them. In some places Liébard's mare would stop all of a sudden. Patiently he would wait for her to go on again; meantime he talked about the people whose property bordered the road, interpolating moral reflections on the story told. Thus, while they were in the middle of Toucques, as they were passing under a window full of nasturtiums, he remarked, shrugging his shoulders: "There's that Mme. Lehoussais, who instead of taking in a young man . . ." Félicité did not hear the rest; the horses were trotting; the donkey was galloping. They all filed down the path, a gate swung open, two boys appeared, and they dismounted in front of a dung heap on the very threshold.

When Mme. Liébard spotted her mistress, she was profuse in her expressions of delight. She served her a luncheon of sirloin of beef, tripe, black pudding, a fricassee of chicken, frothy cider, a fruit tart, and plums in brandy—all the time paying the Madame polite compliments, saying how wonderful she looked, how Mademoiselle was becoming "magnificent," and how Paul was growing so strong. Nor did she forget their deceased grandparents, whom the Liébards had known, as they had been in the service of the family for generations. The farm, like them, had the quality of oldness. The ceiling beams were worm-eaten, the walls black with smoke, the window panes gray with dust. On an oak sideboard were set all sorts of utensils, jugs, dishes, pewter bowls, wolf-traps, and sheep shears; and a big syringe made the children laugh. There was not a tree in the three courtyards that did not have mushrooms growing at its base or a tuft of mistletoe on its branches. The wind had blown some of the trees down. They had begun to grow again in the middle; and all of them were bent under the weight of the apples. The thatched roofs, like brown velvet and varying in thickness, had withstood the most violent gales. However, the wagon shed was falling into ruin. Mme. Aubain said she would tend to it later, and ordered the animals to be resaddled.

It was another half hour before they arrived in Trouville. The little caravan dismounted to pass Écores—a cliff jutting out over some boats—and three minutes later, at the end of the quay, they entered the courtyard of the "Golden Lamb" kept by Mme. David.

Virginie, from the very first days there, began to feel less weak—the result of the change of air and the effect of the baths, which she took in her chemise, for want of a bathing costume. Her nurse dressed her in a custom-house shed, which was used by the bathers.

In the afternoon, with the donkey, they rode off beyond the Roches-Noires, in the direction of Hennequeville. The path rose, at first, over hilly terrain like the lawn of a park; then it reached a plateau where meadows alternated with plowed fields. By the edge of the road, in briar thickets, stood holly bushes; here and there, a great lifeless tree made zigzags in the blue sky with its naked branches.

Nearly always they would rest awhile in a meadow, with Deauville to their left, Le Havre to the right, and before them the open sea. It sparkled in the sun, smooth like a mirror, so calm that you could hardly hear its murmuring. Unseen sparrows chirped, and the immense vault of heaven hung over everything. Mme. Aubain sat on the ground, doing her sewing; Virginie, next to her, plaited rushes; Félicité was weeding some lavender flowers; Paul was bored and wanted to go back.

On other occasions, they would go by boat across the Toucques, looking for shells. At low tide, they found sea urchins, starfish, and jellyfish; and the children would chase the flakes of foam carried by the wind. The waves, breaking on the sand, unrolled sleepily along the beach. The latter stretched as far as you could see, but on the landward side, it ended in the dunes that separated it from the Marais, a wide meadow shaped like an arena. When they returned that way, Trouville, on the hill slope in the background, loomed larger with every step, and its houses, with their uneven rooftops, seemed to be spread in colorful disorder.

On days when it was too hot, they did not leave their room. The dazzling brightness from outside made golden streaks through the venetian blinds. The village was silent. No one was to be seen on the sidewalks below. The all-pervading silence intensified the peacefulness. In the distance the hammers of the caulkers tapped on the hulls of the boats and a warm breeze wafted up the odor of tar.

The chief amusement was watching the ships return. As soon as they had passed the buoys, they began to maneuver. They lowered the sails on two of the three masts, and, with the foresail swelling like a balloon, they moved in gliding fashion over the chopping waves, until they reached the middle of the harbor where they suddenly dropped anchor. Then the boat docked against the pier. The sailors threw squirming fish over the side; a line of carts was awaiting them, and women in cotton bonnets rushed forward to take the baskets and to kiss their men.

One day one of them came up to Félicité, who, a little later, went to her room overjoyed. She had found a sister, Nastasie Barette, whose married name was Leroux, nursing an infant; and on her right-hand side was another child, and at her left was a little cabin boy with his hands on his hips and a beret cocked over his ear.

After fifteen minutes, Mme. Aubain sent them away.

But they were always to be seen outside her kitchen or on their walks. The husband never appeared.

Félicité took a liking to them. She bought them a blanket, some shirts, and a stove; it was obvious they were taking advantage of her. And this weakness of hers annoyed Mme. Aubain, who, moreover, did not like the familiar ways of Félicité's nephew with her son. And, as Virginie was coughing and the weather was no longer good, she decided to go back to Pont-l'Évêque.

M. Bourais advised her on the choice of a school for Paul. The one at Caen was considered to be the best, so he was sent there. He said his goodbyes bravely and was content to be going to live in a house where he would have companions his age.

Mme. Aubain resigned herself to her son's departure, because it was necessary. Virginie thought about it less and less. Félicité missed his noise. But a new interest diverted her: from Christmas time onward, she took the little girl to her catechism lesson every day.

III

When she had made her genuflection at the door of the church, Félicité walked under the lofty nave between the double row of chairs, opened Mme. Aubain's pew, sat down, and gazed around.

The choir stalls were filled with boys on the right and girls on the left; the curé was standing next to the lectern. One stained-glass window in the apse depicted the Holy Ghost hovering over the Virgin; another showed her on her knees before the Christ Child, and behind the tabernacle a group carved in wood depicted St. Michael overcoming the dragon.

The priest began with an outline of Sacred History. Félicité formed vivid pictures in her mind of Paradise, the Flood, the Tower of Babel, cities in flames, people dying, idols being overturned. She learned from these bewildering scenes a reverence for the Most High and a fear of His wrath. Then, she wept when the Passion was narrated. Why had they crucified Him—He who loved the little children, He who fed the multitudes, He who cured the blind, and He who had consented, out of meekness, to be born among the poor in a stable? The sowings, the harvests, the wine presses, all these familiar things the Gospel speaks of, were a part of her life; they had been sanctified by God's sojourn on earth. She loved lambs more tenderly out of love for the Lamb, and doves because of the Holy Ghost.

She found it difficult to imagine His person, for He was not only a bird, but a flame as well, and at still other times, a breath. She thought perhaps it is His light that hovers at night on the edge of the marshes, His breath that moves the clouds, His voice that gives the bells their harmony! Thus she sat in adoration, delighting in the cool walls and the peacefulness of the church.

As for Church dogmas, she did not understand or even try to understand them. The priest gave his sermon, the children recited, and she finally fell asleep. She woke up again with a start, when the people, leaving the church, clattered with their wooden shoes on the flagstones.

This is how Félicité, whose religious education had been neglected in her youth, learned her catechism—by hearing it repeated; and from that time on she imitated all of Virginie's practices, fasting when she did and going to confession with her. On Corpus Christi they made a small altar together.

She had looked forward with consternation to Virginie's first communion. Félicité made much ado about the little girl's rosary beads, her shoes, her prayerbook, her gloves. How she trembled as she helped Virginie's mother dress the child!

All through the mass, Félicité felt a terrible anxiety. She could not see one side of the choir—M. Bourais was in the way; but just in front of her, the band of young virgins, wearing white crowns over their lowered veils, looked to her like a field of snow. From afar she could recognize her precious little Virginie by her slender neck and by her enraptured bearing.

The altar bell tinkled. Heads bowed. There was silence. When the organ began to play again, the choir members and the whole congregation chanted the *Agnus Dei*. Then the boys began to move from their pews. After them the girls rose. Reverently, with their hands joined, they made their way to the brilliantly lit altar, and knelt on the first step, to receive the Divine Host in turn. Afterward they came back to their *prie-dieus* in the same order.

When it was Virginie's turn, Félicité leaned forward to see her; and in imagination, stimulated by genuine affection, she felt that she herself was this child. Virginie's face became her own; Virginie's dress clothed her; Virginie's heart throbbed in her own breast; when Virginie opened her mouth and closed her eyes, Félicité almost fainted.

Early the next morning, she went to the sacristy and asked M. le Curé to give her communion. She received it with devotion, but she did not feel the same ecstatic rapture.

Mme. Aubain wanted to make an accomplished person of her daughter; and, as Guyot could not teach her either English or music, she decided to board Virginie in the Ursuline Convent at Honfleur.

Virginie did not object. Félicité sighed and thought Madame was unfeeling. Then she decided that her mistress was, perhaps, right. These things were too much for Félicité to grasp.

So, one day, an old coach stopped in front of the door, and out stepped a nun who had come to fetch Virginie. Félicité lifted Virginie's baggage to the top of the vehicle, gave some instructions to the driver, and put on the seat six jars of jam, a dozen pears, and a bouquet of violets.

Virginie, at the last moment, began to sob; she hugged her mother who kissed her on the forehead and kept saying, "Come on, now! Be brave. Don't cry!" The side step was raised and the coach drove off.

Then Mme. Aubain broke down. That evening all her friends—the Lormeau family, Mme. Lechaptois, the Rochefeville ladies, M. de Houppeville, and Bourais—came to comfort her.

At first, her daughter's absence caused Mme. Aubain much grief. But three times a week she received a letter from Virginie. She wrote to her daughter on the other days, took strolls in the garden, or read a little, and in this way managed to fill the lonely hours.

Every morning, regularly, Félicité would go into Virginie's room and look around. It distressed her not to have to comb the girl's hair any more, not to lace her shoes, not to tuck her into bed—not to see her perpetually radiant face, not to hold her hand anymore when they went out together. For want of something to do, Félicité tried making lace, but her clumsy fingers broke the threads; she could not do anything, she could not sleep, and was, to use her own expression, "done in." To "distract herself," she asked permission to have her nephew Victor visit her.

He came on Sundays after mass—rosy-cheeked, barechested, and smelling of the fields he had crossed. Immediately Félicité set the table and they sat down to lunch facing each other. Félicité, eating as little as possible to save expense, stuffed him so much that finally he fell asleep. When vespers sounded, she woke him, brushed his trousers, knotted his tie, and went to the church with him, leaning on his arm with a kind of maternal pride.

His parents always instructed him to get something out of her—either a box of brown sugar, some soap, some brandy, or sometimes even money. He always brought his old clothes to Félicité to be mended. She was happy to do this task because it meant he had to come back.

In August his father took him off on a cruise along the coast.

It was vacation time, and the arrival of the children consoled her in the absence of her nephew. But Paul was getting contrary and Virginie was now too old to be addressed familiarly. Now there was a barrier—a feeling of uneasiness—between Virginie and Félicité.

Victor went to Morlaix, Dunkirk, and then to Brighton; and on his return from each trip he brought Félicité a present. The first time it was a box made of sea shells; then it was a coffee cup; from his third trip it was a large gingerbread man. Victor was becoming good-looking: he was well-built, he wore a small mustache, his eyes were attractively frank, and he cocked his small leather cap back like a pilot's. He amused her by telling stories mixed with sailors' lingo.

One Monday, July 14, 1819 (she never forgot the date), Victor told her that he had signed up for a long voyage, and that during the night of the following day, he would take the Honfleur boat to join his schooner which was to weigh anchor from Le Havre soon afterward. He would, perhaps, be gone for two years.

The thought of such a long absence dismayed Félicité, and, to say goodbye to him again, on Wednesday evening, after Madame's dinner, she put on her clogs and traveled the long twelve miles between Pont-l'Évêque and Honfleur.

When she arrived at the Calvary instead of turning left, she went right, got lost in the shipyards, and had to retrace her steps. Some people whom she approached advised her to hurry along. She went all around the ship-filled harbor, stumbling over the moorings. Where the ground sloped, lights criss-crossed. Félicité thought she was losing her mind, for she saw horses in the heavens.

On the wharf's edge, horses, frightened by the sea, were neighing. A crane was lifting them and lowering them into a boat where passengers were jostling one another amid cider casks, baskets of cheese, and grain sacks. Over the cackling of the chickens, one could hear the captain cursing. A cabin boy, undisturbed by all the confusion, leaned over the bow.

Félicité, who had not recognized him, suddenly called, "Victor!" He raised his head; she darted toward him, but at that moment the gangplank was raised.

The boat, towed by singing women, eased away from the wharf. Her hull creaked, and heavy water lashed against the prow. The sail had been turned around, hence no one could be seen any longer on her decks. On the silvery, moonlit sea, she became a black spot that gradually faded out of sight, then sank below the horizon.

As Félicité passed Calvary she wanted to commend to God this boy whom she loved most. She stood there a long time praying, her face bathed in tears, her eyes raised to heaven.

The town slept; only custom officials walked about. There was the sound of water, like that of a torrent, pouring through the holes of a sluice. The town clock struck two.

The convent reception room would not be open before morning. If she was late, Madame would surely be annoyed; so, in spite of a great desire to see Virginie, she returned home. The serving girls of the inn were just getting up when she reached Pont-l'Évêque.

"For months and months that poor boy is going to be tossing about on the waves!" thought Félicité. She had not been frightened by his previous voyages. One always returned safely from England or Brittany; but America, the colonies, the islands—all these were lost in a hazy region at the other end of the world.

From this moment on, Félicité thought of nothing but her nephew. On sunny days, she imagined he was thirsty; when it was stormy, she feared for him the lightning. As she listened to the wind howling down the chimney or heard it carrying off the slates, she saw him battered by this same storm, as he clung to the top of a broken masthead, his body bent back under the wash of the waves. At other times—remembering the geography prints—she imagined him being eaten by cannibals, captured by apes in the jungle, or lying dead on some deserted beach. But never did she speak of these secret apprehensions.

Mme. Aubain had her own apprehensions about her daughter.

The good nuns thought Virginie an affectionate but delicate child. The least bit of excitement upset her. She had to give up her piano lessons.

Her mother demanded from the convent authorities a regular flow of letters. One morning when there was no mail, she became very impatient; she walked up and down her room from the chair to the window. It was very strange indeed! No mail in four days!

To console her, Félicité said, "Look at me, Madame, it has been six months since I received any . . . !"

"From whom? . . ."

"Why . . . from my nephew!" meekly replied the servant.

"Oh! your nephew!" Mme. Aubain began to pace again, shrugging her shoulders as if to say: "I wasn't thinking of him! . . . Besides, he is nothing to me! A cabin boy, a little scamp! . . . While my daughter . . . just think!"

Félicité, though accustomed to rudeness, felt indignant at Madame, but overlooked it as usual.

It seemed very natural to her that one could lose one's head over a little girl.

The two children, Virginie and her nephew, were equally dear to her—they both shared her heart! And their destinies were to be the same.

The druggist told her that Victor's boat had docked in Havana. He had read this bit of news in a newspaper.

On account of cigars, she imagined Havana to be a country where everyone did nothing but smoke. She could visualize Victor moving among the Negroes in a cloud of tobacco fumes. Could one "in case of necessity" return from Havana by land, she wondered. How far was it from Pont-l'Évêque? For answers to these questions, she turned to M. Bourais.

He took out his atlas and began explaining longitudes; and smiled in a pedantic manner at Félicité's amazement. Then with his pencil he pointed to an almost imperceptible black dot on an oval spot, and said, "Here it is." She leaned over the map. This network of colored lines blurred her vision and meant nothing to her; and when Bourais asked her to say what was puzzling her, she begged him to point to the house where Victor was staying. Bourais threw up his arms, sneezed, and roared with laughter; such simplicity was sheer joy to him. But Félicité did not understand why he was so amused—how could she when she perhaps expected to see her nephew's portrait on the map—so limited was her understanding!

It was two weeks afterward that Liébard came into the kitchen at market time as usual, and handed her a letter from her brother-in-law. Since neither of them could read, she took it to her mistress.

Mme. Aubain, who was counting stitches in her knitting, put her work aside, opened the letter, trembled, and with a look full of meaning, said in a low voice, "It is bad news . . . that they have to tell you. Your nephew. . . ."

He was dead. The letter said no more.

Félicité slumped into a chair, and leaned her head back. She closed her eyelids which had suddenly become pink. Then, with her head down, her hands hanging idly, her eyes fixed, she kept saying over and over, "Poor boy! Poor little boy!"

Liébard, murmuring sighs of consolation, watched her. Mme. Aubain was still shaking a little. She suggested to Félicité that she go visit with her sister at Trouville.

Félicité made a gesture to indicate there was no need to do so.

There was silence. Liébard thought it wise that they leave Félicité alone.

Then Félicité said, "They don't care! It means nothing to them!"

She dropped her head again, but, from time to time, she mechanically picked up the long knitting needles from the worktable.

Women passed in the courtyard with their barrows of dripping linen.

Seeing them through the window, Félicité remembered her own washing. Having soaked it the day before, she had to rinse it today; and she left the room.

Her plank and wooden bucket were down by the Toucques. She threw a pile of underclothing on the river bank, rolled up her sleeves, and took the paddle in her hand. The heavy beating she gave her laundry could be heard in the nearby gardens. The meadows were empty, the wind made ripples on the surface of the water; while deep down, tall weeds swayed, like the hair of corpses floating in the water. Félicité suppressed her grief and was very brave till evening; but in her room, she broke down completely and lay on her bed with her face buried in the pillow and her hands clenched against her temples.

Much later, she heard from the captain himself the circumstances of Victor's death. He had had yellow fever. Four doctors had held him while they bled him—too much—at the hospital. He died immediately and the head doctor said: "There! Another one!"

Victor's parents had always been brutal to him. Félicité preferred not to see them again; and they in turn made no attempt to see her, either because they had forgotten about her, or because of the callousness of the poor.

Meanwhile, at the convent, Virginie became weaker. Congestion in her lungs, coughing, a continuous fever, and splotches on her cheekbones indicated some deep-seated illness. M. Poupart prescribed a few days in Provence. Mme. Aubain agreed to that, and would have brought her daughter home at once were it not for the climate of Pont-l'Évêque.

She chartered a carriage and was driven to the convent every Tuesday. There is a terrace in the garden from which you can see the Seine. Virginie would walk there on her mother's arm, over the fallen vine leaves. Sometimes the sun piercing through the clouds made her blink, as she gazed at the distant sails and the whole horizon—from the Château of Tancarville to the lighthouse of Le Havre. Then they would rest under an arbor. Her mother had with her a little flask of excellent Malaga wine, and, laughing at the idea of getting a little tipsy, Virginie would drink just a little, no more.

She regained strength. Autumn passed pleasantly. Félicité reassured Mme. Aubain. But, one evening when she had been running errands in the neighborhood, she saw on her return M. Poupart's carriage in front of the door. He was in the vestibule. Mme. Aubain was tying on her hat.

"Give me my foot warmer, my handbag, and gloves! Hurry!"

Virginie had pneumonia. Perhaps her case was already hopeless.

"Not yet!" said the doctor and both got into his carriage, under whirling flakes of snow. Night was falling. It was very cold.

Félicité rushed into church to light a candle. Then she ran after the carriage which she overtook an hour later. She had jumped nimbly on behind, and was holding on to the straps, when she suddenly thought: "The courtyard isn't locked! Suppose thieves break in!" And she jumped off.

At dawn of the following day, she went to the doctor's house. He had returned, but had left again for the country. Then she stayed at the inn, thinking some stranger would bring a letter. Finally, at dusk, she took the Lisieux stagecoach.

The convent was at the bottom of a steep lane. About half way down, Félicité heard strange sounds—a death knell. "It's for someone else," she thought. But she knocked violently on the door.

After several minutes, she heard the shuffling of slippers; the door was opened a crack and a nun appeared.

The good sister, with a compassionate air, said that Virginie "had just passed away." At that moment, the tolling at Saint-Léonard's became louder.

Félicité went up to the second floor of the convent.

From the doorway she could see Virginie lying on her back, her hands folded, her mouth open, and her head tilted back under an overhanging black cross between two motionless curtains, less pale than her face. Mme. Aubain, clutching the foot of the bed, was sobbing uncontrollably. The Mother Superior was standing on the right. Three candles on the dresser made shafts of red light, and mist whitened the windowpanes. Some nuns led Mme. Aubain away.

For two nights Félicité did not leave her death watch. She repeated the same prayers, sprinkled the sheets with holy water, sat down again, and gazed at the dead girl. At the end of the first night, she noticed that the face had yellowed, the lips had turned blue, the nose was sharper and the eyes were deeper. She kissed them several times, and would not have been surprised if they had opened again; for to minds like hers the supernatural is quite simple. She dressed her, wrapped her in a shroud, laid her body in the coffin, arranged her hair and placed a wreath upon her head. The hair was blond and extraordinarily long for her age. Félicité cut a thick lock of it and slipped half of it into Virginie's bosom. She resolved never to part with hers.

The corpse was brought back to Pont-l'Évêque, according to the wishes of Mme. Aubain, who followed the hearse in a closed carriage.

After the mass, it took another three-quarters of an hour to reach the cemetery. Paul, sobbing, walked ahead of the cortege. M. Bourais walked behind, followed by the principal residents of the village, the women wearing black mantles, and Félicité. She was thinking of her nephew, and because she had not been able to pay these respects to him, her sadness was intensified, as if he were being interred with Virginie.

Mme. Aubain's despair knew no limits.

At first she cried out against God, thinking it unjust for Him to have taken her daughter—Virginie who had never hurt anyone, and whose soul was so pure! But no! She should have taken her to the south. Other doctors could have saved her! She railed at herself, she wanted to join Virginie in death, she cried out distressfully in her dreams. One dream especially haunted her. Her husband, dressed like a sailor, came back from a long voyage and told her tearfully that he had received orders to take Virginie away. Then, they both tried to find a hiding place somewhere.

Once Mme. Aubain came in from the garden terribly upset. A little while before (she could point out the spot) the father and daughter, standing side by side, had appeared to her; they did nothing; they just looked at her.

For several months she kept to her room—apathetic. Félicité reproached her gently, saying her mistress must take care of herself for the sake of her son, and in remembrance of "her."

"Her?" replied Mme. Aubain as though she were emerging from sleep. "Ah yes! . . . Yes! You do not forget her!" This was an allusion to the cemetery which Mme. Aubain was strictly forbidden to visit.

Félicité went there every day.

At exactly four o'clock, she would go by the houses, climb the hill, open the gate, and come to Virginie's grave. There was a little column of pink marble with a plaque at its base, to which was fastened a chain that enclosed a miniature garden. The borders disappeared under beds of flowers. Félicité watered the plants, upturned the gravel, and knelt down better to dress the ground. Mme. Aubain, when at last she could visit the grave, felt a relief and a kind of consolation.

The years slipped by uneventfully and without any incidents other than the return of the great feast days: Easter, Assumption, All Saints' Day. Only household events were spoken of as important in the years that followed: for example, in 1825, two workmen whitewashed the vestibule; in 1827, part of the roof, falling into the courtyard, almost killed a man; in the summer of 1827, it became Madame's turn to offer the consecrated bread; Bourais, about this time, was mysteriously not around; and the old acquaintances one by one went away: Guyot, Liébard, Mme. Lechaptois, Robelin, Uncle Gremanville, who had been paralyzed for a long time now.

One night the driver of the mail coach announced in Pont-l'Évêque the July Revolution. A new subprefect was appointed a few days later: Baron de Larsonnière, an ex-consular official in America, and a man who had brought with him, in addition to his wife, his sister-in-law and her three daughters, almost grown up. They could be seen on their lawn, dressed in loose-fitting blouses; they had a Negro servant and a parrot. They paid a visit to Mme. Aubain, who returned their call promptly. Whenever Félicité saw them coming, she always ran to her mistress to forewarn her. But the only thing really capable of arousing Madame was letters from her son.

He could not follow any profession, since he spent most of his time in taverns. She paid his debts, but he contracted others; and the sighs that Mme. Aubain uttered, as she sat knitting by the window, reached Félicité as she turned her spinning wheel in the kitchen.

They took walks together along the espalier, and talked always about Virginie, wondering whether such and such would have pleased her, or what she would probably have said on this or that occasion.

All her little belongings were in a cupboard in the room with two beds. Mme. Aubain inspected them as seldom as possible. One summer day she resigned herself to doing so, and moths flew out of the cupboard.

Her dresses were arranged under a shelf on which sat three dolls, some hoops, a doll's house, and the basin that she used daily. They took out her petticoats, stockings, and handkerchiefs and spread them on the two beds, before folding them again. The sun, shining on these pitiful objects, brought out the spots and the creases made by the movements of Virginie's body. Outside the sky was blue, the air was warm, a blackbird warbled. Everything seemed vibrant with a heartfelt sweetness. They found a little hat of deeply piled plush, chestnut-colored; but it was all motheaten. Félicité wanted it for herself. They looked at each other and their eyes filled with tears; at last the mistress opened her arms and the servant threw herself into them. They held each other close, assuaging their grief in a kiss that made them equal.

This was the first time in their lives, for Mme. Aubain was not demonstrative by nature. Félicité was as grateful as if she had been presented with a gift; and from then on she cherished Mme. Aubain with a devotion that was almost animal and with an almost religious veneration.

The kindness of her heart grew.

When she heard in the street the drums of a marching regiment, she stood at the front door with a pitcher of cider and asked the soldiers to drink. She took care of cholera patients. She protected the Poles, and there was even one who wanted to marry her. But they quarreled, for one morning, returning from the Angelus, she found that he had entered her kitchen, prepared a salad, and was nonchalantly eating it.

After the Poles came Papa Colmiche, an old man who was supposed to have been guilty of some atrocities in '93. He lived along the riverbank, in a tumble-down pigsty. The little boys used to spy on him through cracks in the wall and throw stones at him that always landed on the squalid bed where he lay, continually racked by a cough. His hair was long, his eyes inflamed, and on his arm grew a tumor bigger than his head. Félicité supplied him with linen and tried to keep his miserable hut clean. It was her wish to have him installed in the bakehouse without his annoying Madame. When the tumor opened, she dressed it every day. Sometimes she brought him some cake. She used to lay him in the sun on a bed of straw. The poor old fellow, slobbering and shaking, would thank her in his weak voice. He was afraid of losing her, and would stretch out his hand when he saw her going away. He died. She had a mass said for the repose of his soul.

On that day, fortune smiled on her: at the dinner hour, the Negro servant of Mme. de Larsonniére came carrying the parrot in a cage, with perch, chain, and padlock. A note from the baroness informed Mme. Aubain that, because her husband was promoted to a prefecture, they were leaving that evening; and she begged her to accept the bird as a remembrance and a mark of her esteem.

For a long time this bird had occupied Félicité's thoughts, because he came from America and America reminded her of Victor—so much so that she questioned the Negro about that country. Once she had even remarked: "How happy Madame would be to have him!"

The Negro had told this to his mistress, and since she could not take the bird with her, she disposed of him in this fashion.

IV

The parrot was called Loulou. His body was green, the tip of his wings pink, his forehead blue, and his throat golden.

But he had the tiresome habit of biting his perch, plucking his feathers, scattering his mess about, and spattering the water of his bath. Mme. Aubain thought the bird was a nuisance and gave him to Félicité to keep.

She set out to train the parrot; soon he could repeat: "Nice boy," "Your servant, sir," "Hello, Mary!" He was placed next to the door, and people were surprised that he would not answer to Jacquot, for weren't all parrots called Jacquot? They likened him to a turkey, to a log of wood; and each time they did so Félicité was hurt to the quick! But Loulou was curiously stubborn! He stopped talking when one looked at him!

Yet he liked company, for on Sunday, while those Rochefeuille ladies, M. de Houppeville, and some new habitués—Onfray the apothecary, M. Varin, and Captain Mathieu—were playing cards, he would beat the windowpanes with his wings, and would fling himself about so violently that it was impossible to hear oneself speak.

Bourais' face, undoubtedly, struck him as being very funny. As soon as he spotted Bourais, he would begin to laugh—to laugh with all his might. His noises reverberated through the courtyard, echoes repeated them, the neighbors stood at their windows and laughed too. Therefore, so as not to be seen by the parrot, M. Bourais would slither along the wall, hiding his face under his hat, and, getting down to the river, would enter the house by the garden door. The looks he then shot at the bird were far from tender.

Loulou had been slapped by the butcher boy for taking the liberty of putting his head into the meat basket. Since then, the bird always tried to pinch him through his shirt. Fabu threatened to wring Loulou's neck, although he was not cruel, in spite of his tattooed arms and long sideburns. On the contrary! He was rather fond of the parrot and, in a jovial mood, he even wanted to teach him some curse words. Félicité, alarmed by all these tricks, removed the parrot to the kitchen.

Later, his little chain was removed and he roamed about the house. He would come downstairs by hooking his curved beak on the steps, lifting first his right leg, then his left. Félicité was afraid that all these gymnastics would make the bird dizzy. Sure enough, he did become ill and could neither talk nor eat. There was a thickness under his tongue such as chickens sometimes develop. She cured him by scratching out this thickness with her fingernail.

M. Paul, one day, had the effrontery to blow cigar smoke into the parrot's nostrils. Another time, when Mme. Lormeau was teasing him with the end of her parasol, Loulou snapped at the metal ring. Finally, the bird got lost.

Félicité had put him on the grass to give him some fresh air and had gone away for a minute. When she returned, the parrot was gone! First, she searched in the bushes, then by the riverbank, and on the roofs, paying no attention to her mistress who was screaming, "Be careful! You must be out of your mind!"

Then Félicité looked in all the gardens of Pont-l'Évêque, and she stopped everyone passing by—"You haven't seen my parrot, by chance, have you?" To those who did not know the bird, she gave a description. Suddenly, she thought she spotted something green fluttering behind the mill at the bottom of the hill. But when she approached—nothing! A peddler told her he had seen a parrot a little while ago at Saint-Melaine, in Mère Simon's shop. She ran all the way. They didn't know what she was talking about. Finally, she came home, exhausted, her slippers in shreds, her heart broken by disappointment. As she was sitting on a bench close to Mme. Aubain and was telling her everywhere she had been, a light weight fell on her shoulder. It was Loulou! What the devil had he been doing? Probably taking a stroll in the neighborhood!

Félicité had trouble getting over this—or rather, she never did recover from it.

As a result of a cold, Félicité had an attack of quinsy, and a little later an ear infection. Three years later she was deaf; and she spoke very loud, even in church. Though her sins might have been bruited abroad to all corners of the diocese without shame to her or scandal to anyone, the parish priest thought it best henceforth to hear her confession only in the sacristy.

Imaginary buzzings in the head added to her afflictions. Often her mistress would say to her: "My word, how stupid you are!" She would simply answer, "Yes, Madame," and go look for something to do near her.

The small scope of her ideas became smaller still, and the pealing of the church bells and the lowing of the cattle ceased to exist for her. All living creatures moved about silently as ghosts. The only sound that she could hear now was the voice of the parrot.

As if to distract her, Loulou would mimic the tic-tac of the turnspit, the shrill cry of the the fish vendor, the noise of the carpenter's saw across the road, and when the bell rang, he would imitate Mme. Aubain—"Félicité! The door, the door!"

They had conversations, Loulou incessantly repeating the three short phrases in his repertory, to which Félicité would reply with phrases just as disconnected, but in which there was deep sincerity. Loulou was almost a son and lover to her in her isolated world. He would climb on her fingers, nibble at her lips, and cling to her kerchief; and, when she leaned forward, shaking her head as nurses do, the long wings of her bonnet and those of the bird moved together.

When the clouds were banked on top of one another and the thunder began to roll, Loulou would utter cries, remembering, perhaps, the downpours in his native forests. Teeming rain made him absolutely mad with joy; he fluttered about wildly, he climbed the ceiling, knocked everything over, and went out through the window to splash in the garden; but he would come back quickly and alight on one of the andirons, and hopping about to dry his feathers, he would show first his tail, then his beak.

One morning in the terrible winter of 1837, when Félicité had put Loulou in front of the fireplace because of the cold, she found him dead, in the center of his cage, his head down, and his claws clutching the wire bars. Undoubtedly, he had died of a congestion. But Félicité thought he had been poisoned with parsley, and despite all lack of evidence, she suspected Fabu.

She wept so bitterly that her mistress said to her: "Well then, have the bird stuffed."

She asked the pharmacist's advice, since he had always been kind to the parrot.

He wrote to LeHavre. A certain man named Fellacher undertook the job. But as parcels sometimes got lost when sent by the stage-coach, she decided to take it herself as far as Honfleur.

Leafless apple trees lined both sides of the road. Ice covered the ditches. Dogs barked on the farms. Félicité, with her hands under her cloak, carrying her basket, and wearing her little black sabots, walked briskly along in the middle of the road.

She went through the forest, passed Haut-Chêne, and reached Saint-Gatien.

Behind her, in a cloud of dust, gathering speed down a steep hill, came a mail coach, with horses at full gallop, like the wind. Seeing this woman who was not paying any attention, the driver stood up, and the postilion shouted, too. All the while the four horses which the driver could not hold back gained speed. The first two horses grazed Félicité. With a pull on the reins, he veered to the side, but, furious, he raised his arm, and in full flight, with his heavy whip he gave her such a lash from her stomach to her neck that she fell on her back.

Her first action, when she regained consciousness, was to open the basket. Fortunately, Loulou was all right. She felt a burning on her right cheek, and when she touched it, her hands were red. The blood was streaming.

She sat down on a pile of stones and dabbed her face with a handkerchief; then she ate a crust of bread which she had put in her basket just in case, and took consolation for her own wound in gazing at the bird.

When she arrived at Ecquemauville, she could see below the lights of Honfleur, which twinkled in the night like a cluster of stars; the sea, beyond, spread out indistinctly. Then weakness forced her to stop; and her wretched childhood, the disillusion of her first love, the departure of her nephew, Virginie's death, all came back to her like the waves of a tide, rising to her throat and choking her.

Later she spoke to the captain of the boat; and without telling him what she was sending, she gave him instructions.

Fellacher kept the parrot a long time. He was always promising it for the following week. At the end of six months he announced it had been dispatched in a box; and then nothing more was heard about it. It seemed that Loulou was never coming back. "They have stolen him from me!" she thought.

Finally he did arrive—and how wonderful he looked, sitting upright on a branch that was screwed to a mohogany base. One foot was held in the air. His head was tilted sidewise, and he was biting on a nut that the taxidermist, carried away by a flair for the grandiose, had painted gold!

Félicité put Loulou in her room.

This place, to which she admitted few, had so many religious objects and so many unusual things that it looked like a chapel and a bazaar combined.

A large wardrobe made it difficult to open the door. Opposite the window overlooking the garden, a small circular window looked down upon the courtyard. On a table near the folding bed stood a water pitcher, two combs, and a bar of blue soap on a chipped plate. On the walls hung rosary beads, medallions, several statues of the Virgin, and a holy water font made of a coconut; on the commode, covered with a cloth like that on altars, stood the box made of shells which Victor had given to her, a watering can, a balloon, some writing books, the geography picture book, and a pair of boots. Fastened by its ribbons to a nail on the mirror hung the small plush hat! Félicité carried this kind of respect to such extremes that she even kept one of Monsieur's frock coats. All the old things Mme. Aubain no longer wanted Félicité took to her room. For this reason there were artificial flowers on the edge of the commode, and a portrait of the Comte d'Artois in the recess of the dormer window.

By means of a small shelf, Loulou was set prominently on the chimney piece that projected into the room. Every morning, when Félicité woke up, she could see him in the dawn's light, and she would recall painlessly and peacefully the old days with their insignificant events down to their last detail.

Communicating with no one, she lived in a kind of sleepwalking trance. The Corpus Christi processions rejuvenated her. She would go to her neighbors begging tapers and mats with which to decorate the altar being erected in the street.

In church she always sat gazing at the stained-glass window that portrayed the Holy Ghost, and noticed there was something of the parrot about it. The resemblance seemed to her more pronounced in a picture that depicted the Baptism of Our Lord. With its purple wings and its emerald body, it was really Loulou's portrait.

She bought this picture and hung it in the place formerly occupied by the Comte d'Artois—so that, with one glance, she could see them together. They became associated in her mind, the parrot becoming sanctified by this association with the Holy Ghost, which became more real in her eyes and easier to comprehend. God the Father, to reveal Himself, could not have chosen a dove, since those birds have no voices, but rather one of Loulou's ancestors. And Félicité, although she looked at the picture as she said her prayers, would turn from time to time toward the parrot.

She wanted to join the Ladies of the Blessed Virgin, but Mme. Aubain dissuaded her.

Then a great event occurred: Paul's marriage.

After having been in succession a clerk in a notary's office, in business, in the customs office, in the revenue service, and having even made efforts to get into the bureau of waters and forests—suddenly, at thirty-six, by an inspiration from heaven, he had discovered his career: that of registrar! He showed such aptitude for this kind of work that an inspector had offered him his daughter in marriage, promising to use his influence on Paul's behalf.

Paul, serious-minded now, brought the girl to see his mother.

She sniffed at the ways of Pont-l'Évêque, gave herself the airs of a princess, and hurt Félicité's feelings. Mme. Aubain felt relieved when the visitor left.

The following week news was brought of Bourais' death in an inn in lower Brittany. Rumors of suicide were later confirmed and doubts of his integrity were raised. Mme. Aubain pored over his accounts, and it didn't take her long to discover a long list of his misdeeds: embezzlements, fictitious sales of wood, forged receipts, etc. Besides that, he had an illegitimate child, and "relations with a certain person from Dozulé."

These scandalous acts distressed Madame very much. In March 1853, she was seized with a pain in her chest; her tongue was coated, and leeches did not give her any relief. On the ninth evening she died, having just reached her seventy-second birthday.

Everyone thought she was younger than she really was, because of her brown hair, braids of which framed her pallid, pockmarked face. Few friends regretted her passing, for with her haughty manner she kept people at a distance.

But Félicité mourned her as masters are seldom mourned. That Madame should have died before her disturbed her thoughts, seemed to her contrary to the nature of things, something inadmissible and monstrous.

Ten days later (the time it took to travel from Besançon) the heirs arrived. The daughter-in-law rummaged through drawers, selected certain pieces of furniture, sold the rest. Then they left, and Paul returned to his registering.

Madame's armchair, her small round table, her foot warmer, the eight chairs were gone! On the walls were yellow squares that marked where pictures used to hang. They had carried off the two beds, with the mattresses, and Virginie's belongings were no longer to be seen in the cupboard! Félicité, numb with sadness, wandered from floor to floor.

Next day there was a notice on the door. The apothecary shouted in her ear that the house was for sale.

She staggered and had to sit down. What distressed her most of all was that she might have to give up her room—so comfortable for poor little Loulou. Gazing at the bird with a look of anguish, she prayed to the Holy Ghost. She had formed the idolatrous habit of saying her prayers on her knees in front of the parrot. Sometimes the sun breaking through the window caught his glass eye, and a long luminous ray would dart from it, throwing Félicité into ecstasy.

She had an income of three hundred and eighty francs a year, willed to her by Mme. Aubain. The garden provided her with vegetables. As for clothes, she had enough to last till the end of her days, and she saved on lighting by going to bed at dusk.

She rarely went out, in order to avoid the secondhand shop where some pieces of the old furniture were displayed for sale. Ever since her shock, she dragged one leg; and as her strength was failing Mère Simon, whose grocery business had fallen into ruin, used to come every morning to chop her wood and pump her water.

Félicité's eyesight became weak.

The shutters of the house would no longer open. Many years passed, but the place was not rented or sold.

For fear of being turned out, Félicité never asked for repairs. The laths of the roof began to rot, so that for a whole year the bolster of her bed was damp. After Easter she began to spit blood.

This time Mère Simon called a doctor. Félicité wanted to know what was the matter with her. But, too deaf to hear, she caught only one word: "Pneumonia." It was familiar enough to her and she answered, softly, "Ah! like Madame," thinking it natural that she should thus follow her mistress.

The time for preparing the altars was nearing. The first of them was always erected at the bottom of the hill, the second in front of the post office, and the third about halfway down the street. There was some difference of opinion concerning this last-mentioned, and the parishioners at last decided to put it in Mme. Aubain's courtyard.

The pain in Félicité's chest and her fever continued to increase. Félicité was annoyed because she could do nothing for the altar. If only she could have at least put something on it. Then she thought of the parrot. But the neighbors objected: it wasn't proper. However, the curé granted permission and this made her so happy that she begged him to accept Loulou, her sole valuable possession, when she died.

From Tuesday to Saturday, the eve of Corpus Christi, she coughed more and more. By the evening, her face was pinched, her lips clung to her gums, and she began to vomit, and next day at early dawn, feeling very weak, she sent for a priest.

Three kindly old women stood around while she received extreme unction. Then she said she wanted to speak to Fabu.

He came in his Sunday clothes, ill at ease in this sad atmosphere.

"Forgive me," she said, with an effort to extend her arm, "I thought it was you who had killed him!"

What did she mean by this nonsense? Suspecting a man like him of being a murderer! He was indignant, and was about to make a scene.

"As you can see, she makes no sense at all."

Every once in a while Félicité would talk to shadows. The three ladies went away and Mère Simon went to breakfast.

A little later Mère Simon took Loulou and, holding him near Félicité, said: "Come, now, say goodbye to him!"

Though he was not a corpse, the worms had begun to devour the dead bird; one of his wings was broken, and the stuffing was coming out of his body. But Félicité, now blind, kissed Loulou's forehead, and pressed him against her cheek. Mère Simon took him away and placed him on the altar.

V

A scent of summer drifted from the meadow; flies buzzed; the sun made the surface of the river glisten and heated the slate roofs. Mère Simon had come back into the room, and was dozing peacefully.

The tolling of the church bell awakened her; the people were coming from vespers. Félicité's delirium ceased. She thought of the procession, and saw it as if she had been there.

All the children from the schools, the choir singers, together with the firemen, walked along on the pavement, while in the middle of the road marched first the verger armed with his halberd, the beadle carrying his large cross, the schoolmaster watching his small charges, and the sister anxious for her little girls; three of the cutest of these, with curls like angels, were throwing rose petals in the air; the deacon, with his arms outstretched, was leading the music; and two incense bearers bowed at every step in front of the Blessed Sacrament, carried by M. le Curé wearing a beautiful chasuble, beneath a flaming red canopy, held by four churchwardens. Waves of people surged behind, between the white cloths covering the walls of the houses. They arrived at the foot of the hill.

Beads of cold sweat dampened Félicité's temples. Mère Simon sponged them with a piece of cloth, saying to herself that one day she would have to go too.

The murmur of the crowd mounted; for a moment, it was very loud, then it faded.

A fusillade rattled the windowpanes. It was the postilions saluting the monstrance. Félicité rolled her eyes and said as softly as she could:

"Is he all right?" She was anxiously thinking of her parrot.

Her death agony began. A rattle, more and more violent, shook her sides. Froth appeared at the corners of her mouth and her whole body was trembling.

Soon, above the blaring of the wind instruments, the clear voices of the children and the deep voices of men could be distinguished. At intervals, all was silent, except for the tread of feet shuffling over the strewn flowers, sounding like sheep on the grass.

The priests appeared in the courtyard. Mère Simon climbed on one of the chairs to look through the round window. In this way she could look down upon the altar.

Green wreaths hung from the altar, which was decorated with a flounce of English lace. In the middle there was a small receptacle containing relics; two orange trees stood at the corners, and all along were silver candlesticks and porcelain vases, filled with sunflowers, lilies, peonies, foxgloves, and tufts of hydrangea. This mass of brilliant colors banked from the level of the altar to the rug spread over the pavement. Strange objects caught the eye: a vermilion sugar bowl held a wreath of violets; pendants of Alençon stone glittered on the moss; two Chinese screens depicted landscapes. Loulou, concealed by the roses, showed nothing but his blue forehead, like a piece of lapis lazuli.

The churchwardens, choristers, and children stood in rows on three sides of the courtyard. The priest ascended the steps slowly, and put down his great, shining, golden monstrance on the lacework cloth. All knelt. There was a deep silence; and the censers, swinging to and fro, glided on their little chains.

A blue cloud of smoke rose to Félicité's room. She distended her nostrils, breathing it in with a mystical sensuousness; then she closed her eyes. Her lips were smiling. The beating of her heart became fainter and fainter, softer like an exhausted fountain, like a fading echo; and when she breathed her last breath, she thought she saw in the opening heavens a gigantic parrot, hovering above her head.

Questions

1. **What account does Flaubert give of Félicité's background? How is it relevant to her life with the Aubains?**
2. **Cite instances of juxtaposition in the story. What is the effect in each instance?**
3. **How does Flaubert show the passage of time?**
4. **Why does Félicité ask Fabu to forgive her? Why did Flaubert have her do this?**
5. **What role does religion play in Félicité's life?**

Guy de Maupassant

At Sea

MAUPASSANT was Flaubert's prize pupil. For seven years the author of "A Simple Heart" would not let the younger man publish a word of what he wrote. The result was that when he burst upon the French literary scene, with "Boule de Suif," he appeared as an already polished master of his art.

Maupassant's best stories involve neither the trick plots nor the mawkish sentimentality so commonly associated in the popular mind with his fiction. They do, however, usually revolve around strong dramatic situations, and they are more often than not ironic stories. There always hovers the suspicion that life is somehow a joke, that a hoax has been played on man.

Many of his best stories are set in the maritime Normandy of his childhood and deal with peasants and fishermen, types which he understood well. "At Sea," for example, deals with a peasant trait which is the subject of more than one of his stories: avarice. But while Maupassant understands the roots of human conduct, it is not his method to analyze them. "For me," he once said, "psychology in a novel or story consists in this: to show the inner man by his life." Thus he presents the visible surface of human action and implies the rest.

With such a fictional strategy, Maupassant makes great use in his stories of custom, of habitual action and habitual response. It is more than a cultural backdrop for events. It is the prime mover in these events, circumscribing the lives of his characters and even dictating the rôle that fate plays.

THE following item recently appeared in the papers under the dateline "Boulogne-sur-Mer, January 22":

> A frightful disaster has caused consternation among our coastal population, which has already been so hard-hit during the last two years. A fishing trawler commanded by Captain Javel was carried westward off its course as it was entering port and thrown against the breakwater.
>
> Despite the efforts of the lifeboat and the life lines thrown to them, four men and a boy were lost.
>
> The bad weather continues and fresh disasters are feared.

Who was Captain Javel? Could it be the brother of one-armed Javel?

Was the poor man swept away by the waves, or perhaps dead under the debris of his wrecked ship, the Javel I'm thinking of? If so, he had once before witnessed a tragedy at sea, terrible and simple as are all great tragedies of the deep.

It happened eighteen years ago. The elder Javel was then master of a smack, which is an ideal fishing boat. Sturdy, fearing no weather, round-bellied, constantly bobbing on the waves like a cork, always out at sea, forever whipped by the biting, salty winds of the Channel, it plows the billows tirelessly—its sails ballooning, trailing at its side a great net that sweeps over the ocean bottom, grabbing and tearing loose all the sleeping creatures of the rocks: the flat fish that hug the sands, the heavy crabs with their hooked claws, and the lobsters with their pointed whiskers. When the breeze is fresh and the waves are short and choppy, the smack begins to trawl. The net is tied to a long, iron-sheathed wooden bar that is lowered by means of two cables running through two blocks rigged one at each end of the boat. And so the smack, drifting with the wind and the current, drags along this rig which ravages and robs the sea floor.

Javel's crew consisted of his younger brother, four other men, and a boy. They set out from Boulogne on a clear day, hoping to trawl. But when they were out, the wind rose and a squall chased the smack. They reached the English coast, but the stormy seas smashing against the cliffs made it impossible to enter a port. The smack then turned back to sea and returned toward the coast of France. The storm was still so violent that the breakwaters could not be negotiated, and the harbor entrances were wrapped in froth, din, and danger. The little smack turned away once more. The waves tossed it around, shook it, and battered it; but it took all this pluckily, accustomed as it was to rough weather that had sometimes forced it to wander for five or six days between the two neighboring countries without being able to put into a port on either side.

Finally, while the craft was out in the open sea, the storm subsided somewhat, and although the waves were still quite big, the skipper ordered the trawl lowered.

The heavy net was passed overboard and two men forward and two aft began to pay out the cables that held it through the blocks. But when the trawl touched the bottom, a large wave tipped the boat; and the younger Javel, who was on the forward block directing the maneuver, slipped and got his arm caught between the ship's side and the rope that had been slackened for a second when the net had reached the bottom and then had tightened again when the boat was lifted by the waves. He made a desperate effort to loosen the rope with his free hand, but by now it was taut and wouldn't budge.

Shaken by pain, he called for help. They all rushed to him. His brother abandoned the wheel and also joined them. They all took hold of the rope and pulled, trying to slacken it and free the arm that it was crushing. It was all in vain.

"Must be cut," a seaman said, and he produced a big, sharp jackknife that in two slashes could have saved the younger Javel's arm.

But of course, cutting the rope meant losing the trawl net and that meant losing money, a great deal of money—fifteen hundred francs—and it was the property of the elder Javel who hated to let go of what he had. So, his heart filled with agony, he shouted:

"Wait, don't cut it! I'll try to luff. . . ." And he rushed to the wheel and tried to bring the boat closer to the wind. But the smack hardly responded because the net made it unmaneuverable; in addition, it was drifting with the wind and current.

The younger Javel slipped down to his knees, his teeth clenched, his eyes haggard. He said nothing. His brother came back, still worried about the jackknife.

"Wait, wait, don't cut it yet. We'll anchor. . . ."

The anchor was dropped, the chain paid out. Then they tried to wind the cables around the capstan to slacken the ropes that held the trawl. Finally they got enough slack and released the lifeless arm in its blood-stained, woolen sleeve.

The younger Javel's face was blank. They removed his jacket and saw a horrible mass of flesh with blood gushing from it in many streams, as if someone were pumping it out. The man looked at his arm and said:

"I've had it!"

As the blood formed a river on the deck, a seaman shouted:

"Why, he'll empty himself like that. We must tie it off."

So they got a rope, a dark, tarred piece of rope, turned it around the arm above the wound, and tied it as tight as they could. The jets of blood diminished gradually and finally the bleeding stopped completely.

The younger Javel got up, his arm hanging at his side. He took it in his other hand, lifted it, turned it, and shook it. It was quite loose. The bones were broken and only the tendons held it to the rest of his body. He looked at it gloomily, thinking something over. Then he sat down on a folded sail and the others advised him to keep wetting his injured arm with brine to prevent the "black rot."

They placed a bucket of water next to him and every minute or so, he would dip a glass into it and pour a thin, transparent stream over his horrible wound.

"You'd be better off down below," his brother said, and he went down. But within an hour he was back on deck, for he hadn't felt too good down there all by himself. Besides, he preferred to be out in the fresh air. So he sat down on the folded sail and started bathing his arm again.

The fishing was good. Big, white-bellied fish lay next to him, jerking in their death agony, and he watched them as he poured the seawater on his wounded limb.

When they were about to return to Boulogne, a new squall came up and the little fishing boat resumed its mad rush back and forth between the French and English coasts, jouncing, shaking, and rolling the gloomy wounded man.

Night came and the sea remained rough until dawn. As the sun rose, the English coast was once more in sight. But then the weather improved a bit, and they turned back toward France, beating into the wind.

Toward evening the wounded man called his shipmates and showed them some black stains on his arm—the sinister marks of rot on the loose part of the limb.

The sailors examined it and voiced their opinions.

"It could very well be the Black One," one man mused.

"You must keep it in the brine," another seaman advised.

The brought a bucket of seawater and poured it on the arm. The injured man turned livid, his teeth gnashed, his body twisted slightly. But he didn't cry out. And when the scorching pain caused by the salt water had subsided a bit, he said to his brother:

"Give me your knife," and when the other handed it to him, he said: "Hold my arm up straight. That's right, now pull."

His brother did as he was told.

Then the younger Javel began to cut off his own arm. He cut

it slowly, thoughtfully, snapping off the remaining tendons with the razor-sharp blade of the jackknife, and soon he had nothing but a stump left. He gave a deep sigh and said: "Had to do it. I'd had it, otherwise."

He seemed relieved, took a deep breath, then began again to pour water on what was left of his arm.

The night that followed was again too rough to enter port.

When it was day again, the younger Javel picked up his severed arm and examined it at length. The rot was now easily visible. His shipmates came and looked at it too, and it passed from hand to hand, all of them poking and smelling it.

The older brother said:

"Seeing the state it's in, it's best to throw it overboard."

But now the younger brother lost his temper.

"Oh no! No, sir! I don't want it tossed overboard and it's not going to be, since it's my arm!" And he took it back and put it between his knees.

"Still, you can't stop it from rotting," his brother said.

Then the wounded man got an idea: when they stayed at sea for a long time, they preserved their fish in barrels of brine. So he said:

"I guess it'd keep in brine, though?"

"It ought to," the others agreed.

They emptied a barrel which was already full of fish they had caught on an earlier day and put the arm at the bottom of it. They poured brine in over it and then replaced the fish, one by one.

One of the seamen cracked a joke on this occasion:

"Hope we don't sell it in the market by mistake!"

And all except the two Javels laughed.

The wind was still blowing and they had to beat to windward again; they didn't come within sight of Boulogne until ten o'clock. The wounded man kept tirelessly throwing water over his wound. From time to time he would get up and walk from one end of the boat to the other. His brother, who was at the wheel, followed him with his eyes, shaking his head.

Finally they put into Boulogne.

A doctor examined the wound and declared it to be in good shape. He dressed it and prescribed rest for the patient. But Javel wouldn't lie down until he had recovered his arm. He rushed back to port, went on board his brother's smack, and found the barrel that he had marked with a cross in chalk. They emptied it while he watched, then he picked up his limb, which had been very nicely preserved in the brine. It looked rather fresher than before, although it was strangely wrinkled. He wrapped it in a napkin that he had brought with him for the purpose and returned home.

His wife and children examined this piece of their father at length, touching the fingers and removing the traces of salt from under the nails. Then they called the carpenter and asked him to make a little coffin.

The following day, the full crew of the smack followed the funeral of their shipmate's severed limb. The two brothers, side by side, led the procession. The parish sexton carried the little corpse under his arm.

The younger Javel didn't go back to sea. He got a job in the port; and later, when he would speak of the incident, he would confide to his listener in a low voice:

"If my brother had been willing to cut loose his trawl, I'd still have my arm, no doubt about that. . . . But he sure didn't like to part with his goods, my brother."

Questions

1. What function does the newspaper clipping serve? Why does Maupassant begin his story in this way? What is he trying to suggest by the narrator's questions in the two opening paragraphs?
2. Does avarice triumph in this story? If so, whose?
3. What motivates the younger Javel to preserve his arm? Is the same trait manifested in any way in the elder Javel?
4. Do you see any irony in the story? If so, where?

TOWARD A MODERN TRADITION

Henry James

The Real Thing

JOSEPH CONRAD called Henry James "the historian of fine consciences." He was also the historian of fine manners. Both these aspects of his fiction come through in "The Real Thing," in which the artist-narrator worries over his responsibility toward Major and Mrs. Monarch, the upper-class British couple whom he has employed as models.

Because of the Monarchs the narrator comes close to losing a profitable commission to illustrate a whole series of novels for a de luxe edition. His sense of the ironies involved in the situation, as well as his understanding of the perplexity of the Monarchs, in the face of their failure as models and the success of the cockney Miss Churm and the manservant Oronte, gives us one dimension of the sensibility called into play in James's novels and stories. A second can be found in the dialogue of the story, with its ceremonial nature. In spite of its formal surface Jamesian dialogue is designed to pick up nuance and suggestion and to expose them to the full light of reflection and understanding.

The principle of progression in Jamesian fiction is typically a series of controlled revelations; the plot, one of ignorance-to-knowledge. A central character, acting with impartial and imperfect knowledge, makes a commitment to a line of action. In the working out of the plot, the character learns of the shortcomings of his choice and something of the true nature of circumstances and events. In "The Real Thing" this outline is only partially preserved, for James is less interested in the narrator as a person than as a device. The story's major focus is the nature of appearance and reality, and its meaning for art.

James's contributions to "the art of fiction" are various and significant. Many of his interests were technical, and he is in part responsible for our concern today with such aspects of fiction as "point of view." In the short story he worked largely in the conventional mode. We have to turn to such novellas as "The Beast in the Jungle" and his novels to see the full range of his powers.

WHEN the porter's wife, who used to answer the house-bell, announced "A gentleman and a lady, sir," I had, as I often had in those days—the wish being father to the thought—an immediate vision of sitters. Sitters my visitors in this case proved to be; but not in the sense I should have preferred. There was nothing at first however to indicate that they mightn't have come for a portrait. The gentleman, a man of fifty, very high and very straight, with a moustache slightly grizzled and a dark grey walking-coat admirably fitted, both of which I noted professionally—I don't mean as a barber or yet as a tailor—would have struck me as a celebrity if celebrities often were striking. It was a truth of which I had for some time been conscious that a figure with a good deal of frontage was, as one might say, almost never a public institution. A glance at the lady helped to remind me of this paradoxical law: she also looked too distinguished to be a "personality." Moreover one would scarcely come across two variations together.

Neither of the pair immediately spoke—they only prolonged the preliminary gaze suggesting that each wished to give the other a chance. They were visibly shy; they stood there letting me take them in—which, as I afterwards perceived, was the most practical thing they could have done. In this way their embarrassment served their cause. I had seen people painfully reluctant to mention that they desired anything so gross as to be represented on canvas; but the scruples of my new friends appeared almost insurmountable. Yet the gentleman might have said "I should like a portrait of my wife," and the lady might have said "I should like a portrait of my husband." Perhaps they weren't husband and wife—this naturally would make the matter more delicate. Perhaps they wished to be done together—in which case they ought to have brought a third person to break the news.

"We come from Mr. Rivet," the lady finally said with a dim smile that had the effect of a moist sponge passed over a "sunk" piece of painting, as well as of a vague allusion to vanished beauty. She was as tall and straight, in her degree, as her companion, and with ten years less to carry. She looked as sad as a woman could look whose face was not charged with expression; that is her tinted oval mask showed waste as an exposed surface shows friction. The hand of time had played over her freely, but to an effect of elimination. She was slim and stiff, and so well-dressed, in dark blue cloth, with lappets and pockets and buttons, that it was clear she employed the same tailor as her husband. The couple had an indefinable air of prosperous thrift—they evidently got a good deal of luxury for their money. If I was to be one of their luxuries it would behoove me to consider my terms.

"Ah, Claude Rivet recommended me?" I echoed; and I added that it was very kind of him, though I could reflect that, as he only painted landscape, this wasn't a sacrifice.

The lady looked very hard at the gentleman, and the gentleman looked round the room. Then staring at the floor a moment and stroking his moustache, he rested his pleasant eyes on me with the remark: "He said you were the right one."

"I try to be, when people want to sit."

"Yes, we should like to," said the lady anxiously.

"Do you mean together?"

My visitors exchanged a glance. "If you could do anything with *me* I suppose it would be double," the gentleman stammered.

"Oh yes, there's naturally a higher charge for two figures than for one."

"We should like to make it pay," the husband confessed.

"That's very good of you," I returned, appreciating so unwonted a sympathy—for I supposed he meant pay the artist.

A sense of strangeness seemed to dawn on the lady. "We mean for the illustrations—Mr. Rivet said you might put one in."

"Put in—an illustration?" I was equally confused.

"Sketch her off, you know," said the gentleman, colouring.

It was only then that I understood the service Claude Rivet had rendered me; he had told them how I worked in black-and-white, for magazines, for storybooks, for sketches of contemporary life, and consequently had copious employment for models. These things were true, but it was not less true—I may confess it now; whether because the aspiration was to lead to everything or to nothing I leave the reader to guess—that I couldn't get the honours, to say nothing of the emoluments, of a great painter of portraits out of my head. My "illustrations" were my pot-boilers; I looked to a different branch of art—far and away the most interesting it had always seemed to me—to perpetuate my fame. There was no shame in looking to it also to make my fortune; but that fortune was by so much further from being made from the moment my visitors wished to be "done" for nothing. I was disappointed; for in the pictorial sense I had immediately *seen* them. I had seized their type—I had already settled what I would do with it. Something that wouldn't absolutely have pleased them, I afterwards reflected.

"Ah you're—you're—a?" I began as soon as I had mastered my surprise. I couldn't bring out the dingy word "models": it seemed so little to fit the case.

"We haven't had much practice," said the lady.

"We've got to *do* something, and we've thought that an artist in your line might perhaps make something of us," her husband threw off. He further mentioned that they didn't know many artists and that they had gone first, on the off-chance—he painted views of course, but sometimes put in figures; perhaps I remembered—to Mr. Rivet, whom they had met a few years before at a place in Norfolk where he was sketching.

"We used to sketch a little ourselves," the lady hinted.

"It's very awkward, but we absolutely *must* do something," her husband went on.

"Of course we're not so *very* young," she admitted with a wan smile.

With the remark that I might as well know something more about them the husband had handed me a card extracted from a neat new pocket-book—their appurtenances were all of the freshest—and inscribed with the words "Major Monarch." Impressive as these words were they didn't carry my knowledge much further; but my visitor presently added: "I've left the army and we've had the misfortune to lose our money. In fact our means are dreadfully small."

"It's awfully trying—a regular strain," said Mrs. Monarch.

They evidently wished to be discreet—to take care not to swagger because they were gentlefolk. I felt them willing to recognise this as something of a drawback, at the same time that I guessed at an underlying sense—their consolation in adversity—that they *had* their points. They certainly had; but these advantages struck me as preponderantly social; such for instance as would help to make a drawing-room look well. However, a drawing-room was always, or ought to be, a picture.

In consequence of his wife's allusion to their age Major Monarch observed: "Naturally it's more for the figure that we thought of going in. We can still hold ourselves up." On the instant I saw that the figure was indeed their strong point. His "naturally" didn't sound vain, but it lighted up the question. "*She* has the best one," he continued, nodding at his wife with a pleasant after-dinner absence of circumlocution. I could only reply, as if we were in fact sitting over our wine, that this didn't prevent his own from being very good;

which led him in turn to make answer: "We thought that if you ever have to do people like us we might be something like it. *She* particularly—for a lady in a book, you know."

I was so amused by them that, to get more of it, I did my best to take their point of view; and though it was an embarrassment to find myself appraising physically, as if they were animals on hire or useful blacks, a pair whom I should have expected to meet only in one of the relations in which criticism is tacit, I looked at Mrs. Monarch judicially enough to be able to exclaim after a moment with conviction: "Oh yes, a lady in a book!" She was singularly like a bad illustration.

"We'll stand up, if you like," said the Major; and he raised himself before me with a really grand air.

I could take his measure at a glance—he was six feet two and a perfect gentleman. It would have paid any club in process of formation and in want of a stamp to engage him at a salary to stand in the principal window. What struck me at once was that in coming to me they had rather missed their vocation; they could surely have been turned to better account for advertising purposes. I couldn't of course see the thing in detail, but I could see them make somebody's fortune—I don't mean their own. There was something in them for a waistcoat-maker, an hotel-keeper or a soap-vendor. I could imagine "We always use it" pinned on their bosoms with the greatest effect; I had a vision of the brilliancy with which they would launch a table d'hôte.

Mrs. Monarch sat still, not from pride but from shyness, and presently her husband said to her: "Get up, my dear, and show how smart you are." She obeyed, but she had no need to get up to show it. She walked to the end of the studio and then came back blushing, her fluttered eyes on the partner of her appeal. I was reminded of an incident I had accidentally had a glimpse of in Paris—being with a friend there, a dramatist about to produce a play, when an actress came to him to ask to be entrusted with a part. She went through her paces before him, walked up and down as Mrs. Monarch was doing. Mrs. Monarch did it quite as well, but I abstained from applauding. It was very odd to see such people apply for such poor pay. She looked as if she had ten thousand a year. Her husband had used the word that described her: she was in the London current jargon essentially and typically "smart." Her figure was, in the same order of ideas, conspicuously and irreproachably "good." For a woman of her age her waist was surprisingly small; her elbow moreover had the orthodox crook. She held her head at the conventional angle, but why did she come to *me?* She ought to have tried on jackets at a big shop. I feared my visitors were not only destitute but "artistic"—which would be a great complication. When she sat down again I thanked her, observing that what a draughtsman most valued in his model was the faculty of keeping quiet.

"Oh *she* can keep quiet," said Major Monarch. Then he added jocosely: "I've always kept her quiet."

"I'm not a nasty fidget, am I?" It was going to wring tears from me, I felt, the way she hid her head, ostrich-like, in the other broad bosom.

The owner of this expanse addressed his answer to me. "Perhaps it isn't out of place to mention—because we ought to be quite business-like, oughtn't we?—that when I married her she was known as the Beautiful Statue."

"Oh dear!" said Mrs. Monarch ruefully.

"Of course I should want a certain amount of expression," I rejoined.

"Of *course!"*—and I had never heard such unanimity.

"And then I suppose you know that you'll get awfully tired."

"Oh we *never* get tired!" they eagerly cried.

"Have you had any kind of practice?"

They hesitated—they looked at each other. "We've been photographed—*immensely,"* said Mrs. Monarch.

"She means the fellows have asked us themselves," added the Major.

"I see—because you're so good-looking."

"I don't know what they thought, but they were always after us."

"We always got our photographs for nothing," smiled Mrs. Monarch.

"We might have brought some, my dear," her husband remarked.

"I'm not sure we have any left. We've given quantities away," she explained to me.

"With our autographs and that sort of thing," said the Major.

"Are they to be got in the shops?" I enquired as a harmless pleasantry.

"Oh yes, *hers*—they used to be."

"Not now," said Mrs. Monarch, with her eyes on the floor.

II

I could fancy the "sort of thing" they put on the presentation copies of their photographs, and I was sure they wrote a beautiful hand. It was odd how quickly I was sure of everything that concerned them. If they were now so poor as to have to earn shillings and pence they could never have had much of a margin. Their good looks had been their capital, and they had good-humouredly made the most of the career that this resource marked out for them. It was in their faces, the blankness, the deep intellectual repose of the twenty years of country-house visiting that had given them pleasant intonations. I could see the sunny drawing-rooms, sprinkled with periodicals she didn't read, in which Mrs. Monarch had continuously sat; I could see the wet shrubberies in which she had walked, equipped to admiration for either exercise. I could see the rich covers the Major had helped to shoot and the wonderful garments in which, late at night, he repaired to the smoking-room to talk about them. I could imagine their leggings and waterproofs, their knowing tweeds and rugs, their rolls of sticks and cases of tackle and neat umbrellas; and I could evoke the exact appearance of their servants and the compact variety of their luggage on the platforms of country stations.

They gave small tips, but they were liked; they didn't do anything themselves, but they were welcome. They looked so well everywhere; they gratified the general relish for stature, complexion and "form." They knew it without fatuity or vulgarity, and they respected themselves in consequence. They weren't superficial; they were thorough and kept themselves up—it had been their line. People with such a taste for activity had to have some line. I could feel how even in a dull house they could have been counted on for the joy of life. At present something had happened—it didn't matter what, their little income had grown less, it had grown least—and they had to do something for pocket-money. Their friends could like them, I made out, without liking to support them. There was something about them that represented credit—their clothes, their manners, their type; but if credit is a large empty pocket in which an occasional chink reverberates, the chink at least must be audible. What they wanted of me was to help to make it so. Fortunately they had no children—I soon divined that. They would also perhaps wish our relations to be kept secret: this was why it was "for the figure"—the reproduction of the face would betray them.

I liked them—I felt, quite as their friends must have done—they were so simple; and I had no objection to them if they would suit. But somehow with all their perfections I didn't easily believe in them. After all they were amateurs, and the ruling passion of my life was the detestation of the amateur. Combined with this was another perversity—an innate preference for the represented subject over the real one: the defect of the real one was so apt to be a lack of representation. I like things that appeared; then one was sure. Whether they *were* or not was a subordinate and almost always a profitless question. There were other considerations, the first of which was that I already had two or three recruits in use, notably a young person with big feet, in alpaca, from Kilburn, who for a couple of years had come to me regularly for my illustrations and with whom I was still—perhaps ignobly—satisfied. I frankly explained to my visitors how the case stood, but they had taken more precautions than I supposed. They had reasoned out their opportunity, for Claude Rivet had told them of the projected *édition de luxe* of one of the writers of our day—the rarest of the novelists—who, long neglected by the multitudinous vulgar and dearly prized by the attentive (need I mention Philip Vincent?), had had the happy fortune of seeing, late in life, the dawn and then the full light of a higher criticism; an estimate in which on the part of the public there was something really of expiation. The edition preparing, planned by a publisher of taste, was practically an act of high reparation; the wood-cuts with which it was to be enriched were the homage of English art to one of the most independent representatives of English letters. Major and Mrs. Monarch confessed to me they had hoped I might be able to work *them* into my branch of the enterprise. They knew I was to do the first of the books, "Rutland Ramsay," but I had to make clear to them that my participation in the rest of the affair—this first book was to be a test—must depend on the satisfaction I should give. If this should be limited my employers would drop me with scarce common forms. It was therefore a crisis for me, and naturally I was making special preparations, looking about for new people, should they be necessary, and securing the best types. I admitted however that I should like to settle down to two or three good models who would do for everything.

"Should we have often to—a—put on special clothes?" Mrs. Monarch timidly demanded.

"Dear yes—that's half the business."

"And should we be expected to supply our own costumes?"

"Oh no; I've got a lot of things. A painter's models put on—or put off—anything he likes."

"And you mean—a—the same?"

"The same?"

Mrs. Monarch looked at her husband again.

"Oh she was just wondering," he explained, "if the costumes are in *general* use." I had to confess that they were, and I mentioned further that some of them—I had a lot of genuine greasy last-century things—had served their time, a hundred years ago, on living world-stained men and women; on figures not perhaps so far removed, in that vanished world, from *their* type, the Monarchs', *quoi!* of a breeched and bewigged age. "We'll put on anything that *fits,"* said the Major.

"Oh I arrange that—they fit in the pictures."

"I'm afraid I should do better for the modern books. I'd come as you like," said Mrs. Monarch.

"She has got a lot of clothes at home: they might do for contemporary life," her husband continued.

"Oh I can fancy scenes in which you'd be quite natural." And indeed I could see the slipshod rearrangements of stale properties—the stories I tried to produce pictures for without the exasperation of reading them—whose sandy tracts the good lady might help to people. But I had to return to the fact that for this sort of work—the daily mechanical grind—I was already equipped: the people I was working with were fully adequate.

"We only thought we might be more like *some* characters," said Mrs. Monarch mildly, getting up.

Her husband also rose; he stood looking at me with a dim wistfulness that was touching in so fine a man. "Wouldn't it be rather a pull sometimes to have—a—to have—?" He hung fire; he wanted me to help him by phrasing what he meant. But I couldn't—I didn't know. So he brought it out awkwardly: "The *real* thing; a gentleman, you know, or a lady." I was quite ready to give a general assent—I admitted that there was a great deal in that. This encouraged Major Monarch to say, following up his appeal with an unacted gulp: "It's awfully hard—we've tried everything." The gulp was communicative; it proved too much for his wife. Before I knew it Mrs. Monarch had dropped again upon a divan and burst into tears. Her husband sat down beside her, holding one of her hands; whereupon she quickly dried her eyes with the other, while I felt embarrassed as she looked up at me. "There isn't a confounded job I haven't applied for—waited for—prayed for. You can fancy we'd be pretty bad first. Secretaryships and that sort of thing? You might as well ask for a peerage. I'd be *anything*—I'm strong; a messenger or a coalheaver. I'd put on a gold-laced cap and open carriage-doors in front of the haberdasher's; I'd hang about a station to carry portmanteaux; I'd be a postman. But they won't *look* at you; there are thousands as good as yourself already on the ground. *Gentlemen,* poor beggars, who've drunk their wine, who've kept their hunters!"

I was as reassuring as I knew how to be, and my visitors were presently on their feet again while, for the experiment, we agreed on an hour. We were discussing it when the door opened and Miss Churm came in with a wet umbrella. Miss Churm had to take the omnibus to Maida Vale and then walk half a mile. She looked a trifle blowsy and slightly splashed. I scarcely ever saw her come in without thinking afresh how odd it was that, being so little in herself, she should yet be so much in others. She was a meagre little Miss Churm, but was such an ample heroine of romance. She was only a freckled cockney, but she could represent everything, from a fine lady to a shepherdess; she had the faculty as she might have had a fine voice or long hair. She couldn't spell and she loved beer, but she had two or three "points," and practice, and a knack, and mother-wit, and a whimsical sensibility, and a love of the theatre, and seven sisters, and not an ounce of respect, especially for the *h*. The first thing my visitors saw was that her umbrella was wet, and in their spotless perfection they visibly winced at it. The rain had come on since their arrival.

"I'm all in a soak; there *was* a mess of people in the 'bus. I wish you lived near a stytion," said Miss Churm. I requested her to get ready as quickly as possible, and she passed into the room in which she always changed her dress. But before going out she asked me what she was to get into this time.

"It's the Russian princess, don't you know?" I answered; "the one with the 'golden eyes,' in black velvet, for the long thing in the *Cheapside*."

"Golden eyes? I *say!*" cried Miss Churm, while my companions watched her with intensity as she withdrew. She always arranged herself, when she was late, before I could turn round; and I kept my visitors a little on purpose, so that they might get an idea, from seeing her, what would be expected of themselves. I mentioned that she was quite my notion of an excellent model—she was really very clever.

"Do you think she looks like a Russian princess?" Major Monarch asked with lurking alarm.

"When I make her, yes."

"Oh if you have to *make* her—!" he reasoned, not without point.

"That's the most you can ask. There are so many who are not makeable."

"Well now, *here's* a lady"—and with a persuasive smile he passed his arm into his wife's—"who's already made!"

"Oh I'm not a Russian princess," Mrs. Monarch protested a little coldly. I could see she had known some and didn't like them. There at once was a complication of a kind I never had to fear with Miss Churm.

This young lady came back in black velvet—the gown was rather rusty and very low on her lean shoulders—and with a Japanese fan in her red hands. I reminded her that in the scene I was doing she had to look over some one's head. "I forget whose it is; but it doesn't matter. Just look over a head."

"I'd rather look over a stove," said Miss Churm; and she took her station near the fire. She fell into position, settled herself into a tall attitude, gave a certain backward inclination to her head and a certain forward droop to her fan, and looked, at least to my prejudiced sense, distinguished and charming, foreign and dangerous. We left her looking so while I went downstairs with Major and Mrs. Monarch.

"I believe I could come about as near it as that," said Mrs. Monarch.

"Oh you think she's shabby, but you must allow for the alchemy of art."

However, they went off with an evident increase of comfort founded on their demonstrable advantage in being the real thing. I could fancy them shuddering over Miss Churm. She was very droll about them when I went back, for I told her what they wanted.

"Well, if *she* can sit I'll tyke to book-keeping," said my model.

"She's very ladylike," I replied as an innocent form of aggravation.

"So much the worse for *you*. That means she can't turn round."

"She'll do for the fashionable novels."

"Oh yes, she'll *do* for them!" my model humorously declared. "Ain't they bad enough without her?" I had often sociably denounced them to Miss Churm.

III

It was for the elucidation of a mystery in one of these works that I first tried Mrs. Monarch. Her husband came with her, to be useful if necessary—it was sufficiently clear that as a general thing he would prefer to come with her. At first I wondered if this were for "propriety's" sake—if he were going to be jealous and meddling. The idea was too tiresome, and if it had been confirmed it would speedily have brought our acquaintance to a close. But I soon saw there was nothing in it and that if he accompanied Mrs. Monarch it was—in addition to the chance of being wanted—simply because he had nothing else to do. When they were separate his occupation was gone and they never *had* been separate. I judged rightly that in their awkward situation their close union was their main comfort and that this union had no weak spot. It was a real marriage, an encouragement to the hesitating, a nut for pessimists to crack. Their address was humble—I remember afterwards thinking it had been the only thing about them that was really professional—and I could fancy the lamentable lodgings in which the Major would have been left alone. He could sit there more or less grimly with his wife—he couldn't sit there anyhow without her.

He had too much tact to try and make himself agreeable when he couldn't be useful; so when I was too absorbed in my work to talk he simply sat and waited. But I liked to hear him talk—it made my work, when not interrupting it, less mechanical, less special. To listen to him was to combine the excitement of going out with the economy of staying at home. There was only one hindrance—that I seemed not to know any of the people this brilliant couple had known. I think he wondered extremely, during the term of our intercourse, whom the deuce I *did* know. He hadn't a stray sixpence of an idea to fumble for, so we didn't spin it very fine; we confined ourselves to questions of leather and even of liquor—saddlers and breeches-makers and how to get excellent claret cheap—and matters like "good trains" and the habits of small game. His lore on these last subjects was astonishing—he managed to interweave the station-master with the ornithologist. When he couldn't talk about greater things he could talk cheerfully about smaller, and since I couldn't accompany him into reminiscences of the fashionable world he could lower the conversation without a visible effort to my level.

So earnest a desire to please was touching in a man who could so easily have knocked one down. He looked after the fire and had an opinion on the draught of the stove without my asking him, and I could see that he thought many of my arrangements not half knowing. I remember telling him that if I were only rich I'd offer him a salary to come and teach me how to live. Sometimes he gave a random sigh of which the essence might have been: "Give me even such a bare old barrack as *this,* and I'd do something with it!" When I wanted to use him he came alone; which was an illustration of the superior courage of women. His wife could bear her solitary second floor, and she was in general more discreet; showing by various small reserves that she was alive to the propriety of keeping our relations markedly professional—not letting them slide into sociability. She wished it to remain clear that she and the Major were employed, not cultivated, and if she approved of me as a superior, who could be kept in his place, she never thought me quite good enough for an equal.

She sat with great intensity, giving the whole of her mind to it, and was capable of remaining for an hour almost as motionless as before a photographer's lens. I could see she had been photographed often, but somehow the very habit that made her good for that purpose unfitted her for mine. At first I was extremely pleased with her ladylike air, and it was a satisfaction, on coming to follow her lines, to see how good they were and how far they could lead the pencil. But after a little skirmishing I began to find her too insurmountably stiff; do what I would with it my drawing looked like a photograph or a copy of a photograph. Her figure had no variety of expression—she herself had no sense of variety. You may say that this was my business and was only a question of placing her. Yet I placed her in every conceivable position and she managed to obliterate their differences. She was always a lady certainly, and into the bargain was always the same lady. She was the real thing, but always the same thing. There were moments when I rather writhed under the serenity of her confidence that she *was* the real thing. All her dealings with me and all her husband's were an implication that this was lucky for *me*. Meanwhile I found myself trying to invent types that approached her own, instead of making her own transform itself—in the clever way that was not impossible for instance to poor Miss Churm. Arrange as I would and take the precautions I would, she always came out, in my pictures, too tall—landing me in the dilemma of having represented a fascinating woman as seven feet high, which (out of respect perhaps to my own very much scantier inches) was far from my idea of such a personage.

The case was worse with the Major—nothing I could do would keep *him* down, so that he became useful only for the representation of brawny giants. I adored variety and range, I cherished human accidents, the illustrative note; I wanted to characterise closely, and the thing in the world I most hated was the danger of being ridden by a type. I had quarreled with some of my friends about it; I had parted company with them for maintaining that one *had* to be, and that if the type was beautiful—witness Raphael and Leonardo—the servitude was only a gain. I was neither Leonardo nor Raphael—I might only be a presumptuous young modern searcher; but I held that everything was to be sacrificed sooner than character. When they claimed that the obsessional form could easily *be* character I retorted, perhaps superficially, "Whose?" It couldn't be everybody's—it might end in being nobody's.

After I had drawn Mrs. Monarch a dozen times I felt surer even than before that the value of such a model as Miss Churm resided precisely in the fact that she had no positive stamp, combined of course with the other fact that what she did have was a curious and inexplicable talent for imitation. Her usual appearance was like a curtain which she could draw up at request for a capital performance. This performance was simply suggestive; but it was a word to the wise—it was vivid and pretty. Sometimes even I thought it, though she was plain herself, too insipidly pretty; I made it a reproach to her that the figures drawn from her were monotonously (*bêtement,* as we used to say) graceful. Nothing made her more angry; it was so much her pride to feel she could sit for characters that had nothing in common with each other. She would accuse me at such moments of taking away her "reputytion."

It suffered a certain shrinkage, this queer quantity, from the repeated visits of my new friends. Miss Churm was greatly in demand, never in want of employment, so I had no scruple in putting her off occasionally, to try them more at my ease. It was certainly amusing at first to do the real thing—it was amusing to do Major Monarch's trousers. They *were* the real thing, even if he did come out colossal. It was amusing to do his wife's back hair—it was so mathematically neat—and the particular "smart" tension of her tight stays. She lent herself especially to positions in which the face was somewhat averted or blurred; she abounded in ladylike back views and *profils perdus*. When she stood erect she took naturally one of the attitudes in which court-painters represent queens and princesses; so that I found myself wondering whether, to draw out this accomplishment, I couldn't get the editor of the *Cheapside* to publish a really royal romance, "A Tale of Buckingham Palace." Sometimes however the real thing and the make-believe came into contact; by which I mean that Miss Churm, keeping an appointment or coming to make one on days when I had much work in hand, encountered her invidious rivals. The encounter was not on their part, for they noticed her no more than if she had been the housemaid; not from intentional loftiness, but simply because as yet, professionally, they didn't know how to fraternise, as I could imagine they would have liked—or at least that the Major would. They couldn't talk about the omnibus—they always walked; and they didn't know what else to try—she wasn't interested in good trains or cheap claret. Besides, they must have felt—in the air—that she was amused at them, secretly derisive of their ever knowing how. She wasn't a person to conceal the limits of her faith if she had had a chance to show them. On the other hand Mrs. Monarch didn't think her tidy; for why else did she take pains to say to me—it was going out of the way, for Mrs. Monarch—that she didn't like dirty women?

One day when my young lady happened to be present with my

other sitters—she even dropped in, when it was convenient, for a chat—I asked her to be so good as to lend a hand in getting tea, a service with which she was familiar and which was one of a class that, living as I did in a small way, with slender domestic resources, I often appealed to my models to render. They liked to lay hands on my property, to break the sitting, and sometimes the china—it made them feel Bohemian. The next time I saw Miss Churm after this incident she surprised me greatly by making a scene about it—she accused me of having wished to humiliate her. She hadn't resented the outrage at the time, but had seemed obliging and amused, enjoying the comedy of asking Mrs. Monarch, who sat vague and silent, whether she would have cream and sugar, and putting an exaggerated simper into the question. She had tried intonations—as if she too wished to pass for the real thing—till I was afraid my other visitors would take offence.

Oh they were determined not to do this, and their touching patience was the measure of their great need. They would sit by the hour, uncomplaining, till I was ready to use them; they would come back on the chance of being wanted and would walk away cheerfully if it failed. I used to go to the door with them to see in what magnificent order they retreated. I tried to find other employment for them—I introduced them to several artists. But they didn't "take," for reasons I could appreciate, and I became rather anxiously aware that after such disappointments they fell back upon me with a heavier weight. They did me the honour to think me most *their* form. They weren't romantic enough for the painters, and in those days there were few serious workers in black-and-white. Besides, they had an eye to the great job I had mentioned to them—they had secretly set their hearts on supplying the right essence for my pictorial vindication of our fine novelist. They knew that for this undertaking I should want no costume-effects, none of the frippery of past ages—that it was a case in which everything would be contemporary and satirical and presumably genteel. If I could work them into it their future would be assured, for the labour would of course be long and the occupation steady.

One day Mrs. Monarch came without her husband—she explained his absence by his having had to go to the City. While she sat there in her usual relaxed majesty there came at the door a knock which I immediately recognised as the subdued appeal of a model out of work. It was followed by the entrance of a young man whom I at once saw to be a foreigner and who proved in fact an Italian acquainted with no English word but my name, which he uttered in a way that made it seem to include all others. I hadn't then visited his country, nor was I proficient in his tongue; but as he was not so meanly constituted—what Italian is?—as to depend only on that member for expression he conveyed to me, in familiar but graceful mimicry, that he was in search of exactly the employment in which the lady before me was engaged. I was not struck with him at first, and while I continued to draw I dropped few signs of interest or encouragement. He stood his ground however—not importunately, but with a dumb dog-like fidelity in his eyes that amounted to innocent impudence, the manner of a devoted servant—he might have been in the house for years—unjustly suspected. Suddenly it struck me that this very attitude and expression made a picture; whereupon I told him to sit down and wait till I should be free. There was another picture in the way he obeyed me, and I observed as I worked that there were others still in the way he looked wonderingly, with his head thrown back, about the high studio. He might have been crossing himself in Saint Peter's. Before I finished I said to myself "The fellow's a bankrupt orange-monger, but a treasure."

When Mrs. Monarch withdrew he passed across the room like a flash to open the door for her, standing there with the rapt pure gaze of the young Dante spellbound by the young Beatrice. As I never insisted, in such situations, on the blankness of the British domestic, I reflected that he had the making of a servant—and I needed one, but couldn't pay him to be only that—as well as of a model; in short I resolved to adopt my bright adventurer if he would agree to officiate in the double capacity. He jumped at my offer, and in the event my rashness—for I had really known nothing about him—wasn't brought home to me. He proved a sympathetic though a desultory ministrant, and had in a wonderful degree the *sentiment de la pose*. It was uncultivated, instinctive, a part of the happy instinct that had guided him to my door and helped him to spell out my name on the card nailed to it. He had had no other introduction to me than a guess, from the shape of my high north window, seen outside, that my place was a studio and that as a studio it would contain an artist. He had wandered to England in search of fortune, like other itinerants, and had embarked, with a partner and a small green hand-cart, on the sale of penny ices. The ices had melted away and the partner had dissolved in their train. My young man wore tight yellow trousers with reddish stripes and his name was Oronte. He was sallow but fair, and when I put him into some old clothes of my own he looked like an Englishman. He was as good as Miss Churm, who could look, when requested, like an Italian.

IV

I thought Mrs. Monarch's face slightly convulsed when, on her coming back with her husband, she found Oronte installed. It was strange to have to recognise in a scrap of a lazzarone a competitor to her magnificent Major. It was she who scented danger first, for the Major was anecdotically unconscious. But Oronte gave us tea, with a hundred eager confusions—he had never been concerned in so queer a process—and I think she thought better of me for having at last an "establishment." They saw a couple of drawings that I had made of the establishment, and Mrs. Monarch hinted that it never would have struck her he had sat for them. "Now the drawings you make from us, they look exactly like us," she reminded me, smiling in triumph; and I recognised that this was indeed just their defect. When I drew the Monarchs I couldn't anyhow get away from them—get into the character I wanted to represent; and I hadn't the least desire my model should be discoverable in my picture. Miss Churm never was, and Mrs. Monarch thought I hid her, very properly, because she was vulgar; whereas if she was lost it was only as the dead who go to heaven are lost—in the gain of an angel the more.

By this time I had got a certain start with "Rutland Ramsay," the first novel in the great projected series; that is I had produced a dozen drawings, several with the help of the Major and his wife, and I had sent them in for approval. My understanding with the publishers, as I have already hinted, had been that I was to be left to do my work, in this particular case, as I liked, with the whole book committed to me; but my connexion with the rest of the series was only contingent. There were moments when, frankly, it *was* a comfort to have the real thing under one's hand; for there were characters in "Rutland Ramsay" that were very much like it. There were people presumably as erect as the Major and women of as good a fashion as Mrs. Monarch. There was a great deal of country-house life—treated, it is true, in a fine fanciful ironical generalised way—and there was a considerable implication of knickerbockers and kilts. There were certain things I had to settle at the outset; such things for instance as the exact appearance of the hero and the particular bloom and figure of the heroine. The author of course gave me a lead, but there was a margin for interpretation. I took the Monarchs into my confidence, I told them frankly what I was about, I mentioned my embarrassments and alternatives. "Oh take *him!*" Mrs. Monarch murmured sweetly, looking at her husband; and "What could you want better than my wife?" the Major enquired with the comfortable candour that now prevailed between us.

I wasn't obliged to answer these remarks—I was only obliged to place my sitters. I wasn't easy in mind, and I postponed a little timidly perhaps the solving of my question. The book was a large canvas, the other figures were numerous, and I worked off at first some of the episodes in which the hero and the heroine were not concerned. When once I had set *them* up I should have to stick to them—I couldn't make my young man seven feet high in one place and five feet nine in another. I inclined on the whole to the latter measurement, though the Major more than once reminded me that he looked about as young as any one. It was indeed quite possible to arrange him, for the figure, so that it would have been difficult to detect his age. After the spontaneous Oronte had been with me a month, and after I had given him to understand several times over that his native exuberance would presently constitute an insurmountable barrier to our further intercourse, I waked to a sense of his heroic capacity. He was only five feet seven, but the remaining inches were latent. I tried him almost secretly at first, for I was really rather afraid of the judgement my other models would pass on such a choice. If they regarded Miss Churm as little better than a snare what would they think of the representation by a person so little the real thing as an Italian street-vendor of a protagonist formed by a public school?

If I went a little in fear of them it wasn't because they bullied me, because they had got an oppressive foothold, but because in their really pathetic decorum and mysteriously permanent newness they counted on me so intensely. I was therefore very glad when Jack Hawley came home: he was always of such good counsel. He painted badly himself, but there was no one like him for putting his finger on the place. He had been absent from England for a year; he had been somewhere—I don't remember where—to get a fresh eye. I was in a good deal of dread of any such organ, but we were old friends; he had been away for months and a sense of emptiness was creeping into my life. I hadn't dodged a missile for a year.

He came back with a fresh eye, but with the same old black velvet blouse, and the first evening he spent in my studio we smoked cigarettes till the small hours. He had done no work himself, he had only got the eye; so the field was clear for the production of my little things. He wanted to see what I had produced for the *Cheapside,* but he was disappointed in the exhibition. That at least seemed the meaning of two or three comprehensive groans which, as he lounged on my big divan, his leg folded under him, looking at my latest drawings, issued from his lips with the smoke of the cigarette.

"What's the matter with you?" I asked.

"What's the matter with *you?"*

"Nothing save that I'm mystified."

"You are indeed. You're quite off the hinge. What's the meaning of this new fad?" And he tossed me, with visible irreverence, a drawing in which I happened to have depicted both my elegant models. I asked if he didn't think it good, and he replied that it struck him as execrable, given the sort of thing I had always represented myself to him as wishing to arrive at; but I let that pass—I was so anxious to see exactly what he meant. The two figures in the picture looked colossal, but I supposed this was *not* what he meant, inasmuch as, for aught he knew to the contrary, I might have been trying for some such effect. I maintained that I was working exactly in the same way as when he last had done me the honour to tell me I might do something some day. "Well, there's a screw loose somewhere," he answered; "wait a bit and I'll discover it." I depended upon him to do so: where else was the fresh eye? But he produced at last nothing more luminous than "I don't know—I don't like your types." This was lame for a critic who had never consented to discuss with me anything but the question of execution, the direction of strokes and the mystery of values.

"In the drawings you've been looking at I think my types are very handsome."

"Oh they won't do!"

"I've been working with new models."

"I see you have. *They* won't do."

"Are you very sure of that?"

"Absolutely—they're stupid."

"You mean *I* am—for I ought to get round that."

"You *can't*—with such people. Who are they?"

I told him, so far as was necessary, and he concluded heartlessly: "Ce sont des gens qu'il faut mettre à la porte."

"You've never seen them; they're awfully good"—I flew to their defence.

"Not seen them? Why all this recent work of yours drops to pieces with them. It's all I want to see of them."

"No one else has said anything against it—the *Cheapside* people are pleased."

"Every one else is an ass, and the *Cheapside* people the biggest asses of all. Come, don't pretend at this time of day to have pretty illusions about the public, especially about publishers and editors. It's not for *such* animals you work—it's for those you know, *coloro che sanno;* so keep straight for *me* if you can't keep straight for yourself. There was a certain sort of thing you used to try for—and a very good thing it was. But this twaddle isn't *in* it." When I talked with Hawley later about "Rutland Ramsay" and its possible successors he declared that I must get back into my boat again or I should go to the bottom. His voice in short was the voice of warning.

I noted the warning, but I didn't turn my friends out of doors. They bored me a good deal; but the very fact that they bored me admonished me not to sacrifice them—if there was anything to be done with them—simply to irritation. As I look back at this phase they seem to me to have pervaded my life not a little. I have a vision of them as most of the time in my studio, seated against the wall on an old velvet bench to be out of the way, and resembling the while a pair of patient courtiers in a royal ante-chamber. I'm convinced that during the coldest weeks of the winter they held their ground because it saved them fire. Their newness was losing its gloss, and it was impossible not to feel them objects of charity. Whenever Miss Churm arrived they went away, and after I was fairly launched in "Rutland Ramsay" Miss Churm arrived pretty often. They managed to express to me tacitly that they supposed I wanted her for the low life of the book, and I let them suppose it, since they had attempted to study the work—it was lying about the studio—without discovering that it dealt only with the highest circles. They had dipped into the most brilliant of our novelists without deciphering many passages. I still took an hour from them, now and again, in spite of Jack Hawley's warning: it would be time enough to dismiss them, if dismissal should be necessary, when the rigour of the season was over. Hawley had made their acquaintance—he had met them at my fireside—and thought them a ridiculous pair. Learning that he was a painter they tried to approach him, to show him too that they were the real thing; but he looked at them, across the big room, as if they were miles away: they were a compendium of everything he most objected to in the social system of his country. Such people as that, all convention and patent-leather, with ejaculations that stopped conversation, had no business in a studio. A studio was a place to learn to see, and how could you see through a pair of feather-beds?

The main inconvenience I suffered at their hands was that at first I was shy of letting it break upon them that my artful little servant had begun to sit to me for "Rutland Ramsay." They knew I had been odd enough—they were prepared by this time to allow oddity to artists—to pick a foreign vagabond out of the streets when I might have had a person with whiskers and credentials; but it was some time before they learned how high I rated his accomplishments. They found him in an attitude more than once, but they never doubted I was doing him as an organ-grinder. There were several things they never guessed, and one of them was that for a striking scene in the novel, in which a footman briefly figured, it occurred to me to make use of Major Monarch as the menial. I kept putting this off, I didn't like to ask him to don the livery—besides the difficulty of finding a livery to fit him. At last, one day late in the winter, when I was at work on the despised Oronte, who caught one's idea on the wing, and was in the glow of feeling myself go very straight, they came in, the Major and his wife, with their society laugh about nothing (there was less and less to laugh at); came in like country-callers—they always reminded me of that—who have walked across the park after church and are presently persuaded to stay to luncheon. Luncheon was over, but they could stay to tea—I knew they wanted it. The fit was on me, however, and I couldn't let my ardour cool and my work wait, with the fading daylight, while my model prepared it. So I asked Mrs. Monarch if she would mind laying it out—a request which for an instant brought all the blood to her face. Her eyes were on her husband's for a second, and some mute telegraphy passed between them. Their folly was over the next instant; his cheerful shrewdness put an end to it. So far from pitying their wounded pride, I must add, I was moved to give it as complete a lesson as I could. They bustled about together and got out the cups and saucers and made the kettle boil. I know they felt as if they were waiting on my servant, and when the tea was prepared I said: "He'll have a cup, please—he's tired." Mrs. Monarch brought him one where he stood, and he took it from her as if he had been a gentleman at a party squeezing a crush-hat with an elbow.

Then it came over me that she had made a great effort for me—made it with a kind of nobleness—and that I owed her a compensation. Each time I saw her after this I wondered what the compensation could be. I couldn't go on doing the wrong thing to oblige them. Oh it *was* the wrong thing, the stamp of the work for which they sat—Hawley was not the only person to say it now. I sent in a large number of the drawings I had made for "Rutland Ramsay," and I received a warning that was more to the point than Hawley's. The artistic adviser of the house for which I was working was of opinion that many of my illustrations were not what had been looked for. Most of these illustrations were the subjects in which the Monarchs had figured. Without going into the question of what *had* been looked for, I had to face the fact that at this rate I shouldn't get the other books to do. I hurled myself in despair on Miss Churm—I put her through all her paces. I not only adopted Oronte publicly as my hero, but one morning when the Major looked in to see if I didn't require him to finish a *Cheapside* figure for which he had begun to sit the week before, I told him I had changed my mind—I'd do the drawing from my man. At this my visitor turned pale and stood looking at me. "Is *he* your idea of an English gentleman?" he asked.

I was disappointed, I was nervous, I wanted to get on with my work; so I replied with irritation: "Oh my dear Major—I can't be ruined for *you!*"

It was a horrid speech, but he stood another moment—after which, without a word, he quitted the studio. I drew a long breath, for I said to myself that I shouldn't see him again. I hadn't told him definitely that I was in danger of having my work rejected, but I was vexed at his not having felt the catastrophe in the air, read with me the moral of our fruitless collaboration, the lesson that in the deceptive atmosphere of art even the highest respectability may fail of being plastic.

I didn't owe my friends money, but I did see them again. They reappeared together three days later, and, given all the other facts, there was something tragic in that one. It was a clear proof they could find nothing else in life to do. They had threshed the matter out in a dismal conference—they had digested the bad news that they were not in for the series. If they weren't useful to me even for the *Cheapside* their function seemed difficult to determine, and I could only judge at first that they had come, forgivingly, decorously, to take a last leave. This made me rejoice in secret that I had little leisure for a scene; for I had placed both my other models in position together and I was pegging away at a drawing from which I hoped to derive glory. It had been suggested by the passage in which Rutland Ramsay, drawing up a chair to Artemisia's piano-stool, says extraordinary things to her while she ostensibly fingers out a difficult piece of music. I had done Miss Churm at the piano before—it was an attitude in which she knew how to take on an absolutely poetic grace. I wished the two figures to "compose" together with intensity, and my little Italian had entered perfectly into my conception. The pair were vividly before me, the piano had been pulled out; it was a charming show of blended youth and murmured love, which I had only to catch and keep. My visitors stood and looked at it, and I was friendly to them over my shoulder.

They made no response, but I was used to silent company and went on with my work, only a little disconcerted—even though exhilarated by the sense that *this* was at least the ideal thing—at not having got rid of them after all. Presently I heard Mrs. Monarch's sweet voice beside or rather above me: "I wish her hair were a little better done." I looked up and she was staring with a strange fixedness at Miss Churm, whose back was turned to her. "Do you mind my just touching it?" she went on—a question which made me spring up for an instant as with the instinctive fear that she might do the young lady a harm. But she quieted me with a glance I shall never forget—I confess I should like to have been able to paint *that*—and went for a moment to my model. She spoke to her softly, laying a hand on her shoulder and bending over her; and as the girl, understanding, gratefully assented, she disposed her rough curls, with a few quick passes, in such a way as to make Miss Churm's head twice as charming. It was one of the most heroic personal services I've ever seen rendered. Then Mrs. Monarch turned away with a low sigh and, looking about her as if for something to do, stooped to the floor with a noble humility and picked up a dirty rag that had dropped out of my paint-box.

The Major meanwhile had also been looking for something to do, and, wandering to the other end of the studio, saw before him my breakfast-things neglected, unremoved. "I say, can't I be useful *here?*" he called out to me with an irrepressible quaver. I assented with a laugh that I fear was awkward, and for the next ten minutes, while I worked, I heard the light clatter of china and the tinkle of spoons and glass. Mrs. Monarch assisted her husband—they washed up my crockery, they put it away. They wandered off into my little scullery, and I afterwards found that they had cleaned my knives and that my slender stock of plate had an unprecedented surface. When it came over me, the latent eloquence of what they were doing, I confess that my drawing was blurred for a moment—the picture swam. They had accepted their failure, but they couldn't accept their fate. They had bowed their heads in bewilderment to the perverse and cruel law in virtue of which the real thing could be so much less precious than the unreal; but they didn't want to starve. If my servants were my models, then my models might be my servants. They would reverse the parts—the others would sit for the ladies and gentlemen and *they* would do the work. They would still be in the studio—it was an intense dumb appeal to me not to turn them out. "Take us on," they wanted to say—"we'll do *anything.*"

My pencil dropped from my hand; my sitting was spoiled and I got rid of my sitters, who were also evidently rather mystified and awe-struck. Then, alone with the Major and his wife I had a most uncomfortable moment. He put their prayer into a single sentence: "I say, you know—just let *us* do for you, can't you?" I couldn't—it was dreadful to see them emptying my slops; but I pretended I could, to oblige them, for about a week. Then I gave them a sum of money to go away, and I never saw them again. I obtained the remaining books, but my friend Hawley repeats that Major and Mrs. Monarch did me a permanent harm, got me into false ways. If it be true I'm content to have paid the price—for the memory.

Questions

1. In his private jottings about the story James noted that it had to be "an idea," not merely "a 'story' in the vulgar sense of the word." He thought of making the major jealous of the artist, in other words of developing a triangle situation. But this he rejected as "vulgar and obvious—worth nothing" in terms of his idea. What is the "idea" that James is trying to illustrate in "The Real Thing"? Why is the story-line he first conceived "vulgar and obvious"?
2. Characterize the Monarchs as fully as you can. Describe the class to which they belong.
3. What is the function of Jack Hawley in the story? Of Miss Churm and Oronte?
4. What does the narrator mean, in the fourth section, when he says that "A studio was a place to learn to see, and how could you see through a pair of feather beds?"?
5. What problems did James face in bringing his story to a close?

Stephen Crane

The Bride Comes to Yellow Sky

WITH Stephen Crane the modern voice in American literature is heard for the first time—the flat, rapid voice that we recognize as ourselves talking. This may not be as obvious in "The Bride Comes to Yellow Sky" as it is in "The Open Boat" and THE RED BADGE OF COURAGE, *though it can be clearly heard, particularly in the dialogue in the Weary Gentleman saloon. It is less obvious here because the main characters, Jack Potter and Scratchy Wilson, are, at least in part, grotesques. They are figures in whom certain traits have been accentuated for purposes other than character portrayal.*

In "The Bride Comes to Yellow Sky" Crane is intent on writing a passage of cultural history. He is also making a commentary on the nature of civilization. Both of these intentions become obvious in the first section of the story in the attention Crane devotes to Jack Potter and his bride, their features and manners, their innocence, and the reaction of the passengers and the porter to them. It is also obvious in the detail with which he describes the Pullman, and, later in the story, the origin of the clothes worn by Scratchy Wilson.

"The Bride Comes to Yellow Sky" can also be viewed as a parable about the passing of the American west. In this sense it is a kind of

Ur-western, suggestive of the movies and television series with which we are familiar today. But Crane's methods here are, in general, not those of the film maker. For one thing, there is an element of the mock heroic in the conflict between Jack Potter and Scratchy Wilson.

Crane drew his subject matter directly from the mainstream of American life, and also from his own experience as a journalist. The resources of his art are more various. He has been called a "philosophical naturalist," also an "impressionist." Both terms have a relevance to his achievements, though their full implication can be understood only in the context of his other stories and novels. For the moment, a good deal of his art can be observed in "The Bride Comes to Yellow Sky," particularly in the sentence with which the story closes.

I

THE great Pullman was whirling onward with such dignity of motion that a glance from the window seemed simply to prove that the plains of Texas were pouring eastward. Vast flats of green grass, dull-hued spaces of mesquit and cactus, little groups of frame houses, woods of light and tender trees, all were sweeping into the east, sweeping over the horizon, a precipice.

A newly married pair had boarded this coach at San Antonio. The man's face was reddened from many days in the wind and sun, and a direct result of his new black clothes was that his brick-colored hands were constantly performing in a most conscious fashion. From time to time he looked down respectfully at his attire. He sat with a hand on each knee, like a man waiting in a barber's shop. The glances he devoted to other passengers were furtive and shy.

The bride was not pretty, nor was she very young. She wore a dress of blue cashmere, with small reservations of velvet here and there, and with steel buttons abounding. She continually twisted her head to regard her puff sleeves, very stiff, straight, and high. They embarrassed her. It was quite apparent that she had cooked, and that she expected to cook, dutifully. The blushes caused by the careless scrutiny of some passengers as she had entered the car were strange to see upon this plain, under-class countenance, which was drawn in placid, almost emotionless lines.

They were evidently very happy. "Ever been in a parlor-car before?" he asked, smiling with delight.

"No," she answered; "I never was. It's fine, ain't it?"

"Great! And then after a while we'll go forward to the diner, and get a big lay-out. Finest meal in the world. Charge a dollar."

"Oh, do they?" cried the bride. "Charge a dollar? Why, that's too much—for us—ain't it, Jack?"

"Not this trip, anyhow," he answered bravely. "We're going to go the whole thing."

Later he explained to her about the trains. "You see, it's a thousand miles from one end of Texas to the other; and this train runs right across it, and never stops but four times." He had the pride of an owner. He pointed out to her the dazzling fittings of the coach; and in truth her eyes opened wider as she contemplated the sea-green figured velvet, the shining brass, silver, and glass, the wood that gleamed as darkly brilliant as the surface of a pool of oil. At one end a bronze figure sturdily held a support for a separated chamber, and at convenient places on the ceiling were frescos in olive and silver.

To the minds of the pair, their surroundings reflected the glory of their marriage that morning in San Antonio; this was the environment of their new estate; and the man's face in particular beamed with an elation that made him appear ridiculous to the Negro porter. This individual at times surveyed them from afar with an amused and superior grin. On other occasions he bullied them with skill in ways that did not make it exactly plain to them that they were being bullied. He subtly used all the manners of the most unconquerable kind of snobbery. He oppressed them; but of this oppression they had small knowledge, and they speedily forgot that infrequently a number of travelers covered them with stares of derisive enjoyment. Historically there was supposed to be something infinitely humorous in their situation.

"We are due in Yellow Sky at 3:42," he said, looking tenderly into her eyes.

"Oh, are we?" she said, as if she had not been aware of it. To evince surprise at her husband's statement was part of her wifely amiability. She took from a pocket a little silver watch; and as she held it before her, and stared at it with a frown of attention, the new husband's face shone.

"I bought it in San Anton' from a friend of mine," he told her gleefully.

"It's seventeen minutes past twelve," she said, looking up at him with a kind of shy and clumsy coquetry. A passenger, noting this play, grew excessively sardonic, and winked at himself in one of the numerous mirrors.

At last they went to the dining-car. Two rows of Negro waiters, in glowing white suits, surveyed their entrance with the interest, and also the equanimity, of men who had been forewarned. The pair fell to the lot of a waiter who happened to feel pleasure in steering them through their meal. He viewed them with the manner of a fatherly pilot, his countenance radiant with benevolence. The patronage, entwined with the ordinary deference, was not plain to them. And yet, as they returned to their coach, they showed in their faces a sense of escape.

To the left, miles down a long purple slope, was a little ribbon of mist where moved the keening Rio Grande. The train was approaching it at an angle, and the apex was Yellow Sky. Presently it was apparent that, as the distance from Yellow Sky grew shorter, the husband became commensurately restless. His brick-red hands were more insistent in their prominence. Occasionally he was even rather absent-minded and far-away when the bride leaned forward and addressed him.

As a matter of truth, Jack Potter was beginning to find the shadow of a deed weigh upon him like a leaden slab. He, the town marshal of Yellow Sky, a man known, liked, and feared in his corner, a prominent person, had gone to San Antonio to meet a girl he believed he loved, and there, after the usual prayers, had actually induced her to marry him, without consulting Yellow Sky for any part of the transaction. He was now bringing his bride before an innocent and unsuspecting community.

Of course people in Yellow Sky married as it pleased them, in accordance with a general custom; but such was Potter's thought of his duty to his friends, or of their idea of his duty, or of an unspoken form which does not control men in these matters, that he felt he was heinous. He had committed an extraordinary crime. Face to face with this girl in San Antonio, and spurred by his sharp impulse, he had gone headlong over all the social hedges. At San Antonio he was like a man hidden in the dark. A knife to sever any friendly duty, any form, was easy to his hand in that remote city. But the hour of Yellow Sky—the hour of daylight—was approaching.

He knew full well that his marriage was an important thing to his town. It could only be exceeded by the burning of the new hotel. His friends could not forgive him. Frequently he had reflected on the advisability of telling them by telegraph, but a new cowardice had been upon him. He feared to do it. And now the train was hurrying him toward a scene of amazement, glee, and reproach. He glanced out of the window at the line of haze swinging slowly in toward the train.

Yellow Sky had a kind of brass band, which played painfully, to the delight of the populace. He laughed without heart as he thought of it. If the citizens could dream of his prospective arrival with his bride, they would parade the band at the station and escort them, amid cheers and laughing congratulations, to his adobe home.

He resolved that he would use all the devices of speed and plainscraft in making the journey from the station to his house. Once within that safe citadel, he could issue some sort of vocal bulletin, and then not go among the citizens until they had time to wear off a little of their enthusiasm.

The bride looked anxiously at him. "What's worrying you, Jack?"

He laughed again. "I'm not worrying, girl; I'm only thinking of Yellow Sky."

She flushed in comprehension.

A sense of mutual guilt invaded their minds and developed a finer tenderness. They looked at each other with eyes softly aglow. But Potter often laughed the same nervous laugh; the flush upon the bride's face seemed quite permanent.

The traitor to the feelings of Yellow Sky narrowly watched the speeding landscape. "We're nearly there," he said.

Presently the porter came and announced the proximity of Potter's home. He held a brush in his hand, and, with all his airy superiority gone, he brushed Potter's new clothes as the latter slowly turned this way and that way. Potter fumbled out a coin and gave it to the porter, as he had seen others do. It was a heavy and muscle-bound business, as that of a man shoeing his first horse.

The porter took their bag, and as the train began to slow they moved forward to the hooded platform of the car. Presently the two engines and their long string of coaches rushed into the station of Yellow Sky.

"They have to take water here," said Potter, from a constricted throat and in mournful cadence, as one announcing death. Before the train stopped his eye had swept the length of the platform, and he was glad and astonished to see there was none upon it but the station agent, who, with a slightly hurried and anxious air, was walking toward the water-tanks. When the train had halted, the porter alighted first, and placed in position a little temporary step.

"Come on, girl," said Potter, hoarsely. As he helped her down they each laughed on a false note. He took the bag from the Negro, and bade his wife cling to his arm. As they slunk rapidly away, his hang-dog glance perceived that they were unloading the two trunks, and also that the station-agent, far ahead near the baggage-car, had turned and was running toward him, making gestures. He laughed, and groaned as he laughed, when he noted the first effect of his marital bliss upon Yellow Sky. He gripped his wife's arm firmly to his side, and they fled. Behind them the porter stood, chuckling fatuously.

II

The California express on the Southern Railway was due at Yellow Sky in twenty-one minutes. There were six men at the bar of the Weary Gentleman saloon. One was a drummer who talked a great deal and rapidly; three were Texans who did not care to talk at that time; and two were Mexican sheep-herders, who did not talk as a general practice in the Weary Gentleman saloon. The barkeeper's dog lay on the boardwalk that crossed in front of the door. His head was on his paws, and he glanced drowsily here and there with the constant vigilance of a dog that is kicked on occasion. Across the sandy street were some vivid green grass-plots, so wonderful in appearance, amid the sands that burned near them in a blazing sun, that they caused a doubt in the mind. They exactly resembled the grass mats used to represent lawns on the stage. At the cooler end of the railway station, a man without a coat sat in a tilted chair and smoked his pipe. The fresh-cut bank of the Rio Grande circled near the town, and there could be seen beyond it a great plum-colored plain of mesquit.

Save for the busy drummer and his companions in the saloon, Yellow Sky was dozing. The new-comer leaned gracefully upon the bar, and recited many tales with the confidence of a bard who has come upon a new field.

"—and at the moment that the old man fell downstairs with the bureau in his arms, the old woman was coming up with two scuttles of coal, and of course—"

The drummer's tale was interrupted by a young man who suddenly appeared in the open door. He cried: "Scratchy Wilson's drunk, and has turned loose with both hands." The two Mexicans at once set down their glasses and faded out of the rear entrance of the saloon.

The drummer, innocent and jocular, answered: "All right, old man. S'pose he has? Come in and have a drink, anyhow."

But the information had made such an obvious cleft in every skull in the room that the drummer was obliged to see its importance. All had become instantly solemn. "Say," said he, mystified, "what is this?" His three companions made the introductory gesture of eloquent speech; but the young man at the door forestalled them.

"It means, my friend," he answered, as he came into the saloon, "that for the next two hours this town won't be a health resort."

The barkeeper went to the door, and locked and barred it; reaching out of the window, he pulled in heavy wooden shutters, and barred them. Immediately a solemn, chapel-like gloom was upon the place. The drummer was looking from one to another.

"But say," he cried, "what is this, anyhow? You don't mean there is going to be a gun-fight?"

"Don't know whether there'll be a fight or not," answered one man, grimly; "but there'll be some shootin'—some good shootin'."

The young man who had warned them waved his hand. "Oh, there'll be a fight fast enough, if any one wants it. Anybody can get a fight out there in the street. There's a fight just waiting."

The drummer seemed to be swayed between the interest of a foreigner and a perception of personal danger.

"What did you say his name was?" he asked.

"Scratchy Wilson," they answered in chorus.

"And will he kill anybody? What are you going to do? Does this happen often? Does he rampage around like this once a week or so? Can he break in that door?"

"No; he can't break down that door," replied the barkeeper. "He's tried it three times. But when he comes you'd better lay down on the floor, stranger. He's dead sure to shoot at it, and a bullet may come through."

Thereafter the drummer kept a strict eye upon the door. The time had not yet been called for him to hug the floor, but, as a minor precaution, he sidled near to the wall. "Will he kill anybody?" he said again.

The men laughed low and scornfully at the question.

"He's out to shoot, and he's out for trouble. Don't see any good in experimentin' with him."

"But what do you do in a case like this? What do you do?"

A man responded: "Why, he and Jack Potter—"

"But," in chorus the other men interrupted, "Jack Potter's in San Anton'."

"Well, who is he? What's he got to do with it?"

"Oh, he's the town marshal. He goes out and fights Scratchy when he gets on one of these tears."

"Wow!" said the drummer, mopping his brow. "Nice job he's got."

The voices had toned away to mere whisperings. The drummer wished to ask further questions, which were born of an increasing anxiety and bewilderment; but when he attempted them, the men merely looked at him in irritation and motioned him to remain silent. A tense waiting hush was upon them. In the deep shadows of the room their eyes shone as they listened for sounds from the street. One man made three gestures at the barkeeper; and the latter, moving like a ghost, handed him a glass and a bottle. The man poured a full glass of whisky, and set down the bottle noiselessly. He gulped the whisky in a swallow, and turned again toward the door in immovable silence. The drummer saw that the barkeeper, without a sound, had taken a Winchester from beneath the bar. Later he saw this individual beckoning to him, so he tiptoed across the room.

"You better come with me back of the bar."

"No, thanks," said the drummer, perspiring; "I'd rather be where I can make a break for the back door."

Whereupon the man of bottles made a kindly but peremptory gesture. The drummer obeyed it, and, finding himself seated on a box with his head below the level of the bar, balm was laid upon his soul at sight of various zinc and copper fittings that bore a resemblance to armor-plate. The barkeeper took a seat comfortably upon an adjacent box.

"You see," he whispered, "this here Scratchy Wilson is a wonder with a gun—a perfect wonder; and when he goes on the war-trail, we hunt our holes—naturally. He's about the last one of the old gang that used to hang out along the river here. He's a terror when he's drunk. When he's sober he's all right—kind of simple—wouldn't hurt a fly—nicest fellow in town. But when he's drunk—whoo!"

There were periods of stillness. "I wish Jack Potter was back from San Anton'," said the barkeeper. "He shot Wilson up once—in the leg—and he would sail in and pull out the kinks in this thing."

Presently they heard from a distance the sound of a shot, followed by three wild yowls. It instantly removed a bond from the men in the darkened saloon. There was a shuffling of feet. They looked at each other. "Here he comes," they said.

III

A man in a maroon-colored flannel shirt, which had been purchased for purposes of decoration, and made principally by some Jewish women on the East Side of New York, rounded a corner and walked into the middle of the main street of Yellow Sky. In either hand the man held a long, heavy, blue-black revolver. Often he yelled, and these cries rang through a semblance of a deserted village, shrilly flying over the roofs in a volume that seemed to have no relation to the ordinary vocal strength of a man. It was as if the surrounding stillness formed the arch of a tomb over him. These cries of ferocious challenge rang against walls of silence. And his boots had red tops with gilded imprints, of the kind beloved in winter by little sledding boys on the hillsides of New England.

The man's face flamed in a rage begot of whisky. His eyes, rolling, and yet keen for ambush, hunted the still doorways and windows. He walked with the creeping movement of the midnight cat. As it occurred to him, he roared menacing information. The long revolvers in his hands were as easy as straws; they were moved with an electric swiftness. The little fingers of each hand played sometimes in a musician's way. Plain from the low collar of the shirt, the cords of his neck straightened and sank, straightened and sank, as passion moved him. The only sounds were his terrible invitations. The calm adobes preserved their demeanor at the passing of this small thing in the middle of the street.

There was no offer of fight—no offer of fight. The man called to the sky. There were no attractions. He bellowed and fumed and swayed his revolvers here and everywhere.

The dog of the barkeeper of the Weary Gentleman saloon had not appreciated the advance of events. He yet lay dozing in front of his master's door. At sight of the dog, the man paused and raised his revolver humorously. At sight of the man, the dog sprang up and walked diagonally away, with a sullen head, and growling. The man yelled, and the dog broke into a gallop. As it was about to enter an alley, there was a loud noise, a whistling, and something spat the ground directly before it. The dog screamed, and, wheeling in terror, galloped headlong in a new direction. Again there was a noise, a whistling, and sand was kicked viciously before it. Fear-stricken, the dog turned and flurried like an animal in a pen. The man stood laughing, his weapons at his hips.

Ultimately the man was attracted by the closed door of the Weary Gentleman saloon. He went to it and, hammering with a revolver, demanded drink.

The door remaining imperturbable, he picked a bit of paper from the walk, and nailed it to the framework with a knife. He then turned his back contemptuously upon this popular resort and, walking to the opposite side of the street and spinning there on his heel quickly and lithely, fired at the bit of paper. He missed it by a half-inch. He swore at himself, and went away. Later he comfortably fusilladed the windows of his most intimate friend. The man was playing with this town; it was a toy for him.

But still there was no offer of fight. The name of Jack Potter, his ancient antagonist, entered his mind, and he concluded that it would be a glad thing if he should go to Potter's house, and by bombardment induce him to come out and fight. He moved in the direction of his desire, chanting Apache scalp-music.

When he arrived at it, Potter's house presented the same still front as had the other adobes. Taking up a strategic position, the man howled a challenge. But this house regarded him as might a great stone god. It gave no sign. After a decent wait, the man howled further challenges, mingling with them wonderful epithets.

Presently there came the spectacle of a man churning himself into deepest rage over the immobility of a house. He fumed at it as the winter wind attacks a prairie cabin in the North. To the distance there should have gone the sound of a tumult like the fighting of two hundred Mexicans. As necessity bade him, he paused for breath or to reload his revolvers.

IV

Potter and his bride walked sheepishly and with speed. Sometimes they laughed together shamefacedly and low.

"Next corner, dear," he said finally.

They put forth the efforts of a pair walking bowed against a strong wind. Potter was about to raise a finger to point the first appearance of the new home when, as they circled the corner, they came face to face with a man in a maroon-colored shirt, who was feverishly pushing cartridges into a large revolver. Upon the instant the man dropped his revolver to the ground and, like lightning, whipped another from its holster. The second weapon was aimed at the bridegroom's chest.

There was a silence. Potter's mouth seemed to be merely a grave for his tongue. He exhibited an instinct to at once loosen his arm from the woman's grip, and he dropped the bag to the sand. As for the bride, her face had gone as yellow as old cloth. She was a slave to hideous rites, gazing at the apparitional snake.

The two men faced each other at a distance of three paces. He of the revolver smiled with a new and quiet ferocity.

"Tried to sneak up on me," he said. "Tried to sneak up on me!" His eyes grew more baleful. As Potter made a slight movement, the man thrust his revolver venomously forward. "No; don't you do it, Jack Potter. Don't you move a finger toward a gun just yet. Don't you move an eyelash. The time has come for me to settle with you, and I'm goin' to do it my own way, and loaf along with no interferin'. So if you don't want a gun bent on you, just mind what I tell you."

Potter looked at his enemy. "I ain't got a gun on me, Scratchy," he said. "Honest, I ain't." He was stiffening and steadying, but yet somewhere at the back of his mind a vision of the Pullman floated: the sea-green figured velvet, the shining brass, silver, and glass, the wood that gleamed as darkly brilliant as the surface of a pool of oil—all the glory of the marriage, the environment of the new estate. "You know I fight when it comes to fighting, Scratchy Wilson; but I ain't got a gun on me. You'll have to do all the shootin' yourself."

His enemy's face went livid. He stepped forward, and lashed his weapon to and fro before Potter's chest. "Don't you tell me you ain't got no gun on you, you whelp. Don't tell me no lie like that. There ain't a man in Texas ever seen you without no gun. Don't take me for no kid." His eyes blazed with light, and his throat worked like a pump.

"I ain't takin' you for no kid," answered Potter. His heels had not moved an inch backward. "I'm takin' you for a damn fool. I tell you I ain't got a gun, and I ain't. If you're goin' to shoot me up, you better begin now; you'll never get a chance like this again."

So much enforced reasoning had told on Wilson's rage; he was calmer. "If you ain't got a gun, why ain't you got a gun?" he sneered. "Been to Sunday school?"

"I ain't got a gun because I've just come from San Anton' with my wife. I'm married," said Potter. "And if I'd thought there was going to be any galoots like you prowling around when I brought my wife home, I'd had a gun, and don't you forget it."

"Married!" said Scratchy, not at all comprehending.

"Yes, married. I'm married," said Potter, distinctly.

"Married?" said Scratchy. Seemingly for the first time, he saw the drooping, drowning woman at the other man's side. "No!" he said. He was like a creature allowed a glimpse of another world. He moved a pace backward, and his arm, with the revolver, dropped to his side. "Is this the lady?" he asked.

"Yes; this is the lady," answered Potter.

There was another period of silence.

"Well," said Wilson at last, slowly, "I s'pose it's all off now."

"It's all off if you say so, Scratchy. You know I didn't make the trouble." Potter lifted his valise.

"Well, I 'low it's off, Jack," said Wilson. He was looking at the ground. "Married!" He was not a student of chivalry; it was merely that in the presence of this foreign condition he was a simple child of the earlier plains. He picked up his starboard revolver, and, placing both weapons in their holsters, he went away. His feet made funnel-shaped tracks in the heavy sand.

Questions

1. Can you further define the way in which Crane uses the grotesque? Is it only a matter of characterization, or does it also involve style? What do you make of the statement, early in the fourth section, that the bride "was a slave to hideous rites, gazing at the apparitional snake"?
2. Crane divides his story into four parts. What does each part accomplish?
3. Why, precisely, is Jack Potter a "traitor to the feelings of Yellow Sky"?
4. What is the function of the porter? The drummer?
5. Explain the meaning of the last sentence of the story. Why "*funnel-shaped* tracks in the heavy sand"?

James Joyce

Counterparts

"COUNTERPARTS" is one of a series of stories by James Joyce which make up the volume DUBLINERS *(1914). It is not surprising then that the events portrayed are a microcosm of Dublin life.*

The true subject of "Counterparts" is not a man but a city. The story of Farrington is the story of a cog within a wheel within wheels—the social machine that is Dublin. Primarily it is a talking machine, and talk dominates the story, from the opening lines, where the voice of Mr. Alleyne, Farrington's employer, beckons him through a tube from the floor above, to the final, importunate appeal of Farrington's son to his father.

There is very little physical action in a Joyce story, indeed, so little that the reader is apt to think that the story is a mere incident, or a series of incidents, instead of a story. Nor is there apt to be any significant change in the lives of the characters within the bounds of the story; it would appear that more of the same kind of life awaits these characters the next day, or the next year. What action there is is apt to seem petty, insignificant; what change, minor and inconsequential. Yet something significant does happen in the course of a Joyce story. Events in themselves trivial lead to a moment of awareness, or revelation, for the reader, and sometimes, though not always, for the main character.

Joyce's method of telling a story has largely become the modern method. Such a method gives a heightened relevance to character and event, to the figures and the particulars of everyday life, which life itself seldom possesses without intense reflection. The stories which result from this method are deceptively simple.

THE BELL rang furiously and, when Miss Parker went to the tube, a furious voice called out in a piercing North of Ireland accent:

"Send Farrington here!"

Miss Parker returned to her machine, saying to a man who was writing at a desk:

"Mr. Alleyne wants you upstairs."

The man muttered *"Blast* him!" under his breath and pushed back his chair to stand up. When he stood up he was tall and of great bulk. He had a hanging face, dark wine-coloured, with fair eyebrows and moustache: his eyes bulged forward slightly and the whites of them were dirty. He lifted up the counter and, passing by the clients, went out of the office with a heavy step.

He went heavily upstairs until he came to the second landing, where a door bore a brass plate with the inscription *Mr. Alleyne.* Here he halted, puffing with labour and vexation, and knocked. The shrill voice cried:

"Come in!"

The man entered Mr. Alleyne's room. Simultaneously Mr. Alleyne, a little man wearing gold-rimmed glasses on a clean-shaven face, shot his head up over a pile of documents. The head itself was so pink and hairless it seemed like a large egg reposing on the papers. Mr. Alleyne did not lose a moment:

"Farrington? What is the meaning of this? Why have I always to complain of you? May I ask you why you haven't made a copy of that contract between Bodley and Kirwan? I told you it must be ready by four o'clock."

"But Mr. Shelley said, sir—"

"Mr. Shelley said, sir. . . . Kindly attend to what I say and not to what *Mr. Shelley says, sir.* You have always some excuse or another for shirking work. Let me tell you that if the contract is not copied before this evening I'll lay the matter before Mr. Crosbie. . . . Do you hear me now?"

"Yes, sir."

"Do you hear me now? . . . Ay and another little matter! I might as well be talking to the wall as talking to you. Understand once for all that you get a half an hour for your lunch and not an hour and a half. How many courses do you want, I'd like to know. . . . Do you mind me now?"

"Yes, sir."

Mr. Alleyne bent his head again upon his pile of papers. The man stared fixedly at the polished skull which directed the affairs of Crosbie & Alleyne, gauging its fragility. A spasm of rage gripped his throat for a few moments and then passed, leaving after it a sharp sensation of thirst. The man recognised the sensation and felt that he must have a good night's drinking. The middle of the month was passed and, if he could get the copy done in time, Mr. Alleyne might give him an order on the cashier. He stood still, gazing fixedly at the head upon the pile of papers. Suddenly Mr. Alleyne began to upset all the papers, searching for something. Then, as if he had been unaware of the man's presence till that moment, he shot up his head again, saying:

"Eh? Are you going to stand there all day? Upon my word, Farrington, you take things easy!"

"I was waiting to see . . ."

"Very good, you needn't wait to see. Go downstairs and do your work."

The man walked heavily towards the door and, as he went out of the room, he heard Mr. Alleyne cry after him that if the contract was not copied by evening Mr. Crosbie would hear of the matter.

He returned to his desk in the lower office and counted the sheets which remained to be copied. He took up his pen and dipped it in the ink but he continued to stare stupidly at the last words he had written: *In no case shall the said Bernard Bodley be* . . . The evening was falling and in a few minutes they would be lighting the gas: then he could write. He felt that he must slake the thirst in his throat. He stood up from his desk and, lifting the counter as before, passed out of the office. As he was passing out the chief clerk looked at him inquiringly.

"It's all right, Mr. Shelley," said the man, pointing with his finger to indicate the objective of his journey.

The chief clerk glanced at the hat-rack, but, seeing the row complete, offered no remark. As soon as he was on the landing the man pulled a shepherd's plaid cap out of his pocket, put it on his head and ran quickly down the rickety stairs. From the street door he walked on furtively on the inner side of the path towards the corner and all at once dived into a doorway. He was now safe in the dark snug of O'Neill's shop, and filling up the little window that looked into the bar with his inflamed face, the colour of dark wine or dark meat, he called out:

"Here, Pat, give us a g.p., like a good fellow."

The curate brought him a glass of plain porter. The man drank it at a gulp and asked for a caraway seed. He put his penny on the counter and, leaving the curate to grope for it in the gloom, retreated out of the snug as furtively as he had entered it.

Darkness, accompanied by a thick fog, was gaining upon the dusk of February and the lamps in Eustace Street had been lit. The man went up by the houses until he reached the door of the office, wondering whether he could finish his copy in time. On the stairs a moist pungent odour of perfumes saluted his nose: evidently Miss Delacour had come while he was out in O'Neill's. He crammed his cap back again into his pocket and re-entered the office, assuming an air of absentmindedness.

"Mr. Alleyne has been calling fo you," said the chief clerk severely. "Where were you?"

The man glanced at the two clients who were standing at the counter as if to intimate that their presence prevented him from answering. As the clients were both male the chief clerk allowed himself a laugh.

"I know that game," he said. "Five times in one day is a little bit . . . Well, you better look sharp and get a copy of our correspondence in the Delacour case for Mr. Alleyne."

This address in the presence of the public, his run upstairs and the porter he had gulped down so hastily confused the man and, as he sat down at his desk to get what was required, he realised how hopeless was the task of finishing his copy of the contract before half past five. The dark damp night was coming and he longed to spend it in the bars, drinking with his friends amid the glare of gas and the clatter of glasses. He got out the Delacour correspondence and passed out of the office. He hoped Mr. Alleyne would not discover that the last two letters were missing.

The moist pungent perfume lay all the way up to Mr. Alleyne's room. Miss Delacour was a middle-aged woman of Jewish appearance. Mr. Alleyne was said to be sweet on her or on her money. She came to the office often and stayed a long time when she came. She was sitting beside his desk now in an aroma of perfumes, smoothing the handle of her umbrella and nodding the great black feather in her hat. Mr. Alleyne had swivelled his chair round to face her and thrown his right foot jauntily upon his left knee. The man put the correspondence on the desk and bowed respectfully but neither Mr. Alleyne nor Miss Delacour took any notice of his bow. Mr. Alleyne tapped a finger on the correspondence and then flicked it towards him as if to say: *"That's all right: you can go."*

The man returned to the lower office and sat down again at his desk. He stared intently at the incomplete phrase: *In no case shall the said Bernard Bodley be . . .* and thought how strange it was that the last three words began with the same letter. The chief clerk began to hurry Miss Parker, saying she would never have the letters typed in time for post. The man listened to the clicking of the machine for a few minutes and then set to work to finish his copy. But his head was not clear and his mind wandered away to the glare and rattle of the public-house. It was a night for hot punches. He struggled on with his copy, but when the clock struck five he had still fourteen pages to write. Blast it! He couldn't finish it in time. He longed to execrate aloud, to bring his fist down on something violently. He was so enraged that he wrote *Bernard Bernard* instead of *Bernard Bodley* and had to begin again on a clean sheet.

He felt strong enough to clear out the whole office singlehanded. His body ached to do something, to rush out and revel in violence. All the indignities of his life enraged him. . . . Could he ask the cashier privately for an advance? No, the cashier was no good, no damn good; he wouldn't give an advance. . . . He knew where he would meet the boys: Leonard and O'Halloran and Nosey Flynn. The barometer of his emotional nature was set for a spell of riot.

His imagination had so abstracted him that his name was called twice before he answered. Mr. Alleyne and Miss Delacour were standing outside the counter and all the clerks had turned round in anticipation of something. The man got up from his desk. Mr. Alleyne began a tirade of abuse, saying that two letters were missing. The man answered that he knew nothing about them, that he had made a faithful copy. The tirade continued: it was so bitter and violent that the man could hardly restrain his fist from descending upon the head of the manikin before him:

"I know nothing about any other two letters," he said stupidly.

"You—know—nothing. Of course you know nothing," said Mr. Alleyne. "Tell me," he added, glancing first for approval to the lady beside him, "do you take me for a fool? Do you think me an utter fool?"

The man glanced from the lady's face to the little egg-shaped head and back again; and, almost before he was aware of it, his tongue had found a felicitous moment:

"I don't think, sir," he said, "that that's a fair question to put to me."

There was a pause in the very breathing of the clerks. Everyone was astounded (the author of the witticism no less than his neighbours) and Miss Delacour, who was a stout amiable person, began to smile broadly. Mr. Alleyne flushed to the hue of a wild rose and his mouth twitched with a dwarf's passion. He shook his fist in the man's face till it seemed to vibrate like the knob of some electric machine:

"You impertinent ruffian! You impertinent ruffian! I'll make short work of you! Wait till you see! You'll apologise to me for your impertinence or you'll quit the office instanter! You'll quit this, I'm telling you, or you'll apologise to me!"

He stood in a doorway opposite the office watching to see if the cashier would come out alone. All the clerks passed out and finally the cashier came out with the chief clerk. It was no use trying to say a word to him when he was with the chief clerk. The man felt that his position was bad enough. He had been obliged to offer an abject apology to Mr. Alleyne for his impertinence but he knew what a hornet's nest the office would be for him. He could remember the way in which Mr. Alleyne had hounded little Peake out of the office in order to make room for his own nephew. He felt savage and thirsty and revengeful, annoyed with himself and with everyone else. Mr. Alleyne would never give him an hour's rest; his life would be a hell to him. He had made a proper fool of himself this time. Could he not keep his tongue in his cheek? But they had never pulled together from the first, he and Mr. Alleyne, ever since the day Mr. Alleyne had overheard him mimicking his North of Ireland accent to amuse Higgins and Miss Parker: that had been the beginning of it. He might have tried Higgins for the money, but sure Higgins never had anything for himself. A man with two establishments to keep up, of course he couldn't. . . .

He felt his great body again aching for the comfort of the public-house. The fog had begun to chill him and he wondered could he touch Pat in O'Neill's. He could not touch him for more than a bob—and a bob was no use. Yet he must get money somewhere or other: he had spent his last penny for the g.p. and soon it would be too late for getting money anywhere. Suddenly, as he was fingering his watch-chain, he thought of Terry Kelly's pawn-office in Fleet Street. That was the dart! Why didn't he think of it sooner?

He went through the narrow alley of Temple Bar quickly, muttering to himself that they could all go to hell because he was going to have a good night of it. The clerk in Terry Kelly's said *A crown!* but the consignor held out for six shillings; and in the end the six shillings was allowed him literally. He came out of the pawn-office joyfully, making a little cylinder of the coins between his thumb and fingers. In Westmoreland Street the footpaths were crowded with young men and women returning from business and ragged urchins ran here and there yelling out the names of the evening editions. The man passed through the crowd, looking on the spectacle generally with proud satisfaction and staring masterfully at the office-girls. His head was full of the noises of tram-gongs and swishing trolleys and his nose already sniffed the curling fumes of punch. As he walked on he preconsidered the terms in which he would narrate the incident to the boys:

"So, I just looked at him—coolly, you know, and looked at her. Then I looked back at him again—taking my time, you know. 'I don't think that that's a fair question to put to me,' says I."

Nosey Flynn was sitting up in his usual corner of Davy Byrne's and, when he heard the story, he stood Farrington a half-one, saying it was as smart a thing as ever he heard. Farrington stood a drink in his turn. After a while O'Halloran and Paddy Leonard came in and the story was repeated to them. O'Halloran stood tailors of malt, hot, all round and told the story of the retort he had made to the chief clerk when he was in Callan's of Fownes's Street; but, as the retort was after the manner of the liberal shepherds in the eclogues, he had to admit that it was not as clever as Farrington's retort. At this Farrington told the boys to polish off that and have another.

Just as they were naming their poisons who should come in but Higgins! Of course he had to join in with the others. The men asked him to give his version of it, and he did so with great vivacity for the sight of five small hot whiskies was very exhilarating. Everyone roared laughing when he showed the way in which Mr. Alleyne shook his fist in Farrington's face. Then he imitated Farrington, saying, *"And here was my nabs, as cool as you please,"* while Farrington looked at the company out of his heavy dirty eyes, smiling and at times drawing forth stray drops of liquor from his moustache with the aid of his lower lip.

When that round was over there was a pause. O'Halloran had money but neither of the other two seemed to have any; so the whole party left the shop somewhat regretfully. At the corner of Duke Street Higgins and Nosey Flynn bevelled off to the left while the other three turned back towards the city. Rain was drizzling down on the cold streets and, when they reached the Ballast Office, Farrington suggested the Scotch House. The bar was full of men and loud with the noise of tongues and glasses. The three men pushed past the whining matchsellers at the door and formed a little party at the corner of the counter. They began to exchange stories. Leonard introduced them to a young fellow named Weathers who was performing at the Tivoli as an acrobat and knockabout *artiste*. Farrington stood a drink all round. Weathers said he would take a small Irish and Apollinaris. Farrington, who had definite notions of what was what, asked the boys would they have an Apollinaris too; but the boys told Tim to make theirs hot. The talk became theatrical. O'Halloran stood a round and then Farrington stood another round, Weathers protesting that the hospitality was too Irish. He promised to get them in behind the scenes and introduce them to some nice girls. O'Halloran said that he and Leonard would go, but that Farrington wouldn't go because he was a married man; and Farrington's heavy dirty eyes leered at the company in token that he understood he was being chaffed. Weathers made them all have just one little tincture at his expense and promised to meet them later on at Mulligan's in Poolbeg Street.

When the Scotch House closed they went round to Mulligan's. They went into the parlour at the back and O'Halloran ordered small hot specials all round. They were all beginning to feel mellow. Farrington was just standing another round when Weathers came back. Much to Farrington's relief he drank a glass of bitter this time. Funds were getting low but they had enough to keep them going. Presently two young women with big hats and a young man in a check suit came in and sat at a table close by. Weathers saluted them and told the company that they were out of the Tivoli. Farrington's eyes wandered at every moment in the direction of one of the young women. There was something striking in her appearance. An immense scarf of peacock-blue muslin was wound round her hat and knotted in a great bow under her chin; and she wore bright yellow gloves, reaching to the elbow. Farrington gazed admiringly at the plump arm which she moved very often and with much grace; and when, after a little time, she answered his gaze he admired still more her large dark brown eyes. The oblique staring expression in them fascinated him. She glanced at him once or twice and, when the party was leaving the room, she brushed against his chair and said *"O, pardon!"* in a London accent. He watched her leave the room in the hope that she would look back at him, but he was disappointed. He cursed his want of money and cursed all the rounds he had stood, particularly to all the whiskies and Apollinaris which he had stood to Weathers. If there was one thing that he hated it was a sponge. He was so angry that he lost count of the conversation of his friends.

When Paddy Leonard called him he found that they were talking about feats of strength. Weathers was showing his biceps muscle to the company and boasting so much that the other two had called on Farrington to uphold the national honour. Farrington pulled up his sleeve accordingly and showed his bisceps muscle to the company. The two arms were examined and compared and finally it was agreed to have a trial of strength. The table was cleared and the two men rested their elbows on it, clasping hands. When Paddy Leonard said *"Go!"* each was to try to bring down the other's hand on to the table. Farrington looked very serious and determined.

The trial began. After about thirty seconds Weathers brought his opponent's hand slowly down on to the table. Farrington's dark wine-coloured face flushed darker still with anger and humiliation at having been defeated by such a stripling.

"You're not to put the weight of your body behind it. Play fair," he said.

"Who's not playing fair?" said the other.

"Come on again. The two best out of three."

The trial began again. The veins stood out on Farrington's forehead, and the pallor of Weathers' complexion changed to peony. Their hands and arms trembled under the stress. After a long struggle Weathers again brought his opponent's hand slowly on to the table. There was a murmur of applause from the spectators. The curate, who was standing beside the table, nodded his red head towards the victor and said with stupid familiarity:

"Ah! that's the knack!"

"What the hell do you know about it?" said Farrington fiercely, turning on the man. "What do you put in your gab for?"

"Sh, sh!" said O'Halloran, observing the violent expression of Farrington's face. "Pony up, boys. We'll have just one little smahan more and then we'll be off."

A very sullen-faced man stood at the corner of O'Connell Bridge waiting for the little Sandymount tram to take him home. He was full of smouldering anger and revengefulness. He felt humiliated and discontented; he did not even feel drunk; and he had only twopence in his pocket. He cursed everything. He had done for himself in the office, pawned his watch, spent all his money; and he had not even got drunk. He began to feel thirsty again and he longed to be back again in the hot reeking public-house. He had lost his reputation as a strong man, having been defeated twice by a mere boy. His heart swelled with fury and, when he thought of the woman in the big hat who had brushed against him and said *Pardon!* his fury nearly choked him.

His tram let him down at Shelbourne Road and he steered his great body along in the shadow of the wall of the barracks. He loathed returning to his home. When he went in by the side-door he found the kitchen empty and the kitchen fire nearly out. He bawled upstairs:

"Ada! Ada!"

His wife was a little sharp-faced woman who bullied her husband when he was sober and was bullied by him when he was drunk. They had five children. A little boy came running down the stairs.

"Who is that?" said the man, peering through the darkness.

"Me, pa."

"Who are you? Charlie?"

"No, pa. Tom."

"Where's your mother?"

"She's out at the chapel."

"That's right. . . . Did she think of leaving any dinner for me?"

"Yes, pa. I—"

"Light the lamp. What do you mean by having the place in darkness? Are the other children in bed?"

The man sat down heavily on one of the chairs while the little boy lit the lamp. He began to mimic his son's flat accent, saying half to himself: *"At the chapel. At the chapel, if you please!"* When the lamp was lit he banged his fist on the table and shouted:

"What's for my dinner?"

"I'm going . . . to cook it, pa," said the little boy.

The man jumped up furiously and pointed to the fire.

"On that fire! You let the fire out! By God, I'll teach you to do that again!"

He took a step to the door and seized the walking-stick which was standing behind it.

"I'll teach you to let the fire out!" he said, rolling up his sleeve in order to give his arm free play.

The little boy cried *"O, pa!"* and ran whimpering round the table, but the man followed him and caught him by the coat. The little boy looked about him wildly but, seeing no way of escape, fell upon his knees.

"Now, you'll let the fire out the next time!" said the man, striking at him vigorously with the stick. "Take that, you little whelp!"

The boy uttered a squeal of pain as the stick cut his thigh. He clasped his hands together in the air and his voice shook with fright.

"O, pa!" he cried. "Don't beat me, pa! And I'll . . . I'll say a *Hail Mary* for you. . . . I'll say a *Hail Mary* for you, pa, if you don't beat me. . . . I'll say a *Hail Mary. . . ."*

Questions

1. The Seven Deadly Sins are pride, lechery, envy, anger, covetousness, gluttony, sloth. How many of these are applicable to Farrington? In what ways? How would you further characterize the man?
2. What is the significance of the title? How is its meaning related to the three sections of the story?
3. Mr. Alleyne is an Ulsterman. What significance does this have for the story? What characters are not Irish? Again, what is the significance?
4. Farrington is a copying-machine. What other machines do you see in the story?
5. What is the significance of Weathers asking for a "small Irish and Apollinaris" and of Farrington's response? What role does alcohol play in the story?

D. H. Lawrence

The Horse Dealer's Daughter

THE MAIN subject of D. H. Lawrence's fiction is the nature of love, what it can do, what thwarts it, what makes it possible. For Lawrence, love is an enabling, life-giving force; but there is also a destructive, false kind of love which leads toward death instead of life. In modern society, Lawrence points out over and over again, we are too apt to use love for death-giving instead of life-giving purposes.

There is nothing radical about Lawrence's attitude toward love, although it borders on the mystical and at times is programmatic. What is radical in his fiction is the passionate intensity with which he approaches his subject and the effort, which is unique in literature, to portray a level of response which is instinctual, non-verbal. It perhaps goes without saying that he has only words with which to accomplish this.

Anyone who would learn a good deal about Lawrence's art has simply to observe closely what goes on in "The Horse Dealer's Daughter" between the opening lines, " 'Well, Mabel, and what are you going to do with yourself?' asked Joe, with foolish flippancy," and the echoing question asked by the young doctor several pages later, "What are you going to do, then, Miss Pervin?" In the interven-

ing pages Lawrence has not only set his scene and characterized the brothers as they sit around the breakfast table. He has also revealed the predicament of the horse dealer's daughter, not merely in terms of her family but as a human being.

The realism of the opening pages of "The Horse Dealer's Daughter" may seem at first in sharp contrast to the events with which the story ends. Yet these too are, from one point of view, realistic. I am not speaking here of the middle events, in which the girl tries to commit suicide in the brackish pond and the young doctor rescues her. These events are also symbolic, ritualistic, without ever abandoning the actual world. Rather I am thinking of the events which occur upon their return to the horse dealer's house. There is nothing symbolic about one person willing another to love, though people are not used to putting in words such psychic actions or the responses that follow.

WELL, Mabel, and what are you going to do with yourself?" asked Joe, with foolish flippancy. He felt quite safe himself. Without listening for an answer, he turned aside, worked a grain of tobacco to the tip of his tongue, and spat it out. He did not care about anything, since he felt safe himself.

The three brothers and the sister sat round the desolate breakfast table, attempting some sort of desultory consultation. The morning's post had given the final tap to the family fortune, and all was over. The dreary dining-room itself, with its heavy mahogany furniture, looked as if it were waiting to be done away with.

But the consultation amounted to nothing. There was a strange air of ineffectuality about the three men, as they sprawled at table, smok-

Lizaveta Ivanovna did not hear her. On returning home she ran to her room, and drew the letter out of her glove: it was not sealed. Lizaveta read it. The letter contained a declaration of love; it was tender, respectful, and copied word for word from a German novel. But Lizaveta did not know anything of the German language, and she was quite delighted with the letter.

For all that, it troubled her exceedingly. For the first time in her life she was entering into secret and intimate relations with a young man. His boldness horrified her. She reproached herself for her imprudent behavior, and knew not what to do. Should she cease to sit at the window and, by assuming an appearance of indifference toward him, put a check upon the young officer's desire to pursue her further? Should she send his letter back to him, or should she answer him in a cold and resolute manner? There was nobody to whom she could turn in her perplexity, for she had neither female friend nor adviser. . . . At length she resolved to reply to him.

She sat down at her little writing table, took pen and paper, and began to think. Several times she began her letter, and then tore it up: the way she had expressed herself seemed to her either too indulgent or too severe. At last she succeeded in writing a few lines with which she felt satisfied.

"I am convinced," she wrote, "that your intentions are honorable, and that you do not wish to offend me by any imprudent action, but our acquaintance should not have begun in such a manner. I return you your letter, and I hope that I shall never have any cause to complain of undeserved disrespect."

The next day, as soon as Hermann made his appearance, Lizaveta rose from her embroidery, went into the drawing room, opened the wicket and threw the letter into the street, trusting to the young officer's alertness.

Hermann hastened forward, picked it up and then repaired to a confectioner's shop. Breaking the seal of the envelope, he found inside it his own letter and Lizaveta's reply. He had expected this, and he returned home, very much taken up with his intrigue.

Three days afterward, a bright-eyed young girl from a milliner's establishment brought Lizaveta a letter. Lizaveta opened it with great uneasiness, fearing that it was a demand for money, when suddenly she recognized Hermann's handwriting.

"You have made a mistake, my dear," said she; "this letter is not for me."

"Oh, yes, it is for you," replied the pert girl, without concealing a sly smile. "Have the goodness to read it."

Lizaveta glanced at the letter. Hermann requested an interview.

"It cannot be," said Lizaveta Ivanovna, alarmed both at the haste with which he had made his request, and the manner in which it had been transmitted. "This letter is certainly not for me."

And she tore it into fragments.

"If the letter was not for you, why have you torn it up?" said the girl. "I should have given it back to the person who sent it."

"Be good enough, my dear," said Lizaveta, disconcerted by this remark, "not to bring me any more letters in future, and tell the person who sent you that he ought to be ashamed. . . ."

But Hermann was not the man to be thus put off. Every day Lizaveta received from him a letter, sent now in this way, now in that. They were no longer translated from the German. Hermann wrote them under the inspiration of passion, and spoke in his own language, and they bore full testimony to the inflexibility of his desire and the disordered condition of his uncontrollable imagination. Lizaveta no longer thought of sending them back to him: she became intoxicated with them and began to reply to them, and little by little her answers became longer and more affectionate. At last she threw out of the window to him the following letter:

"This evening there is going to be a ball at the X. Embassy. The Countess will be there. We shall remain until two o'clock. This is your opportunity of seeing me alone. As soon as the Countess is gone, the servants will very probably go out, and there will be nobody left but the porter, but he, too, usually retires to his lodge. Come at half past eleven. Walk straight upstairs. If you meet anybody in the anteroom, ask if the Countess is at home. If you are told she is not, there will be nothing left for you to do but to go away and return another time. But it is most probable that you will meet nobody. The maidservants all sit together in one room. On leaving the anteroom, turn to the left, and walk straight on until you reach the Countess' bedroom. In the bedroom, behind a screen, you will find two small doors: the one on the right leads to a study, which the Countess never enters; the one on the left leads to a corridor, at the end of which is a narrow winding staircase; this leads to my room."

Hermann quivered like a tiger, as he waited for the appointed time. At ten o'clock in the evening he was already in front of the Countess' house. The weather was terrible; the wind was howling; the sleety snow fell in large flakes; the lamps emitted a feeble light, the streets were deserted; from time to time a sledge, drawn by a sorry-looking hack, passed by, the driver on the lookout for a belated fare. Hermann stood there wearing nothing but his jacket, yet he felt neither the wind nor the snow.

At last the Countess' carriage drew up. Hermann saw two footmen carry out in their arms the bent form of the old lady, wrapped in sables, and immediately behind her, clad in a light mantle, and with a wreath of fresh flowers on her head, followed Lizaveta. The door was closed. The carriage rolled away heavily through the yielding snow. The porter shut the street door; the windows became dark.

Hermann began walking up and down near the deserted house; at length he stopped under a lamp, and glanced at his watch: it was twenty minutes past eleven. He remained standing under the lamp, his eyes fixed upon the watch, impatiently waiting for the remaining minutes to pass. At half past eleven precisely, Hermann ascended the steps of the house, and made his way into the brightly illuminated vestibule. The porter was not there. Hermann ran up the stairs, opened the door of the anteroom and saw a footman sitting asleep in an antique soiled armchair, under a lamp. With a light firm step Hermann walked past him. The reception room and the drawing room were in semi-darkness. They were lit feebly by a lamp in the anteroom.

Hermann entered the bedroom. Before an ikon case, filled with ancient ikons, a golden sanctuary lamp was burning. Armchairs, upholstered in faded brocade, and sofas, the gilding of which was worn off and which were piled with down cushions, stood in melancholy symmetry around the room, the walls of which were hung with China silk. On the wall hung two portraits painted in Paris by Madame Lebrun. One of them represented a plump, pink-cheeked man of about forty in a light green uniform and with a star on his breast; the other—a beautiful young woman, with an aquiline nose, curls at her temples, and a rose in her powdered hair. In all the corners stood porcelain shepherds and shepherdesses, clocks from the workshop of the celebrated Leroy, boxes, roulettes, fans, and the various gewgaws for ladies that were invented at the end of the last century, together with Montgolfier's balloon and Mesmer's magnetism. Hermann stepped behind the screen. Behind it stood a little iron bed; on the right was the door which led to the study; on the left—the other which led to the corridor. He opened the latter, and saw the little winding staircase which led to the room of the poor ward. . . . But he retraced his steps and entered the dark study.

The time passed slowly. All was still. The clock in the drawing room struck twelve; in all the rooms, one clock after another marked the hour, and everything was quiet again. Hermann stood leaning against the cold stove. He was calm; his heart beat regularly, like that of a man resolved upon a dangerous but inevitable undertaking. The clock struck one, then two; and he heard the distant rumbling of carriage wheels. In spite of himself, excitement seized him. The carriage drew near and stopped. He heard the sound of the carriage step being let down. All was bustle within the house. The servants were running hither and thither, voices were heard, and the house was lit up. Three antiquated chambermaids entered the bedroom, and they were shortly afterwards followed by the Countess who, more dead than alive, sank into an armchair. Hermann peeped through a chink. Lizaveta Ivanovna passed close by him, and he heard her hurried steps as she hurried up her staircase. For a moment his heart was assailed by something like remorse, but the emotion was only transitory. He stood petrified.

The Countess began to undress before her looking glass. Her cap, decorated with roses, was unpinned, and then her powdered wig was removed from off her white and closely cropped head. Hairpins fell in showers around her. Her yellow satin dress, embroidered with silver, fell down at her swollen feet.

Hermann witnessed the repulsive mysteries of her toilette; at last the Countess was in her nightcap and nightgown, and in this costume, more suitable to her age, she appeared less hideous and terrifying.

Like all old people in general, the Countess suffered from sleeplessness. Having undressed, she seated herself at the window in an armchair and dismissed her maids. The candles were taken away, and once more the room was lit only by the sanctuary lamp. The Countess sat there looking quite yellow, moving her flaccid lips and swaying from side to side. Her dull eyes expressed complete vacancy of mind, and, looking at her, one would have thought that the rocking of her body was not voluntary, but was produced by the action of some concealed galvanic mechanism.

Suddenly the deathlike face changed incredibly. The lips ceased to move, the eyes became animated: before the Countess stood a stranger.

"Do not be alarmed, for Heaven's sake, do not be alarmed!" said he in a low but distinct voice. "I have no intention of doing you any harm, I have only come to ask a favor of you."

The old woman looked at him in silence, as if she had not heard what he had said. Hermann thought that she was deaf, and, bending down toward her ear, he repeated what he had said. The old woman remained silent as before.

"You can insure the happiness of my life," continued Hermann, "and it will cost you nothing. I know that you can name three cards in succession—"

Hermann stopped. The Countess appeared now to understand what was asked of her; she seemed to be seeking words with which to reply.

"It was a joke," she replied at last. "I swear it was only a joke."

"This is no joking matter," replied Hermann angrily. "Remember Chaplitzky, whom you helped to win back what he had lost."

The Countess became visibly uneasy. Her features expressed strong emotion, but she soon lapsed into her former insensibility.

"Can you not name me these three winning cards?" continued Hermann.

The Countess remained silent; Hermann continued: "For whom are you preserving your secret? For your grandsons? They are rich enough without it; they do not know the worth of money. Your cards would be of no use to a spendthrift. He who cannot preserve his paternal inheritance, will die in want, even though he had a demon at his service. I am not a man of that sort; I know the value of money. Your three cards will not be wasted on me. Come!"

He paused and tremblingly awaited her reply. The Countess remained silent; Hermann fell upon his knees.

"If your heart has ever known the feeling of love," said he, "if you remember its rapture, if you have ever smiled at the cry of your newborn child, if your breast has ever throbbed with any human feeling, I entreat you by the feelings of a wife, a lover, a mother, by all that is most sacred in life, not to reject my plea. Reveal to me your secret. Of what use is it to you? . . . Maybe it is connected with some terrible sin, the loss of eternal bliss, some bargain with the devil. . . . Consider—you are old; you have not long to live—I am ready to take your sins upon my soul. Only reveal to me your secret. Remember that the happiness of a man is in your hands, that not only I, but my children, grandchildren, and great-grandchildren, will bless your memory and reverence it as something sacred. . . ."

The old woman answered not a word.

Hermann rose to his feet.

"You old witch!" he exclaimed, clenching his teeth. "Then I will make you answer!"

With these words he drew a pistol from his pocket.

At the sight of the pistol, the Countess for the second time exhibited strong emotion. She shook her head and raised her hands as if to protect herself from the shot . . . then she fell backward and remained motionless.

"Come, an end to this childish nonsense!" said Hermann, taking hold of her hand. "I ask you for the last time: will you tell me the names of your three cards, or will you not?"

The Countess made no reply. Hermann perceived that she was dead!

IV

7 mai, 18– –
Homme sans moeurs et sans religion!
A CORRESPONDENCE

Lizaveta Ivanovna was sitting in her room, still in her ball dress, lost in deep thought. On returning home, she had hastily dismissed the sleepy maid, who reluctantly came forward to assist her, saying that she would undress herself, and with a trembling heart had gone up to her own room, hoping to find Hermann there, but yet desiring not to find him. At the first glance she convinced herself that he was not there, and she thanked her fate for the obstacle which had prevented their meeting. She sat down without undressing, and began to recall to mind all the circumstances which in so short a time had carried her so far. It was not three weeks since the time when she had first seen the young man from the window—and she already was in correspondence with him, and he had succeeded in inducing her to grant him a nocturnal tryst! She knew his name only through his having written it at the bottom of some of his letters; she had never spoken to him, had never heard his voice, and had never heard anything of him until that evening. But, strange to say, that very evening at the ball, Tomsky, being piqued with the young Princess Pauline N., who, contrary to her usual custom, did not flirt with him, wished to revenge himself by assuming an air of indifference: he therefore engaged Lizaveta Ivanovna and danced an endless mazurka with her. All the time he kept teasing her about her partiality for officers in the Engineers; he assured her that he knew far more than she could have supposed, and some of his jests were so happily aimed, that Lizaveta thought several times that her secret was known to him.

"From whom have you learned all this?" she asked, smiling.

"From a friend of a person very well known to you," replied Tomsky, "from a very remarkable man."

"And who is this remarkable man?"

"His name is Hermann."

Lizaveta made no reply; but her hands and feet turned to ice.

"This Hermann," continued Tomsky, "is a truly romantic character. He has the profile of a Napoleon, and the soul of a Mephistopheles. I believe that he has at least three crimes upon his conscience. . . . How pale you are!"

"I have a headache. . . . But what did this Hermann—or whatever his name is—tell you?"

"Hermann is very much dissatisfied with his friend: he says that in his place he would act very differently. . . . I even think that Hermann himself has designs upon you; at least, he listens not indifferently to his friend's enamored exclamations."

"But where has he seen me?"

"In church, perhaps; or promenading—God alone knows where. It may have been in your room, while you were asleep, for he is capable of it."

Three ladies approaching him with the question: *"Oubli ou regret?"* interrupted the conversation, which had become so tantalizingly interesting to Lizaveta.

The lady chosen by Tomsky was the Princess Pauline herself. She succeeded in effecting a reconciliation with him by making an extra turn in the dance and managing to delay resuming her seat. On returning to his place, Tomsky thought no more either of Hermann or Lizaveta. She longed to renew the interrupted conversation, but the mazurka came to an end, and shortly afterward the old Countess took her departure.

Tomsky's words were nothing more than the small talk of the mazurka, but they sank deep into the soul of the young dreamer. The portrait, sketched by Tomsky, agreed with the picture she had formed in her own mind, and that image, rendered commonplace by current novels, terrified and fascinated her imagination. She was now sitting with her bare arms crossed and her head, still adorned with flowers, was bowed over her half-uncovered breast. Suddenly the door opened and Hermann entered. She shuddered.

"Where have you been?" she asked in a frightened whisper.

"In the old Countess' bedroom," replied Hermann. "I have just left her. The Countess is dead."

"My God! What are you saying?"

"And I am afraid," added Hermann, "that I am the cause of her death."

Lizaveta looked at him, and Tomsky's words found an echo in her soul: "This man has at least three crimes upon his conscience!" Hermann sat down by the window near her, and related all that had happened.

Lizaveta listened to him in terror. So all those passionate letters, those ardent demands, this bold obstinate pursuit—all this was not love! Money—that was what his soul yearned for! She could not satisfy his desire and make him happy! The poor girl had been nothing but the blind accomplice of a robber, of the murderer of her aged benefactress! . . . She wept bitter tears of belated, agonized repentance. Hermann gazed at her in silence: his heart, too, was tormented, but neither the tears of the poor girl, nor the wonderful charm of her beauty, enhanced by her grief, could produce any impression upon his hardened soul. He felt no pricking of conscience at the thought of the dead old woman. One thing only horrified him: the irreparable loss of the secret which he had expected would bring him wealth.

"You are a monster!" said Lizaveta at last.

"I did not wish her death," replied Hermann: "my pistol is not loaded."

Both grew silent.

The day began to dawn. Lizaveta extinguished her candle: a pale light illumined her room. She wiped her tear-stained eyes and raised them toward Hermann: he was sitting on the window sill, with his arms folded and frowning fiercely. In this attitude he bore a striking resemblance to the portrait of Napoleon. This resemblance struck even Lizaveta Ivanovna.

"How shall I get you out of the house?" said she at last. "I thought of conducting you down the secret staircase, but in that case it would be necessary to go through the Countess' bedroom, and I am afraid."

"Tell me how to find this secret staircase—I will go alone."

Lizaveta arose, took from her drawer a key, handed it to Hermann and gave him the necessary instructions. Hermann pressed her cold, unresponsive hand, kissed her bowed head, and left the room.

He descended the winding staircase, and once more entered the Countess' bedroom. The dead old woman sat as if petrified; her face expressed profound tranquillity. Hermann stopped before her, and gazed long and earnestly at her, as if he wished to convince himself of the terrible reality; at last he entered the study, felt behind the tapestry for the door, and then began to descend the dark staircase, agitated by strange emotions. "At this very hour," thought he, "some sixty years ago, a young gallant, who has long been moldering in his grave, may have stolen down this very staircase, perhaps coming from the very same bedroom, wearing an embroidered caftan, with his hair dressed *à l'oiseau royal* and pressing to his heart his three-cornered hat, and the heart of his aged mistress has only today ceased to beat. . . ."

At the bottom of the staircase Hermann found a door, which he opened with the same key, and found himself in a corridor which led him into the street.

V

That night the deceased Baroness von W. appeared to me. She was clad all in white and said to me: "How are you, Mr. Councilor?"

SWEDENBORG

Three days after the fatal night, at nine o'clock in the morning, Hermann repaired to the Convent of ——, where the burial service for the deceased Countess was to be held. Although feeling no remorse, he could not altogether stifle the voice of conscience, which kept repeating to him: "You are the murderer of the old woman!" While he had little true faith, he was very superstitious; and believing that the dead Countess might exercise an evil influence on his life, he resolved to be present at her funeral in order to ask her pardon.

The church was full. It was with difficulty that Hermann made his way through the crowd. The coffin stood on a sumptuous catafalque under a velvet baldachin. The deceased lay within it, her hands crossed upon her breast, and wearing a lace cap and a white satin gown. Around the catafalque stood the members of her household: the servants in black caftans, with armorial ribbons upon their shoulders, and candles in their hands; the relatives—children, grandchildren, and great-grandchildren—in deep mourning.

Nobody wept; tears would have been *une affectation*. The Countess was so old that her death could have surprised nobody, and her relatives had long looked upon her as not among the living. A famous preacher delivered the funeral oration. In simple and touching words he described the peaceful passing away of the saintly woman whose long life had been a serene, moving preparation for a Christian end. "The angel of death found her," said the preacher, "engaged in pious meditation and waiting for the midnight bridegroom."

The service concluded in an atmosphere of melancholy decorum. The relatives went forward first to bid farewell to the deceased. Then followed the numerous acquaintances, who had come to render the last homage to her who for so many years had participated in their frivolous amusements. After these followed the members of the Countess' household. The last of these was the old housekeeper who was of the same age as the deceased. Two young women led her forward, supporting her by the arms. She had not strength enough to bow down to the ground—she was the only one to shed a few tears and kiss the cold hand of her mistress.

Hermann now resolved to approach the coffin. He bowed down to the ground and for several minutes lay on the cold floor, which was strewn with fir boughs; at last he arose, as pale as the deceased

Countess herself, ascended the steps of the catafalque and bent over the corpse. . . . At that moment it seemed to him that the dead woman darted a mocking look at him and winked with one eye. Hermann started back, took a false step and fell to the ground. He was lifted up. At the same moment Lizaveta Ivanovna was carried into the vestibule of the church in a faint. This episode disturbed for some minutes the solemnity of the gloomy ceremony. Among the congregation arose a muffled murmur, and the lean chamberlain, a near relative of the deceased, whispered in the ear of an Englishman who was standing near him, that the young officer was a natural son of the Countess, to which the Englishman coldly replied: "Oh!"

During the whole of that day, Hermann was exceedingly perturbed. Dining in an out-of-the-way restaurant, he drank a great deal of wine, contrary to his usual custom, in the hope of allaying his inward agitation. But the wine only served to excite his imagination still more. On returning home, he threw himself upon his bed without undressing, and fell into a deep sleep.

When he woke up it was already night, and the moon was shining into the room. He looked at his watch: it was a quarter to three. Sleep had left him; he sat down upon his bed and thought of the funeral of the old Countess.

At that moment somebody in the street looked in at his window, and immediately passed on again. Hermann paid no attention to this incident. A few moments afterward he heard the door of the anteroom open. Hermann thought that it was his orderly, drunk as usual, returning from some nocturnal expedition, but presently he heard footsteps that were unknown to him: somebody was shuffling softly across the floor in slippers. The door opened, and a woman, dressed in white, entered the room. Hermann mistook her for his old nurse, and wondered what could bring her there at that hour of the night. But the white woman glided rapidly across the room and stood before him—and Hermann recognized the Countess!

"I have come to you against my will," she said in a firm voice: "but I have been ordered to grant your request. Three, seven, ace will win for you if played in succession, but only on these conditions: that you do not play more than one card in twenty-four hours, and that you never play again during the rest of your life. I forgive you my death, on condition that you marry my ward, Lizaveta Ivanovna."

With these words she turned round very quietly, walked with a shuffling gait toward the door and disappeared. Hermann heard the street door bang, and he saw someone look in at him through the window again.

For a long time Hermann could not recover himself. Then he went into the next room. His orderly was asleep upon the floor, and he had much difficulty in waking him. The orderly was drunk as usual, and nothing could be got out of him. The street door was locked. Hermann returned to his room, lit his candle, and set down an account of his vision.

VI

"Attendez!"
"How dare you say attendez *to me?"*
"Your Excellency, I said: 'Attendez, sir.' "

Two fixed ideas can no more exist together in the moral world than two bodies can occupy one and the same place in the physical world. "Three, seven, ace" soon drove out of Hermann's mind the thought of the dead Countess. "Three, seven, ace" were perpetually running through his head and continually on his lips. If he saw a young girl, he would say: "How slender she is! Quite like the three of hearts." If anybody asked: "What is the time?" he would reply: "Five minutes to seven." Every stout man that he saw reminded him of the ace. "Three, seven, ace" haunted him in his sleep, and assumed all possible shapes. The three bloomed before him in the form of a magnificent flower, the seven was represented by a Gothic portal, and the ace became transformed into a gigantic spider. One thought alone occupied his whole mind—to make use of the secret which he had purchased so dearly. He thought of applying for a furlough so as to travel abroad. He wanted to go to Paris and force fortune to yield a treasure to him in the public gambling houses there. Chance spared him all this trouble.

There was in Moscow a society of wealthy gamblers, presided over by the celebrated Chekalinsky, who had passed all his life at the card table and had amassed millions, accepting bills of exchange for his winnings and paying his losses in ready money. His long experience secured for him the confidence of his companions, and his open house, his famous cook, and his agreeable and cheerful manner gained for him the respect of the public. He came to St. Petersburg. The young men of the capital flocked to his rooms, forgetting balls for cards, and preferring the temptations of faro to the seductions of flirting. Narumov conducted Hermann to Chekalinsky's residence.

They passed through a suite of magnificent rooms, filled with courteous attendants. Several generals and privy counselors were playing whist; young men were lolling carelessly upon the velvet-covered sofas, eating ices and smoking pipes. In the drawing room, at the head of a long table, around which crowded about a score of players, sat the master of the house keeping the bank. He was a man of about sixty years of age, of a very dignified appearance; his head was covered with silvery-white hair; his full, florid countenance expressed good nature, and his eyes twinkled with a perpetual smile. Narumov introduced Hermann to him. Chekalinsky shook him by the hand in a friendly manner, requested him not to stand on ceremony, and then went on dealing.

The game lasted a long time. On the table lay more than thirty cards. Chekalinsky paused after each throw, in order to give the players time to arrange their cards and note down their losses, listened politely to their requests, and more politely still, straightened out the corners of cards that some absent-minded player's hand had turned down. At last the game was finished. Chekalinsky shuffled the cards and prepared to deal again.

"Allow me to play a card," said Hermann, stretching out his hand from behind a stout gentleman who was punting.

Chekalinsky smiled and bowed silently, as a sign of acquiescence.

Narumov laughingly congratulated Hermann on ending his long abstention from cards, and wished him a lucky beginning.

"Here goes!" said Hermann, writing the figure with chalk on the back of his card.

"How much, sir?" asked the banker, screwing up his eyes. "Excuse me, I cannot see quite clearly."

"Forty-seven thousand," replied Hermann.

At these words every head in the room turned suddenly round, and all eyes were fixed upon Hermann.

"He has taken leave of his senses!" thought Narumov.

"Allow me to observe," said Chekalinsky, with his eternal smile, "that that is a very high stake; nobody here has ever staked more than two hundred and seventy-five rubles at a time."

"Well," retorted Hermann, "do you accept my card or not?"

Chekalinsky bowed with the same look of humble acquiescence.

"I only wish to inform you," said he, "that enjoying the full confidence of my partners, I can only play for ready money. For my own part, I am, of course, quite convinced that your word is sufficient, but for the sake of order, and because of the accounts, I must ask you to put the money on your card."

Hermann drew from his pocket a banknote and handed it to Chekalinsky, who, after examining it in a cursory manner, placed it on Hermann's card.

He began to deal. On the right a nine turned up, and on the left a three.

"I win!" said Hermann, showing his card.

A murmur of astonishment arose among the players. Chekalinsky frowned, but the smile quickly returned to his face.

"Do you wish me to settle with you?" he said to Hermann.

"If you please," replied the latter.

Chekalinsky drew from his pocket a number of banknotes and paid up at once. Hermann took his money and left the table. Narumov could not recover from his astonishment. Hermann drank a glass of lemonade and went home.

The next evening he again appeared at Chekalinsky's. The host was dealing. Hermann walked up to the table; the punters immediately made room for him. Chekalinsky greeted him with a gracious bow.

Hermann waited for the next game, took a card and placed upon it his forty-seven thousand rubles, together with his winnings of the previous evening.

Chekalinsky began to deal. A knave turned up on the right, a seven on the left.

Hermann showed his seven.

There was a general exclamation. Chekalinsky was obviously disturbed, but he counted out the ninety-four thousand rubles and handed them over to Hermann, who pocketed them in the coolest manner possible and immediately left the house.

The next evening Hermann appeared again at the table. Everyone was expecting him. The generals and privy counselors left their whist in order to watch such extraordinary play. The young officers jumped up from their sofas, and even the servants crowded into the room. All pressed round Hermann. The other players left off punting, impatient to see how it would end. Hermann stood at the table and prepared to play alone against the pale but still smiling Chekalinsky. Each opened a new pack of cards. Chekalinsky shuffled. Hermann took a card and covered it with a pile of banknotes. It was like a duel. Deep silence reigned.

Chekalinsky began to deal; his hands trembled. On the right a queen turned up, and on the left an ace.

"Ace wins!" cried Hermann, showing his card.

"Your queen has lost," said Chekalinsky sweetly.

Hermann started; instead of an ace, there lay before him the queen of spades! He could not believe his eyes, nor could he understand how he had made such a mistake.

At that moment it seemed to him that the queen of spades screwed up her eyes and sneered. He was struck by the remarkable resemblance. . . .

"The old woman!" he exclaimed, in terror.

Chekalinsky gathered up his winnings. For some time Hermann

remained perfectly motionless. When at last he left the table, the room buzzed with loud talk.

"Splendidly punted!" said the players. Chekalinsky shuffled the cards afresh, and the game went on as usual.

CONCLUSION

Hermann went out of his mind. He is now confined in room Number 17 of the Obukhov Hospital. He never answers any questions, but he constantly mutters with unusual rapidity: "Three, seven, ace! Three, seven, queen!"

Lizaveta Ivanovna has married a very amiable young man, a son of the former steward of the old Countess. He is a civil servant, and has a considerable fortune. Lizaveta is bringing up a poor relative.

Tomsky has been promoted to the rank of captain, and is marrying Princess Pauline.

Nikolai Gogol

The Nose

I

AN INCREDIBLE THING happened in Petersburg on March 25th. Ivan Yakovlevich, the barber on Voznesensky Avenue (his last name has been lost and does not even figure on the signboard bearing a picture of a gentleman with a soapy cheek and the inscription WE ALSO LET BLOOD HERE), woke up rather early and detected a smell of newly baked bread. He raised himself a little and saw that his wife, a quite respectable woman and one extremely fond of coffee, was taking fresh rolls out of the oven.

"Praskovia Osipovna," he said to his wife, "no coffee for me this morning. I'll have a hot roll with onions instead."

Actually Ivan Yakovlevich would have liked both but he knew his wife frowned on such whims. And, sure enough, she thought:

"It's fine with me if the fool wants bread. That'll leave me another cup of coffee."

And she tossed a roll onto the table.

Mindful of his manners, Ivan Yakovlevich put his frock coat on over his nightshirt, seated himself at the table, poured some salt, got a couple of onions, took a knife and, assuming a dignified expression, proceeded to cut the roll in two.

Suddenly he stopped, surprised. There was something whitish in the middle of the roll. He poked at it with his knife, then felt it with his finger.

"It's quite compact . . ." he muttered under his breath. "Whatever can it be? . . ."

He thrust in two fingers this time and pulled it out. It was a nose.

He almost fell off his chair. Then he rubbed his eyes and felt the thing again. It was a nose all right, no doubt about it. And, what's more, a nose that had something familiar about it. His features expressed intense horror.

But the intensity of the barber's horror was nothing compared with the intensity of his wife's indignation.

"Where," she screamed, "did you lop off that nose, you beast? You crook," she shouted, "you drunkard! I'll report you to the police myself, you thug! Three customers have complained to me before this about the way you keep pulling their noses when you shave them, so that it's a wonder they manage to stay on at all."

But Ivan Yakovlevich, at that moment more dead than alive, was immune to her attack. He had remembered where he had seen the nose before and it was on none other than Collegiate Assessor Kovalev, whom he shaved regularly each Wednesday and Sunday.

"Wait, my dear, I'll wrap it in a rag and put it away somewhere in a corner. Let it stay there for a while, then I'll take it away."

"I won't even listen to you! Do you really imagine that I'll allow a cut-off nose to remain in my place, you old crumb! All you can do is strop your damn razor and when it comes to your duties, you're no good. You stupid, lousy, skirt-chasing scum! So you want me to get into trouble with the police for your sake? Is that it, you dirty mug? You're a stupid log, you know. Get it out of here. Do what you like with it, you hear me, but don't let me ever see it here again."

The barber stood there dumfounded. He thought and thought but couldn't think of anything.

"I'll be damned if I know how it happened," he said in the end, scratching behind his ear. "Was I drunk last night when I came home? I'm not sure. Anyway, it all sounds quite mad: bread is a baked product while a nose is something else again. Makes no sense to me. . . ."

So he fell silent. The thought that the police would find the nose on him and accuse him drove him to despair. He could already see the beautiful silver-braided, scarlet collars of the police and started trembling all over.

Still, in the end he stirred and went to get his trousers and his boots. He pulled on these sorry garments, wrapped the nose in a rag, and left under Praskovia Osipovna's unendearing barrage of recriminations.

He wanted to get rid of the nose, to leave it under a seat, stick it in a doorway, or just drop it as if by accident and then rush down a side street. But he kept meeting acquaintances who immediately proceeded to inquire where he was going or whom he was planning to shave so early in the morning, and he missed every opportunity. At one point he actually dropped the nose, but a watchman pointed to it with his halberd and informed him that he'd lost something. And Ivan Yakovlevich had to pick up the nose and stuff it back into his pocket. Things began to look completely hopeless for him when the stores began opening and the streets became more and more crowded.

Then he decided to try throwing the nose into the Neva from the Isakievsky Bridge. . . .

But, at this point, we should say a few words about Ivan Yakovlevich, a man who had a number of good points.

Like every self-respecting Russian tradesman, Ivan Yakovlevich was a terrible drunkard. And although he shaved other people's chins every day, his own looked permanently unshaven. His frock coat (he never wore an ordinary coat) was piebald. That is to say, it had been black originally but now it was studded with yellowish-brown and gray spots. His collar was shiny and three threads dangling from his coat indicated where the missing buttons should have been. Ivan Yakovlevich was a terrible cynic.

While being shaved the collegiate assessor often complained:

"Your hands always stink, Ivan Yakovlevich!"

He would answer: "How can they stink?"

"I don't know how, man, but they stink!" the other would say.

In answer Ivan Yakovlevich would take a pinch of snuff and proceed to soap Kovalev's cheeks and under his nose and behind his ears and under his chin, in fact, anywhere he felt like.

By and by, this worthy citizen reached the Isakievsky Bridge. He glanced around and then, leaning over the parapet, peered under the bridge as if to ascertain the whereabouts of some fish. But actually he discreetly dropped the rag containing the nose. He felt as if a three-hundred-pound weight had been taken off his back. He let out a little laugh and, instead of going back to shave the chins of government employees, he decided he had to recuperate. He was setting out for an establishment which operated under the sign MEALS AND TEA, to treat himself to a glass of punch, when all of a sudden he saw a police inspector of most imposing appearance—handlebar mustache, three-cornered hat, saber and all. He froze in his tracks. The policeman beckoned to him and said:

"Just step over here, fellow!"

Having great respect for this particular uniform, Ivan Yakovlevich pulled off his cap while he was still a good distance away, trotted toward the policeman and said:

"Good morning, officer."

"Instead of good morning, you'd better tell me what you were doing in the middle of the bridge over there."

"I was on my way to shave people, officer, and I wanted to see whether the current was fast——"

"You're lying, man. You won't get away with it. You'd better answer my question."

"Officer, I'll give you two . . . no, three free shaves every week . . . what do you say, officer?" said Ivan Yakovlevich.

"Not a chance. I have three barbers to shave me as it is. And they consider it a great honor, too. So you get on with it and explain what you were doing."

Ivan Yakovlevich turned ashen. . . . But here the incident becomes befogged and it is completely unknown what happened after this point.

II

That morning Collegiate Assessor Kovalev had awakened rather early. He went brrr . . . brrr with his lips as he always did upon waking, although he himself could not explain why. He stretched himself and asked his man for the small mirror that stood on his dressing table. He needed it to examine a pimple that had broken out on his nose the day before. But he was bewildered to find that instead of his nose there was nothing but a bare smooth surface. Horrified, he asked for water and rubbed his eyes with a towel. There was no doubt about it: his nose was not there. He felt himself all over to make sure he was not asleep. It seemed he wasn't. Collegiate Assessor Kovalev jumped up then and shook himself. Still no nose. He called for his clothes and rushed directly to the police inspector.

But, in the meantime, a few things should be said about Kovalev to show what sort of collegiate assessor he was. Collegiate assessors who reach their positions by obtaining academic degrees cannot be compared with the collegiate assessors that used to be appointed in the Caucasus. They are two completely unrelated species. The collegiate assessors equipped with learning . . .

But Russia is a strange place and if we say something about one collegiate assessor, all of them, from Riga to Kamchatka, will take it personally. The same is true of all vocations and ranks.

Kovalev was a Caucasus-made collegiate assessor. Moreover, he had been a collegiate assessor for only two years. In order to feel distinguished and important he never referred to himself as a collegiate assessor but employed the equivalent military rank of major.

"Look here, my good woman," he used to say when he met a woman selling shirt fronts in the street, "I want you to deliver them to my place. I live on Sadovaya Street. Just ask for Major Kovalev's, anybody'll show you."

And if he met someone pretty, he would whisper to her discreetly: "You just ask for Major Kovalev's apartment, deary."

As a rule, Major Kovalev went out for a daily walk along Nevsky Avenue. The collar of his shirt was always clean and well starched. He had whiskers such as are still to be found on provincial surveyors, and architects if they happen to be Russian, among persons performing various police functions, and, in general, on men who have full faces, ruddy cheeks, and play a strong hand at certain games of chance. Whiskers of this type flow straight across the middle of the cheek up to the very nostrils.

Major Kovalev always carried with him a great quantity of seals, both seals engraved with coats of arms and others on which were carved WEDNESDAY, THURSDAY, MONDAY, and that sort of thing. He had come to Petersburg on business, namely, to find a position commensurate with his rank. He hoped, if lucky, to get a Vice-Governorship; otherwise, he would consider a post as executive in some administration. Nor was Major Kovalev averse to matrimony, as long as the bride happened to have a capital of about two hundred thousand rubles.

And now that all this has been said about the major, it can be imagined how he felt when, instead of a quite acceptable-looking, medium-sized nose, he found an absurd, smooth flatness.

And, to make things worse, there was not a cab to be seen in the street and he was forced to walk all the way wrapped in his cloak, his face covered with a handkerchief, pretending he was bleeding, and repeating to himself:

"Maybe it's just imagination. How could I possibly have lost my nose so stupidly? . . ."

He entered a tearoom simply to have a look in a mirror. Fortunately the place was empty except for waiters sweeping the floor and moving chairs around and some others who, with sleepy eyes, were carrying trays with hot buns somewhere. Yesterday's newspapers spotted with coffee were strewn around on tables and chairs.

"Well, thank heaven there's no one here," he said. "I'll be able to have a look."

Gingerly he approached the mirror and looked.

"Filth," he said, spitting, "goddammit. If only there was something to take the nose's place! But it's completely blank!"

He bit his lip in anger and, leaving the tearoom, decided that, contrary to his usual custom, he wouldn't look at the people he met or smile at anyone. Suddenly he stopped dead near the entrance door of a house. An incredible sequence of events unrolled before his eyes. A carriage stopped at the house entrance. Its door opened. A uniformed gentleman appeared. Stooping, he jumped out of the carriage, ran up the steps and entered the house. A combination of horror and amazement swept over Kovalev when he recognized the stranger as his own nose. At this eerie sight, everything swayed before his eyes. But although he could hardly stand on his feet, he felt compelled to wait until the nose returned to the carriage. He waited, shaking as though he had malaria.

After two minutes or so, the nose emerged from the house. He wore a gold-braided, brightly colored uniform, buckskin breeches, a three-cornered hat, and a saber. The plumes on his hat indicated the rank of state councilor. From everything else it could be inferred that he was setting off on some sort of official visit. He looked left, then right, called out to the coachman to bring the carriage up to the very door, got in and was off.

This almost drove poor Kovalev insane. He could no longer think coherently about the whole affair. No, really, how was it possible that the nose, until yesterday on his face, utterly incapable of walking or driving around, should show up like this today and, what's more, wearing a uniform! And Kovalev ran after the carriage, which, luckily for him, did not have far to go. It stopped before Kazan Cathedral.

Kovalev reached the spot and, rushing after the nose, had to elbow his way through a throng of old beggar-women who used to make him laugh because of the way they kept their faces completely wrapped in rags, leaving only slits for their eyes. He entered the cathedral. There were a few worshipers around, all standing near the entrance.

Kovalev was in such a depressed state that he could not possibly muster the strength to pray and instead his eyes scrutinized every recess in search of the gentleman. Finally he discovered him standing in a corner. The nose's face was completely concealed by his high, stand-up collar and he was praying with an expression of the utmost piety.

"How shall I address him?" Kovalev wondered. "From his uniform, his hat, everything about him, he must be a state councilor. Damned if I know what to do. . . ."

He approached and cleared his throat. But the nose never even changed his pious posture and remained absorbed in his worship.

"Excuse me, sir . . ." Kovalev said, scraping up all his courage.

"Yes?" the nose said, turning around.

"I don't know how to put it, sir . . . I would say . . . it seems . . . it seems you ought to know where you belong, and where do I find you? Of all places, in church. You must surely agree——"

"Pardon me, but I can make neither head nor tail of what you're saying. Just what do you want?"

Kovalev tried to think how he could explain to the nose what he had in mind and, taking a deep breath, said:

"Of course, sir, for my part . . . but, after all, I am a major, you know, and it's most improper, in my position, to walk around without a nose. Some old woman selling peeled oranges by the Voskresensky Bridge might be able to get along without a nose. But for someone who is almost certain of a high administrative appointment . . . you can judge for yourself, sir. I really fail to understand . . ." At this point Kovalev shrugged. "You'll excuse me, but if this affair were handled according to the code of honor and duty . . . You can see for yourself——"

"I don't see anything," the nose said. "Kindly come to the point."

"Sir," Kovalev said with dignity, "I don't know how to interpret your words. The matter is quite clear, I believe. Unless you are trying . . . Don't you realize that you are my nose?"

The nose looked at the major and frowned slightly.

"You're mistaken, sir. I'm all on my own. Moreover, there couldn't possibly have been close relations between us. Judging by your dress, you must be employed by the Senate, or possibly by the Ministry of Justice, whereas my field is science."

And having said this, the nose turned away and resumed his prayers.

Kovalev was now completely at a loss. Then he heard the pleasant rustle of a feminine dress. He saw a middle-aged lady covered with lace and, with her, a pretty, slender thing in a white dress which set off a very moving waistline, and with a straw hat as light as whipped cream. Behind them walked a tall man with side whiskers and a very complicated collar.

Kovalev worked his way toward them, pulled up the spotless collar of his shirt front to make sure it showed, straightened the seals that hung on a golden chain, and concentrated his attention on the young lady who, like a spring blossom, raised her white hand with its half-transparent fingers to her forehead. And Kovalev's smile spread twice as wide when, under the hat, he made out a chin of a tender whiteness and a cheek touched by the early spring coloring of a rose. But then he jumped back as though burned. He had remembered that instead of a nose he had absolutely nothing, and the tears sprang to his eyes.

He turned to the gentleman dressed as a state councilor to tell him that he was nothing but a fraud and a crook, nothing but his, Kovalev's, personally owned nose.

But the nose was nowhere to be seen. He must have driven off on another official visit.

Kovalev was in despair. He retraced his steps, stopped for a while under the colonnade, and looked intently around him in the hope of catching sight of the nose. He remembered that the nose had had a plumed hat and a gold-braided uniform, but he hadn't noticed his greatcoat, or the color of his carriage, or his horses, or even whether he had had a footman up behind him and, if so, what livery he wore. And then there were so many carriages rushing back and forth, all going so fast that he would have had difficulty in picking one out and no way of stopping it anyway. It was a lovely sunny day. Nevsky

Avenue was thronged with people; from the central police station to Anichkin Bridge, ladies poured over the sidewalks in a colorful cascade. There went an acquaintance of his, a court councilor, whom he addressed as Lieutenant-Colonel, especially in the presence of outsiders. Then Kovalev saw Yaryzhkin, head clerk in the Senate, a good friend who always lost whenever they played cards together. And there was another major, another Caucasus-made collegiate assessor, beckoning . . .

"Goddammit," Kovalev said, "what the hell does he want from me? Cabbie! To the police commissioner's!"

He got into the cab and kept exhorting the cabbie again and again: "Come on, let's go! Quick! Now turn into Ivanovskaya Street."

"Is the Commissioner in?" he called out, as soon as he entered the house.

"No, sir," the doorman answered. "He left only a minute ago."

"That's really too much. . . ."

"Yes, sir," the doorman said. "If you'd come a minute earlier, you'd have caught him."

Kovalev, still holding his handkerchief to his face, got back into the cab and shouted in a desperate voice:

"Get going."

"Where to?"

"Straight ahead."

"Straight ahead? But this is a dead end. Shall I go right or left?"

Kovalev was caught off balance and forced to give the matter some thought. In his position, he ought first to go to the National Security Administration, not because it was directly connected with the police, but because its orders would be acted on more rapidly than those of others.

Certainly it was no use taking his grievance to the scientific department where the nose claimed to have a post. At best, it would be unwise, since, judging by his statement that he had never seen Kovalev before, it was obvious that he held nothing sacred and he might lie whenever he found it convenient. So Kovalev was about to tell the cabman to drive him to the National Security Administration when it occurred to him that the crook and impostor, who had just behaved so unscrupulously toward him, might very well try to slip out of town, in which case finding him would be quite hopeless or would take, God forbid, a whole month perhaps. Finally, he had what seemed like a divine inspiration. He decided to go straight to the Press Building to have an advertisement put in the papers with a detailed description of the nose in all his aspects, so that anyone who met him could turn him over to Kovalev, or at least inform him of the nose's whereabouts. So, having decided this, he told the cabman to take him to the Press Building and, during the entire ride, he kept pommeling him on the back with his fist and shouting:

"Faster, damn you! Faster!"

"Really, sir!" the cabman said, shaking his head and flicking the reins at his horse, which had hair as long as a lap dog's.

At last the cab came to a stop, and Kovalev, panting, burst into the small outer office where a gray-haired, bespectacled employee in an ancient frock coat was seated at a table, his pen clenched between his teeth, counting out the change someone had paid in.

"Who handles advertisements here?" shouted Kovalev. "Ah," he said, "good morning!"

"Good morning, sir," the gray-haired employee said, raising his eyes for a moment and lowering them again to the little piles of coins before him.

"I want to insert—"

"Excuse me. Would you mind waiting just a moment, please," the employee said, writing down a figure with his right hand while his left hand moved two beads on his abacus.

A footman, whose gold-braided livery and whole appearance testified to his service in an aristocratic house, stood by the old employee holding a piece of paper in his hand and, to prove his worldliness, started chattering away:

"Believe me, I'm quite sure the mutt isn't worth eighty kopeks. In fact, I wouldn't give eight kopeks, if you ask me. But the Countess loves that cur—she has to if she's willing to give a hundred rubles to the person who finds it. Since we are among people who understand, I'll tell you one thing: it's all a matter of taste. I can understand a dog lover. But then, go and get a deerhound or maybe a poodle. Then, if you want to spend five hundred or a thousand on it, it's only natural. But, in my opinion, when you pay you are entitled to a *real* dog . . . ."

The elderly employee was listening to this speech with an important expression and was counting the number of letters in the text of the advertisement the manservant had handed him. The room was full of old women, shopkeepers, and doormen, all holding pieces of paper on which advertisements had been written out. In one a coachman, sober and dependable, was for hire; another announced that a carriage with very little mileage, brought from Paris in 1814, was for sale; a nineteen-year-old girl, a washerwoman's assistant, but suitable for other work too, wanted employment; also for sale were an excellent hansom cab (one spring missing) and a young, seventeen-year-old, dappled-gray horse, as well as a consignment of turnip and radish seeds straight from London, a summer house with a two-carriage coach house and a piece of land very suitable for planting a lovely birch wood. Another advertisement invited persons desirous of buying secondhand shoe soles to present themselves in a certain salesroom between 8 A.M. and 3 P.M.

The reception room in which all these people waited was quite small and the air was getting stuffy. But the smell didn't bother Collegiate Assessor Kovalev because he kept his face covered with a handkerchief and also because his nose happened to be God knew where.

"Excuse me, sir . . . I don't want to bother you, but this is an emergency," he said impatiently at last.

"Wait, wait . . . two rubles, forty-three kopeks, please. One minute, please! . . . One ruble, sixty-four, over there . . ." the old employee said, shoving sheets of paper under the noses of porters and old women. "Now, what can I do for you?" he said finally, turning to Kovalev.

"I wanted," Kovalev said, "to ask you to . . . a fraud, or perhaps a theft, has been committed. I'm still not clear. I want you to run an advertisement simply saying that whoever delivers that robber to me will get a handsome reward."

"Your name, please."

"My name? What for? I can't tell you my name. I have too many acquaintances, such as Mrs. Chekhtareva, the wife of a civil servant, and Palageya Grigorievna Podtochina, who's married to Captain Podtochin, an officer on the Army General Staff. . . . Suppose they found out, God forbid. Write simply 'a collegiate assessor' or, better still, 'a major.'"

"And the runaway, was he a household serf?"

"A household serf. That wouldn't be half so vicious a crime. The runaway is my nose . . . yes, my own nose. . . ."

"Hm . . . odd name. And now may I inquire the sum, the amount, of which this Mr. Nose has defrauded you?"

"No, no, you don't understand. I said nose. My own nose, which has disappeared God knows where. I am the victim of some foul joke. . . ."

"But how could it disappear? I still don't understand, sir."

"Well, I can't explain how, but the main thing is that he mustn't go all over town impersonating a state councilor. That's why I want you to advertise that anyone who catches him should contact me as quickly as possible. Besides, imagine how I feel with such a conspicuous part of my body missing. It's not just a matter of, say, a toe. You could simply stick your foot into your shoe and no one would be the wiser. On Thursdays, I usually visit Mrs. Chekhtareva, the wife of a state councilor. . . . And Mrs. Podtochina, the wife of the staff officer, has an extremely pretty daughter. They are close friends of mine, you see, and now tell me, what am I to do? . . . How can I show myself to them?"

The employee was thinking hard, as could be seen from his tightly pressed lips.

"I am sorry, sir, but I cannot accept your advertisement," he said, after a long silence.

"What's that! Why?"

"I just can't. A newspaper could lose its good name if everybody started advertising vagrant noses. . . . No, sir, as it is, too many absurdities and unfounded rumors manage to slip into print."

"Why is it absurd? I don't see anything so unusual about it."

"It may look that way to you. But just let me tell you . . . Last week, for instance, a government employee came to see me just as you have now. I even remember that his advertisement came to two rubles, seventy-three kopeks. But what it all boiled down to was that a black poodle had run away. You'd think there was nothing to it, wouldn't you? But wait. Turned out to be deliberate libel because the poodle in question happened to be the treasurer of I can't recall exactly what."

"But listen, I'm not advertising about a poodle but about my own nose which is the same as myself."

"Sorry, I can't accept the advertisement."

"But I have lost my nose!"

"If you have, it is a matter for a doctor. I've heard that there are specialists who can fit you with any sort of nose you want. But I'm beginning to think that you are one of these cheerful people who likes to have his little joke."

"But I swear to you by all that's holy! And if it comes to that, I'll show you."

"Why take the trouble," the employee said, taking a pinch of snuff. "But then, after all, if you really don't mind," he added, making a slight movement indicating curiosity, "why, I wouldn't mind having a look."

Kovalev removed the handkerchief from his face.

"My! It *is* strange!" the employee said. "Why, it's as flat as a fresh-cooked pancake, incredibly smooth!"

"Well, now you won't refuse to run my advertisement, will you? It simply must be published. I will be very much obliged to you, and I'm very happy that this accident has given me a chance to make your acquaintance. . . ."

The major, it can be seen, had decided that he'd better make up to him a bit.

"Certainly, running it is no great problem," the employee said, "but I don't see that it would do you any good. However, if you absolutely want to see it in print, why not entrust it to someone who can really write and ask him to present it as a rare natural phenomenon and have it published in the *Northern Bee*"—here he took another pinch of snuff—"for the edification of the young"—here he wiped his nose—"or just as a matter of general interest."

The collegiate assessor was taken aback. He lowered his eyes and his glance happened to fall on the theatrical announcements at the bottom of the page of a newspaper. His face was just about to break into a smile at the sight of the name of a very pretty actress and his hand had already plunged into his pocket to see whether he had a five-ruble bill on him, since, in his opinion, an officer of his rank should sit in the stalls, when he remembered the nose and everything was ruined.

The employee, too, seemed touched by Kovalev's awkward position. To alleviate his distress, he thought it would be appropriate to express his sympathy in a few words:

"I'm very sorry that such a painful thing should have happened to you. Perhaps you'd feel better if you took a pinch of snuff. It eases people's headaches and cheers them up. It's even good for hemorrhoids."

As he said this, the employee offered Kovalev his snuffbox, rather deftly folding back the lid which had a picture on it of some lady in a hat.

At this unintentional provocation, Kovalev's patience snapped.

"I simply don't understand how you can make a joke of it," he said angrily. "Can't you see that I am missing just what I would need to take a pinch of snuff with? You know what you can do with your snuff! I can't even look at it now, especially not at your cheap Berezinsky brand. You might at least have offered me something better. . . ."

Incensed, he rushed out of the Press Building. He decided to take his case to the borough Police Commissioner.

At the moment when Kovalev entered the office of the Commissioner, the latter had just finished stretching himself and reflecting:

"I might as well treat myself to a nap. A couple of hours or so."

Thus it would have been easy to predict that the major's visit was rather poorly timed. Incidentally, the Commissioner, though a great lover of the arts and of commerce, still preferred a bill put in circulation by the Imperial Russian Bank over anything else. His opinion on the matter was as follows:

"It has everything: it doesn't have to be fed, it doesn't take up much room, and, in any case, can always be fitted into a pocket. If you drop it, it doesn't break."

The Commissioner was rather cold with Kovalev. Right after a meal, he said, was not the proper time for investigations. Nature itself, he said, dictated rest when one's belly was full. From this, the collegiate assessor was able to gather that the Commissioner was rather familiar with the maxims of the wise men of antiquity.

"Moreover," the Commissioner said, "they don't tear noses off decent citizens' faces."

Bull's-eye! We must note here that Kovalev was quick to take offense. He could forgive anything that was said about himself personally, but he couldn't stand anything that he considered a slur on his rank and position. He even held the view that, in dramatic works, while a disparaging reference to subaltern ranks was permissible, it became intolerable when applied to officers above the rank of captain. He was so disconcerted by the reception given him by the Commissioner that he shook his head slightly, shrugged, and, on his way out, said in a dignified tone:

"Well, I must say . . . after your offensive remarks I have nothing further to add."

He reached home hardly able to feel his feet beneath him. It was getting dark. After his futile search, his place looked sad and repulsive. As he walked in, he saw Ivan, his manservant, lying on his back on the old leather divan in the entrance hall spitting at the ceiling—very successfully it must be said. Ivan was hitting the same spot again and again. But such indifference enraged Kovalev. He hit him on the head with his hat and said bitterly:

"Swine! You think of nothing but trivialities."

Ivan jumped up and started anxiously to help Kovalev off with his coat.

The major went into his room and let himself fall into an armchair, sad and exhausted. He let out a few sighs, after which he said:

"Good heavens! Why is all this happening to *me*? What have *I* done wrong? It would have been better to have lost an arm or a leg. It would have been bad enough without ears, yet still bearable. But without a nose a man is not a man but God knows what—neither fish nor fowl. He can't even be a proper citizen any more. If only I had had it lopped off during a war or in a duel or if *I* had been responsible for the loss. But I lost it for no reason and for nothing; I haven't even got a kopek out of it! No, it's impossible," he added after a pause, "it is impossible that the nose could have disappeared. Incredible! It is probably a dream or just a hallucination . . . maybe, by mistake, I drank a glassful of the vodka with which I rub my face after shaving? That fool Ivan must have forgotten to put it away and I must have swallowed it inadvertently."

To prove to himself that he was really drunk, the major pinched himself so hard that he let out a moan. The pain convinced him that he was quite sober. Then, slowly, as though stalking something, he approached the mirror, his eyes half closed, in the vague hope that, who knows, perhaps the nose would be in its proper place. But immediately he jumped away.

"What a slanderous sight!"

It was really quite bewildering. Many things get lost: a button, a silver spoon, a watch, or some such object. But to disappear just like that. . . . And what's more, in his own apartment! Having weighed the matter, Major Kovalev came to what seemed to be the most likely explanation: the culprit behind it all was Mrs. Podtochina, who wanted him to marry her daughter. He rather enjoyed the girl's company himself but he was just not ready for a final decision. And when Mrs. Podtochina had told him plainly that she wanted him to marry her daughter, he had quietly beaten a polite retreat, saying that he was still very young and that he ought to devote another five years or so to his career, after which he would be at least forty-two. So, probably, that was when Mrs. Podtochina had decided to maim him and had hired witches or something for the purpose, because by no stretch of the imagination could it be assumed that the nose had been cut off; no one had entered his bedroom; Ivan Yakovlevich, the barber, hadn't shaved him since Wednesday and during the rest of that day and even on Thursday, his nose, all in one piece, had been on his face. He was absolutely certain of it. Moreover, had the nose been cut off he would have felt pain and the wound could never have healed so fast and become as smooth as a pancake. . . .

All sorts of plans clashed in his head: should he take the lady to court or would it be better to go directly to her and denounce her to her face? But his thoughts were interrupted by light seeping in through the cracks in the door, indicating that Ivan had lit a candle in the entrance hall. Soon Ivan appeared carrying the candle high above his head, lighting up the entire room. Kovalev's first thought was to grab the handkerchief and cover the place where, only yesterday, the nose had sat, so that this stupid man should not stand there gaping, noticing the peculiar state of his master's face.

But no sooner had Ivan left than he heard an unknown voice coming from the apartment door ask:

"Does Collegiate Assessor Kovalev live here?"

"Come in. Major Kovalev is in," Kovalev shouted, jumping up and rushing into the hall.

It was a police officer, a quite handsome man with whiskers neither too light nor too dark and with rather full cheeks. In fact it was the same one who, at the beginning of this story, had been standing by the Isakievsky Bridge.

"Did you happen to lose your nose, sir?"

"Yes, I did."

"It has been found."

"Is it possible?"

Joy paralyzed the major's tongue. He stared at the police officer standing in front of him, the reflection of the candlelight shining on his damp, full lips.

"How did it happen?" he managed to say at last.

"By sheer coincidence. Your nose was caught as he was getting on the stagecoach for Riga. He had a passport made out in the name of a government official and the strange thing is that, at first, I myself took him for a gentleman. But luckily I had my glasses with me, so I put them on and recognized immediately that he was a nose. The thing is, I am very shortsighted, sir, and with you standing right in front of me there, I can make out your face but I can't discern your beard, or your nose, or anything else. My mother-in-law, that's the mother of my wife, can't see a thing either."

Kovalev was beside himself with excitement.

"Where is he? Where? I'll run over there now. . . ."

"Don't trouble, sir. I thought you might need it, so I brought it along. But you know, the funny part about it is that the main suspect in the affair is the barber from Voznesensky Avenue, a crook who's now being held at the police station. I've had my eye on him for some time because I suspected him of being a thief and a drunkard. As a matter of fact, he lifted a box of buttons in a store the other day. By the way, your nose is exactly as before, sir."

Saying this, the police officer put his hand in his pocket and extracted the nose wrapped in a piece of paper.

"That's it! That's it!" Kovalev shouted. "No doubt about it! Do come in and have some tea with me, won't you?"

"It would be a great honor, sir, but I am afraid I can't. I must stop over at the house of correction—prices are going up, sir. . . . My mother-in-law, I mean the wife's mother, is living with me . . . we have children too. The eldest son is particularly promising, a very clever boy, but we have no money for his education. . . ."

When the police officer had left, the collegiate assessor remained for some minutes in an indeterminate state, just barely able to see and feel. It was his immense joy that had plunged him into his half-consciousness. Very carefully he held his just-recovered nose in his cupped hands and once again looked it over.

"Yes, that's it, that's it all right. And here, on the left side, is the pimple that sprang up the other day."

The major almost shouted with pleasure.

But there is nothing long-lived in this world and one's joy in the minute that follows the first is no longer as vivid. It further weakens during the third and finally dissolves into one's everyday state just as the circles produced on the surface of a pond by the fall of a pebble dissolve into the smooth surface. Kovalev began to ponder and realized that his troubles were not quite over: the nose had been found. That was fine; but it still had to be put back, fixed in its old place.

"And what if it doesn't stick?"

As he asked himself this question, the major turned white.

With inexpressible anxiety he leapt toward his dressing table and pulled the mirror closer, fearing that he would stick the nose on crooked. His hands trembled. Finally, with infinite hesitations and precautions he pressed the nose into place. Oh, horror! It wouldn't stick! He brought it close to his mouth and warmed it slightly with his breath. Then he placed it again on top of the smooth area between his two cheeks. But the nose would not stay on.

"Come on! Come on now! Stick—you fool!" Kovalev told the nose again and again. But the nose felt as if it were made of wood and kept falling off. And as it hit the dressing table it produced a queer light sound, like a cork. The major's face twisted spasmodically. Panic pervaded him.

"Can it possibly *not* stick?"

He repeatedly pressed the nose against the approximate spot, but his efforts were futile. Then he decided to send Ivan to fetch the doctor who occupied the best apartment in the house where the major lived.

The doctor was a fine figure of a man. He had pitch-black whiskers and a quite fresh and healthy wife. Furthermore, he ate fresh apples in the morning and kept his mouth in a state of incredible cleanliness, rinsing it for about three-quarters of an hour at a time and then brushing his teeth with five different kinds of toothbrush.

The doctor arrived within the minute. Having asked the major how long ago the misfortune had struck, he grabbed him by the chin and tweaked him so hard on the former site of his nose that Kovalev recoiled violently and banged the back of his head against the wall. The doctor said that it was quite all right and, advising him to move a bit further away from the wall, ordered him to bend his head to the right, felt the spot vacated by the nose with his fingers and said, "Hmmm . . ." Then he asked him to bend his head to the left, touched the spot again and said, "Hmmm. . . ." Finally the doctor delivered another tweak with his thumb and forefinger, making Kovalev toss up his head like a horse whose teeth are being inspected.

Having thus completed his examination, the doctor shook his head and declared:

"No. Can't be done. You'd better stay as you are or your condition might deteriorate even further. Of course, it is possible to stick it on. I could have stuck it on now. But, take my advice, that would make it worse for you."

"That's fine! And how can I stay without a nose? And how could I be worse off than I am? It is absolutely disgusting! And where can I show myself in this obscene condition? I have an active social life. Why, even today I was invited to two important parties. And I have many connections . . . Mrs. Chekhtareva, the wife of a state councilor, Mrs. Podtochina, the wife of a senior army officer . . . although after this business I don't want to have anything to do with her, except through the police. . . ."

And Kovalev added imploringly:

"Do me a great favor, Doctor, can't you think of a way? Make it stick somehow. It doesn't matter if it doesn't hold too well—just as long as it stays on somehow. I could even support it with my hand in case of emergency. I don't even dance, you know, and so couldn't jeopardize it by some inadvertent jerk. As to my appreciation of your services, please rest assured that in the measure of my resources——"

"Believe it or not," the doctor said neither too loudly nor too softly but with persuasiveness and magnetic force, "I never dispense my services out of material considerations. It would be contrary to my principles and to professional ethics. True, I do charge for my visits but only in order not to offend people by refusing to accept a fee. Of course I could stick your nose back on, but I assure you, on my honor, if you won't take my simple word for it, that it will be much worse. You're better off letting things take their natural course. Wash often with cold water and I assure you that you'll feel just as healthy without a nose as you felt with one. As to the nose, you can put it in a jar of alcohol or, better still, add two soupspoonfuls of vodka and warmed-up vinegar to it. I'll bet you could make money out of it. In fact, I'd purchase it myself if it weren't too expensive."

"No, no! I'll never sell it," shouted the desolate major, "I'd rather it disappeared again!"

"Forgive me," the doctor said, "I was simply trying to help. Well, I can do no more. At least you see that I tried."

The doctor departed with dignity. Kovalev had not even looked at his face; dazed as he was, he was only aware of the spotless white cuffs sticking out of the black sleeves of the doctor's frock coat.

The next day Kovalev decided to write to Mrs. Podtochina asking her to restore to him voluntarily what was rightfully his and saying that otherwise he would be forced to lodge a complaint. The letter he composed read as follows:

Dear Madam,

I am at a loss to understand your strange action. Rest assured that you will achieve nothing by acting this way, and you certainly won't force me to marry your daughter. Please believe me, Madam, that I am fully aware of exactly what happened to my nose as well as of the fact that you, and nobody else, are the prime instigator of this affair. Its sudden detachment from its assigned place, its desertion, and its masquerading first as a state councilor and then in its natural shape is nothing but the result of witchcraft practiced by you or by those specialized in such pursuits. For my part, I deem it my duty to warn you that if the above-mentioned nose is not back in its proper place this very day, I shall be forced to avail myself of my rights and ask for the protection of the law.

I remain,
Faithfully yours,
Platon Kovalev.

To which the lady sent an immediate reply:

My dear Platon,

I was very surprised by your letter. To be perfectly frank, I never expected anything of this kind from you, especially your unfair reproaches. For your information, I have never received the state councilor you mention at my house, either in disguise or in his natural shape. However, I did receive Philip Ivanovich, but, despite the fact that he asked me for my daughter's hand and was a man of irreproachable character, sober habits, and great learning, I never held out any hopes for him. You also mention your nose. If you mean it symbolically, that I wanted you to stop nosing around my daughter, i.e., that I had decided to refuse you her hand, I am surprised at your saying such things when you are fully aware of my feelings on the subject, namely that, if you asked for her hand formally tomorrow, I would be prepared to grant your request forthwith, since it has always been in agreement with my wishes and in hope of which,

I remain,

Always at your service,

Alexandra Podtochina.

"She," Kovalev said, after he had read the letter, "is certainly not involved. Someone guilty of a crime couldn't write such a letter."

And the collegiate assessor knew what he was talking about because he had taken part in several judicial investigations back in the Caucasus.

"But then, how the devil did it happen, after all? How'll I ever get it straight?" he said, dropping his arms to his sides.

In the meantime, rumors about the extraordinary occurrence spread all over the capital and, as was to be expected, not without all sorts of embellishments. At that time people were prone to fall for supernatural things: only a short time before, experiments with magnetism had caused a sensation. Also, the story about the dancing chairs of Stables Street was still fresh, and people soon began to repeat that Collegiate Assessor Kovalev's nose was to be seen taking a daily walk on Nevsky Avenue at 3:00 P.M. sharp. And every day a multitude of the curious gathered there. Then someone said that the nose was in Junker's Department Store, and, as a result, such a melee developed there that the police had to interfere. A shady character with side whiskers, who nevertheless looked very respectable, and who sold all sorts of dry cakes at the entrance to the theater, got hold of some special wooden benches, perfectly safe to stand on, and invited the curious to do so for a fee of eighty kopeks per person. A highly respected colonel, who had left his home especially early for this purpose, managed to make his way through the dense throng with great difficulty only to see in the display window not a nose but an ordinary woollen sweater and a lithograph of a girl pulling up her stocking with a well-dressed gentleman wearing a waistcoat with lapels and a small beard, a lithograph that had rested there, in the identical spot, for more than ten years. As the colonel left, he declared:

"It shouldn't be allowed—befuddling people with such stupid and improbable rumors!"

Then a rumor spread that Major Kovalev's nose was taking promenades, not on Nevsky Avenue, but in the Tavrichesky Gardens, and that it had been doing so for some time now. In fact, even when Khosrov Mirza lived there he used to marvel at this freak of nature. Students from the School of Surgeons went there. One socially prominent lady wrote a special letter to the director of the park suggesting that he show this rare object to children, if possible with explanations and instructions that would edify the younger generation.

All this was quite welcome to those who never miss a party and like to display their wit before the ladies; without it topics of conversation would have been exhausted. But there was also a dissatisfied and displeased minority among respectable people. One gentleman said he could not understand how it was possible in our enlightened age for such preposterous lies to be believed and that he was flabbergasted at the passivity of the authorities. Apparently this gentleman was one of those who desire the government to interfere in everything, including his daily fights with his wife.

Following these events . . . but here again, things become beclouded and what followed these events has remained completely unknown.

III

The world is full of absolute nonsense. Sometimes it is really unbelievable. Suddenly, the very nose that used to go around as a state councilor and caused such a stir all over the city turned up, as though nothing had happened, in its proper place, namely between the cheeks of Major Kovalev. This happened on April 7. Waking up and chancing to glance in the mirror, what did he see but his nose! He grabbed it with his hand—no doubt about it—it was his nose, all right!

"Aha!" Kovalev said.

And in his infinite joy he would have performed a jig, barefoot as he was, had not Ivan come in at that moment. He ordered Ivan to bring him some water to wash with and, while washing, looked again into the mirror: he had his nose. Drying himself with his towel, he looked again—the nose was still there!

"Here, Ivan, look, I think I have a pimple on my nose," he said, all the while thinking anxiously: "Wouldn't it be terrible if Ivan came out with something like, 'No, sir, not only is there no pimple on your nose, there is no nose on your face.' "

But Ivan simply said:

"Nothing, sir, I see no pimple, the nose is clear."

"Feels good, dammit!" the major said to himself and snapped his fingers gaily.

At that moment, through the partly opened door, there appeared the head of Ivan Yakovlevich, the barber, wearing the expression of a cat that had just been smacked for the theft of a piece of suet.

"Your hands clean?" Kovalev shouted out to him.

"They're clean, sir."

"Liar!"

"I swear they're clean."

"You know, they'd better be."

Kovalev sat down. The barber wrapped a towel around his neck and in one instant transformed the major's whiskers and a part of his cheek into whipped cream of the kind that is likely to be served at a birthday party in the house of a rich merchant.

"Well, I'll be damned!" Ivan Yakovlevich muttered under his breath, looking at the nose. Then he turned the major's head and looked at the nose from the other side and muttered. "Well, well, well . . . who would have thought . . ." and he stared at the nose for a moment.

Then, with a daintiness that can only be imagined, he lifted two fingers to catch the nose by its tip. Such was Ivan Yakovlevich's shaving style.

"Look out, look out, careful!" Kovalev shouted and Ivan Yakovlevich dropped his hand and stood there frozen and embarrassed as never before. Finally he snapped out of it and started carefully tickling the major under his chin with the razor. And although it felt quite awkward and unusual for him to shave someone without holding him by the olfactory organ of the human body, he managed, somehow, by resting his rough thumb on Kovalev's cheek, then on his lower gum, to overcome all the obstacles and complete the shaving operation.

When he was through being shaved, Kovalev hurried to get dressed, rushed out, took a cab and drove to the tearoom. Before even sitting down, he shouted: "Waiter, a cup of chocolate!" then rushed over to the mirror: the nose was there. Happy, he glanced around the room and twisted his face into a sarcastic expression by slightly screwing up his eyes, when he saw two army officers, one of whom had a nose about the size of a waistcoat button. Then he left for the department through which he was trying to get the vice-gubernatorial post or, failing that, a position in the administration. Walking through the reception room, he glanced in the mirror: the nose was in its place.

Then he drove to see another collegiate assessor, that is, a major like himself. This major was a biting wit, and, parrying his digs, Kovalev would often say to him:

"Oh, I see through you clearly, you needler!"

On his way there, Kovalev thought: "Now, if the major does not split his sides with laughter when he sees me, that will be a sure sign that whatever I may have is sitting in its proper place."

And when the other collegiate assessor showed no signs of hilarity, Kovalev thought:

"Fine! It feels good, it feels good, dammit!"

In the street he met Mrs. Podtochina and her daughter and was greeted with joyful exclamations which went to show that they did not find he was missing anything. He had a very long talk with them and, on purpose, took out his snuffbox and filled his nose with great deliberation, through both orifices, muttering under his breath:

"Here, look and admire, you hens! But still, I won't marry the daughter, just *par amour* as they say, but nothing more. . . ."

And from then on, Major Kovalev could be seen on Nevsky Avenue, in theaters, everywhere. And the nose was there, sitting on his face, as though nothing had happened. And after that, Major Kovalev was always in good spirits, smiling, pursuing absolutely every pretty lady without exception and even stopping one day in front of a small shop and purchasing some sort of ribbon for his lapel, although his reason for doing so remained a mystery because he had never been made a knight of any order.

So that's what happened in the northern capital of our vast country. Only now, on further thought, do we see that there is much that is improbable in it. Without even mentioning the strangeness of such a supernatural severance of the nose and its appearance in various places in the form of a state councilor, how could Kovalev have failed to understand that he could not go and advertise about a nose in the press? I don't mean that I think that an advertisement would have cost too much, that would be nonsense and I'm not stingy; but it's not decent, it's not clever, and it's not proper! And then too, how could the nose have got into the roll of bread, and how could Ivan Yakovlevich himself? . . . Now, that I cannot understand. It's absolutely beyond me. But strangest of all, the most incomprehensible thing, is that there are authors who can choose such subjects to write about. This, I confess, is completely inexplicable, it's like . . . no, no, I can't understand it at all. In the first place, there is absolutely no advantage in it for our mother country. Secondly . . . well, what advantage is there in it at all? I simply cannot understand what it is. . . .

However, when all is said and done, and although, of course, we conceive the possibility, one and the other, and maybe even . . . Well, but then what exists without inconsistencies? And still, if you give it a thought, there *is* something to it. Whatever you may say, such things *do* happen—seldom, but they do.

Anton Chekhov

Gooseberries

THE WHOLE SKY had been overcast with rain-clouds from early morning; it was a still day, not hot, but heavy, as it is in gray dull weather when the clouds have been hanging over the country for a long while, when one expects rain and it does not come. Ivan Ivanovich, the veterinary surgeon, and Burkin, the high school teacher, were already tired from walking, and the fields seemed to them endless. Far ahead of them they could just see the windmills of the village of Mironositskoe; on the right stretched a row of hillocks which disappeared in the distance behind the village, and they both knew that this was the bank of the river, that there were meadows, green willows, homesteads there, and that if one stood on one of the hillocks one could see from it the same vast plain, telegraph-wires, and a train which in the distance looked like a crawling caterpillar, and that in clear weather one could even see the town. Now, in still weather, when all nature seemed mild and dreamy, Ivan Ivanovich and Burkin were filled with love of the countryside, and both thought how great, how beautiful a land it was.

"Last time we were in Prokofy's barn," said Burkin, "you were about to tell me a story."

"Yes; I meant to tell you about my brother."

Ivan Ivanovich heaved a deep sigh and lighted a pipe to begin to tell his story, but just at that moment the rain began. And five minutes later heavy rain came down, covering the sky, and it was hard to tell when it would be over. Ivan Ivanovich and Burkin stopped in hesitation; the dogs, already drenched, stood with their tails between their legs gazing at them feelingly.

"We must take shelter somewhere," said Burkin. "Let us go to Alehin's; it's close by."

"Come along."

They turned aside and walked through mown fields, sometimes going straight forward, sometimes turning to the right, till they came out on the road. Soon they saw poplars, a garden, then the red roofs of barns; there was a gleam of the river, and the view opened onto a broad expanse of water with a windmill and a white bathhouse: this was Sofino, where Alehin lived.

The watermill was at work, drowning the sound of the rain; the dam was shaking. Here wet horses with drooping heads were standing near their carts, and men were walking about covered with sacks. It was damp, muddy, and desolate; the water looked cold and malignant. Ivan Ivanovich and Burkin were already conscious of a feeling of wetness, messiness, and discomfort all over; their feet were heavy with mud, and when, crossing the dam, they went up to the barns, they were silent, as though they were angry with one another.

In one of the barns there was the sound of a winnowing machine, the door was open, and clouds of dust were coming from it. In the doorway was standing Alehin himself, a man of forty, tall and stout, with long hair, more like a professor or an artist than a landowner. He had on a white shirt that badly needed washing, a rope for a belt, drawers instead of trousers, and his boots, too, were plastered up with mud and straw. His eyes and nose were black with dust. He recognized Ivan Ivanovich and Burkin, and was apparently much delighted to see them.

"Go into the house, gentlemen," he said, smiling; "I'll come directly, this minute."

It was a big two-storied house. Alehin lived in the lower story, with arched ceilings and little windows, where the bailiffs had once lived; here everything was plain, and there was a smell of rye bread, cheap vodka, and harness. He went upstairs into the best rooms only on rare occasions, when visitors came. Ivan Ivanovich and Burkin were met in the house by a maidservant, a young woman so beautiful that they both stood still and looked at one another.

"You can't imagine how delighted I am to see you, my friends," said Alehin, going into the hall with them. "It is a surprise! Pelageya," he said, addressing the girl, "give our visitors something to change into. And, by the way, I will change too. Only I must first go and wash, for I almost think I have not washed since spring. Wouldn't you like to come into the bathhouse? And meanwhile they will get things ready here."

Beautiful Pelageya, looking so refined and soft, brought them towels and soap, and Alehin went to the bathhouse with his guests.

"It's a long time since I had a wash," he said, undressing. "I have got a nice bathhouse, as you see—my father built it—but I somehow never have time to wash."

He sat down on the steps and soaped his long hair and his neck, and the water round him turned brown.

"Yes, I must say," said Ivan Ivanovich meaningly, looking at his head.

"It's a long time since I washed . . ." said Alehin with embarrassment, giving himself a second soaping, and the water near him turned dark blue, like ink.

Ivan Ivanovich went outside, plunged into the water with a loud splash, and swam in the rain, flinging his arms out wide. He stirred the water into waves which set the white lilies bobbing up and down; he swam to the very middle of the millpond and dived, and came up a minute later in another place, and swam on, and kept on diving, trying to touch bottom.

"Oh, my goodness!" he repeated continually, enjoying himself thoroughly. "Oh, my goodness!" He swam to the mill, talked to the peasants there, then returned and lay on his back in the middle of the pond, turning his face to the rain. Burkin and Alehin were dressed and ready to go, but he still went on swimming and diving. "Oh, my goodness! . . ." he said. "Oh, Lord, have mercy on me! . . ."

"That's enough!" Burkin shouted to him.

They went back to the house. And only when the lamp was lighted in the big drawing-room upstairs, and Burkin and Ivan Ivanovich, attired in silk dressing-gowns and warm slippers, were sitting in armchairs; and Alehin, washed and combed, in a new coat, was walking about the drawing-room, evidently enjoying the feeling of warmth, cleanliness, dry clothes, and light shoes; and when lovely Pelageya, stepping noiselessly on the carpet and smiling softly, handed tea and jam on a tray—only then Ivan Ivanovich began on his story, and it seemed as though not only Burkin and Alehin were listening, but also the ladies, young and old, and the officers who looked down upon them sternly and calmly from their gold frames.

"There are two of us brothers," he began—"I, Ivan Ivanovich, and my brother, Nikolay Ivanovich, two years younger. I went in for a learned profession and became a veterinary surgeon, while Nikolay sat in a government office from the time he was nineteen. Our father, Chimsha-Himalaisky, was the son of a private, but he himself rose to be an officer and left us a little estate and the rank of nobility. After his death the little estate went in debts and legal expenses; but, anyway, we had spent out childhood running wild in the country. Like peasant children, we passed our days and nights in the fields and the woods, looked after horses, stripped the bark off the trees, fished and so on. . . . And, you know, whoever has once in his life caught perch or has seen the migrating of the thrushes in autumn, watched how they float in flocks over the village on bright, cool days, he will never be a real townsman, and will have a yearning for freedom to the day of his death. My brother was miserable in the government office. Years passed by, and he went on sitting in the same place, went on writing the same papers and thinking of one and the same thing—how to get into the country. And this yearning by degrees passed into a definite desire, into a dream of buying himself a little farm somewhere on the banks of a river or a lake.

"He was a gentle, good-natured fellow, and I was fond of him, but I never sympathized with this desire to shut himself up for the rest of his life in a little farm of his own. It's the correct thing to say that a man needs no more than six feet of earth. But six feet is what a corpse needs, not a man. And they say, too, now, that if our intellectual classes are attracted to the land and yearn for a farm, it's a good thing. But these farms are just the same as six feet of earth. To retreat from town, from the struggle, from the bustle of life, to retreat and bury oneself in one's farm—it's not life, it's egoism, laziness, it's monasticism of a sort, but monasticism without good works. A man does not need six feet of earth or a farm, but the whole globe, all nature, where he can have room to display all the qualities and peculiarities of his free spirit.

"My brother Nikolay, sitting in his government office, dreamed of how he would eat his own cabbages, which would fill the whole yard with such a savory smell, take his meals on the green grass, sleep in the sun, sit for whole hours on the seat by the gate gazing at the fields and the forest. Gardening books and the agricultural hints in calendars were his delight, his favorite spiritual sustenance; he enjoyed reading newspapers, too, but the only things he read in them were the advertisements of so many acres of arable land and a grass meadow with farmhouses and buildings, a river, a garden, a mill and millponds, for sale. And his imagination pictured the garden-paths, flowers and fruit, starling cotes, the carp in the pond, and all that sort of thing, you know. These imaginary pictures were of different kinds according to the advertisements which he came across, but for some reason in every one of them he always had to have gooseberries. He could not imagine a homestead, he could not picture an idyllic nook, without gooseberries.

" 'Country life has its conveniences,' he would sometimes say. 'You sit on the veranda and you drink tea, while your ducks swim on the pond, there is a delicious smell everywhere, and . . . and the gooseberries are growing.'

"He used to draw a map of his property, and in every map there were the same things—(a) house for the family, (b) servants' quarters, (c) kitchen-garden, (d) gooseberry-bushes. He lived parsimoniously, was frugal in food and drink, his clothes were beyond description; he looked like a beggar, but kept on saving and putting money in the bank. He grew fearfully avaricious. I did not like to look at him, and I used to give him something and send him presents for Christmas and Easter, but he used to save that too. Once a man is absorbed by an idea there is no doing anything with him.

"Years passed: he was transferred to another province. He was over forty, and he was still reading the advertisements in the papers and saving up. Then I heard he was married. Still with the same object of buying a farm and having gooseberries, he married an elderly and ugly widow without a trace of feeling for her, simply because she had filthy lucre. He went on living frugally after marrying her, and kept her short of food, while he put her money in the bank in his name.

"Her first husband had been a postmaster, and with him she was accustomed to pies and homemade wines, while with her second husband she did not get enough black bread; she began to pine away with this sort of life, and three years later she gave up her soul to God. And I need hardly say that my brother never for one moment imagined that he was responsible for her death. Money, like vodka, makes a man queer. In our town there was a merchant who, before he died, ordered a plateful of honey and ate up all his money and lottery tickets with the honey, so that no one might get the benefit of it. While I was inspecting cattle at a railway-station a cattle-dealer fell under an engine and had his leg cut off. We carried him into the waiting-room, the blood was flowing—it was a horrible thing—and he kept asking them to look for his leg and was very much worried about it; there were twenty roubles in the boot on the leg that had been cut off, and he was afraid they would be lost."

"That's a story from a different opera," said Burkin.

"After his wife's death," Ivan Ivanovich went on, after thinking for half a minute, "my brother began looking out for an estate for himself. Of course, you may look about for five years and yet end by making a mistake, and buying something quite different from what you have dreamed of. My brother Nikolay bought through an agent a mortgaged estate of three hundred and thirty acres, with a house for the family, with servants' quarters, with a park, but with no orchard, no gooseberry-bushes, and no duck-pond; there was a river, but the water in it was the color of coffee, because on one side of the estate there was a brickyard and on the other a factory for burning bones. But Nikolay Ivanovich did not grieve much; he ordered twenty gooseberry-bushes, planted them, and began living as a country gentleman.

"Last year I went to pay him a visit. I thought I would go and see what it was like. In his letters my brother called his estate 'Chumbaroklov Waste, alias Himalaiskoe.' I reached 'alias Himalaiskoe' in the afternoon. It was hot. Everywhere there were ditches, fences, hedges, fir-trees planted in rows, and there was no knowing how to get to the yard, where to put one's horse. I went up to the house, and was met by a fat red dog that looked like a pig. It wanted to bark, but was too lazy. The cook, a fat, barefooted woman, came out of the kitchen, and she, too, looked like a pig, and said that her master was resting. I went in to see my brother. He was sitting up in bed with a quilt over his legs; he had grown older, fatter, wrinkled; his cheeks, his nose, and his mouth all stuck out—he looked as though he might begin grunting into the quilt at any moment.

"We embraced each other, and shed tears of joy and of sadness at the thought that we had once been young and now were both gray-headed and near the grave. He dressed, and led me out to show me the estate.

" 'Well, how are you getting on here?' I asked.

" 'Oh, all right, thank God; I am getting on very well.'

"He was no more a poor timid clerk, but a real landowner, a gentleman. He was already accustomed to it, had grown used to it, and liked it. He ate a great deal, went to the bathhouse, was growing stout, was already at law with the village commune and both factories, and was very much offended when the peasants did not call him 'your Honor.' And he concerned himself with the salvation of his soul in a substantial, gentlemanly manner, and performed deeds of charity, not simply, but with an air of consequence. And what deeds of charity! He treated the peasants for every sort of disease with soda and castor oil, and on his name-day had a thanksgiving service in the middle of the village, and then treated the peasants to a gallon of vodka—he thought that was the thing to do. Oh, those horrible gallons of vodka! One day the fat landowner hauls the peasants up before the district captain for trespass, and next day, in honor of a holiday, treats them to a gallon of vodka, and they drink and shout 'Hurrah!' and when they are drunk bow down to his feet. A change of life for the better and being well fed and idle develop in a Russian the most insolent self-conceit. Nikolay Ivanovich, who at one time in the government office was afraid to have any views of his own, now could say nothing that was not gospel truth, and uttered such truths in the tone of a prime minister. 'Education is essential, but for the peasants it is premature.' 'Corporal punishment is harmful as a rule, but in some cases it is necessary and there is nothing to take its place.'

" 'I know the peasants and understand how to treat them,' he would say. 'The peasants like me. I need only to hold up my little finger and the peasants will do anything I like.'

"And all this, observe, was uttered with a wise, benevolent smile. He repeated twenty times over 'We noblemen,' 'I as a noble'; obviously he did not remember that our grandfather was a peasant, and our father a soldier. Even our surname Chimsha-Himalaisky, in reality so incongruous, seemed to him now melodious, distinguished, and very agreeable.

"But the point just now is not he, but myself. I want to tell you about the change that took place in me during the brief hours I spent at his country place. In the evening, when we were drinking tea, the cook put on the table a plateful of gooseberries. They were not bought, but his own gooseberries, gathered for the first time since the bushes were planted. Nikolay Ivanovich laughed and looked for a minute in silence at the gooseberries, with tears in his eyes; he could not speak for excitement. Then he put one gooseberry in his mouth, looked at me with the triumph of a child who has at last received his favorite toy, and said:

" 'How delicious!'

"And he ate them greedily, continually repeating, 'Ah, how delicious! Do taste them!'

"They were sour and unripe, but, as Pushkin says:

Dearer to us the falsehood that exalts
Than hosts of baser truths.

"I saw a happy man whose cherished dream was so obviously fulfilled, who had attained his object in life, who had gained what he wanted, who was satisfied with his fate and himself. There is always, for some reason, an element of sadness mingled with my thoughts of human happiness, and, on this occasion, at the sight of a happy man I was overcome by an oppressive feeling that was close upon despair. It was particularly oppressive at night. A bed was made up for me in the room next to my brother's bedroom, and I could hear that he was awake, and that he kept getting up and going to the plate of gooseberries and taking one. I reflected how many satisfied, happy people there really are! What an overwhelming force it is! You look at life: the insolence and idleness of the strong, the ignorance and brutishness of the weak, incredible poverty all about us, overcrowding, degeneration, drunkenness, hypocrisy, lying . . . Yet all is calm and stillness in the houses and in the streets; of the fifty thousand living in a town, there is not one who would cry out, who would give vent to his indignation aloud. We see the people going to market for provisions, eating by day, sleeping by night, talking their silly nonsense, getting married, growing old, serenely escorting their dead to the cemetery; but we do not see and we do not hear those who suffer, and what is terrible in life goes on somewhere behind the scenes. . . . Everything is quiet and peaceful, and nothing protests but mute statistics: so many people gone out of their minds, so many gallons of vodka drunk, so many children dead from malnutrition. . . . And this order of things is evidently necessary; evidently the happy man only feels at ease because the unhappy bear their burden in silence, and without that silence happiness would be impossible. It's a case of general hypnotism. There ought to be behind the door of every happy, contented man someone standing with a hammer continually reminding him with a tap that there are unhappy people; that however happy he may be, life will show him her jaws sooner or later, trouble will come for him—disease, poverty, losses, and no one will see or hear, just as now he neither sees nor hears others. But there is no man with a hammer; the happy man lives at his ease, the trivial daily cares faintly agitate him like the wind in the aspen-tree—and all goes well.

"That night I realized that I, too, was happy and contented," Ivan Ivanovich went on, getting up. "I, too, at dinner and at the hunt liked to lay down the law on life and religion, and the way to manage the peasantry. I, too, used to say that science was light, that culture was essential, but for the simple people reading and writing was enough for the time. Freedom is a blessing, I used to say; we can no more do without it than without air, but we must wait a little. Yes, I used to talk like that, and now I ask, 'For what reason are we to wait?'" asked Ivan Ivanovich, looking angrily at Burkin. "Why wait, I ask you? What grounds have we for waiting? I shall be told, it can't be done all at once; every idea takes shape in life gradually, in its due time. But who is it says that? Where is the proof that it's right? You will fall back upon the natural order of things, the uniformity of phenomena; but is there order and uniformity in the fact that I, a living, thinking man, stand over a chasm and wait for it to close of itself, or to fill up with mud at the very time when perhaps I might leap over it or build a bridge across it? And again, wait for the sake of what? Wait till there's no strength to live? And meanwhile one must live, and one wants to live!

"I went away from my brother's early in the morning, and ever since then it has been unbearable for me to be among people. I am oppressed by peace and quiet; I am afraid to look at the windows, for there is no spectacle more painful to me now than the sight of a happy family sitting round the table drinking tea. I am old and am not fit for the struggle; I am not even capable of hatred; I can only grieve inwardly, feel irritated and vexed; but at night my head is hot from the rush of ideas, and I cannot sleep. . . . Ah, if I were young!"

Ivan Ivanovich walked backwards and forwards in excitement, and repeated: "If I were young!"

He suddenly went up to Alehin and began pressing first one of his hands and then the other.

"Pavel Konstantinovich," he said in an imploring voice, "don't be calm and contented, don't let yourself be put to sleep! While you are young, strong, confident, be not weary in well-doing! There is no happiness, and there ought not to be; but if there is a meaning and an object in life, that meaning and object is not our happiness, but something greater and more rational. Do good!"

And all this Ivan Ivanovich said with a pitiful, imploring smile, as though he were asking him a personal favor.

Then all three sat in armchairs at different ends of the drawing-room and were silent. Ivan Ivanovich's story had not satisfied either Burkin or Alehin. When the generals and ladies gazed down from their gilt frames, looking in the dusk as though they were alive, it was dreary to listen to the story of the poor clerk who ate gooseberries. They felt inclined for some reason to talk about elegant people, about women. And their sitting in the drawing-room where everything—the chandeliers in their covers, the armchairs, and the carpet under their feet—reminded them that those very people who were now looking down from their frames had once moved about, sat, drunk tea in this room, and the fact that lovely Pelageya was moving noiselessly about was better than any story.

Alehin was fearfully sleepy; he had got up early, before three o'clock in the morning, to look after his work, and now his eyes were closing; but he was afraid his visitors might tell some interesting story after he had gone, and he lingered on. He did not go into the question whether what Ivan Ivanovich had just said was right and true. His visitors did not talk of groats, nor of hay, nor of tar, but of something that had no direct bearing on his life, and he was glad and wanted them to go on.

"It's bedtime, though," said Burkin, getting up. "Allow me to wish you good night."

Alehin said good night and went downstairs to his own domain, while the visitors remained upstairs. They were both taken for the night to a big room where there stood two old wooden beds decorated with carvings, and in the corner was an ivory crucifix. The big cool beds, which had been made by the lovely Pelageya, smelt agreeably of clean linen.

Ivan Ivanovich undressed in silence and got into bed.

"Lord forgive us sinners!" he said, and put his head under the quilt.

His pipe lying on the table smelt strongly of stale tobacco, and Burkin could not sleep for a long while, and kept wondering where the oppressive smell came from.

The rain was pattering on the windowpanes all night.

Leo Tolstoy

How Much Land Does a Man Need?

AN ELDER SISTER came to visit her younger sister in the country. The elder was married to a shopkeeper in town, the younger to a peasant in the village. As the sisters sat over their tea talking, the elder began to boast of the advantages of town life, saying how comfortably they lived there, how well they dressed, what fine clothes her children wore, what good things they ate and drank, and how she went to the theater, promenades, and entertainments.

The younger sister was piqued, and in turn disparaged the life of a shopkeeper, and stood up for that of a peasant.

"I wouldn't change my way of life for yours," said she. "We may live roughly, but at least we're free from worry. You live in better style than we do, but though you often earn more than you need, you're very likely to lose all you have. You know the proverb, 'Loss and gain are brothers twain.' It often happens that people who're wealthy one day are begging their bread the next. Our way is safer. Though a peasant's life is not a rich one, it's long. We'll never grow rich, but we'll always have enough to eat."

The elder sister said sneeringly:

"Enough? Yes, if you like to share with the pigs and the calves! What do you know of elegance of manners! However much your good man may slave, you'll die as you live—in a dung heap—and your children the same."

"Well, what of that?" replied the younger sister. "Of course our work is rough and hard. But on the other hand, it's sure, and we need not bow to anyone. But you, in your towns, are surrounded by temptations; today all may be right, but tomorrow the Evil One may tempt your husband with cards, wine, or women, and all will go to ruin. Don't such things happen often enough?"

Pahom, the master of the house, was lying on the top of the stove and he listened to the women's chatter.

"It is perfectly true," thought he. "Busy as we are from childhood tilling mother earth, we peasants have no time to let any nonsense settle in our heads. Our only trouble is that we haven't land enough. If I had plenty of land, I shouldn't fear the Devil himself!"

The women finished their tea, chatted a while about dress, and then cleared away the tea things and lay down to sleep.

But the Devil had been sitting behind the stove, and had heard all that had been said. He was pleased that the peasant's wife had led her husband into boasting, and that he had said that if he had plenty of land he would not fear the Devil himself.

"All right," thought the Devil. "We'll have a tussle. I'll give you land enough; and by means of that land I'll get you into my power."

II

Close to the village there lived a lady, a small landowner who had an estate of about three hundred acres. She had always lived on good terms with the peasants until she engaged as her manager an old soldier, who took to burdening the people with fines. However careful Pahom tried to be, it happened again and again that now a horse of his got among the lady's oats, now a cow strayed into her garden, now his calves found their way into her meadows—and he always had to pay a fine.

Pahom paid up, but grumbled, and, going home in a temper, was rough with his family. All through that summer Pahom had much trouble because of this manager, and he was actually glad when winter came and the cattle had to be stabled. Though he grudged the fodder when they could no longer graze on the pasture land, at least he was free from anxiety about them.

In the winter the news got about that the lady was going to sell her land and that the keeper of the inn on the high road was bargaining for it. When the peasants heard this they were very much alarmed.

"Well," thought they, "if the innkeeper gets the land, he'll worry us with fines worse than the lady's manager. We all depend on that estate."

So the peasants went on behalf of their village Council and asked the lady not to sell the land to the innkeeper, offering her a better price for it themselves. The lady agreed to let them have it. Then the peasants tried to arrange for the village Council to buy the whole estate, so that it might be held by them all in common. They met twice to discuss it, but could not settle the matter; the Evil One sowed discord among them and they could not agree. So they decided to buy the land individually, each according to his means; and the lady agreed to this plan as she had to the other.

Presently Pahom heard that a neighbor of his was buying fifty acres, and that the lady had consented to accept one half in cash and to wait a year for the other half. Pahom felt envious.

"Look at that," thought he, "the land is all being sold, and I'll get none of it." So he spoke to his wife.

"Other people are buying," said he, "and we must also buy twenty acres or so. Life is becoming impossible. That manager is simply crushing us with his fines."

So they put their heads together and considered how they could manage to buy it. They had one hundred rubles laid by. They sold a colt and one half of their bees, hired out one of their sons as a farm hand, and took his wages in advance; borrowed the rest from a brother-in-law, and so scraped together half the purchase money.

Having done this, Pahom chose a farm of forty acres, some of it wooded, and went to the lady to bargain for it. They came to an agreement, and he shook hands with her upon it and paid her a deposit in advance. Then they went to town and signed the deeds, he paying half the price down, and undertaking to pay the remainder within two years.

So now Pahom had land of his own. He borrowed seed, and sowed it on the land he had bought. The harvest was a good one, and within a year he had managed to pay off his debts both to the lady and to his brother-in-law. So he became a landowner, plowing and sowing his own land, making hay on his own land, cutting his own trees, and feeding his cattle on his own pasture. When he went out to plow his fields, or to look at his growing corn, or at his grass meadows, his heart would fill with joy. The grass that grew and the flowers that bloomed there seemed to him unlike any that grew elsewhere. Formerly, when he had passed by that land, it had appeared the same as any other land, but now it seemed quite different.

III

So Pahom was well contented, and everything would have been right if the neighboring peasants would only not have trespassed on his wheatfields and meadows. He appealed to them most civilly, but they still went on: now the herdsmen would let the village cows stray into his meadows, then horses from the night pasture would get among his corn. Pahom turned them out again and again, and forgave their owners, and for a long time he forbore to prosecute anyone. But at last he lost patience and complained to the District Court. He knew it was the peasants' want of land, and no evil intent on their part, that caused the trouble, but he thought:

"I can't go on overlooking it, or they'll destroy all I have. They must be taught a lesson."

So he had them up, gave them one lesson, and then another, and two or three of the peasants were fined. After a time Pahom's neighbors began to bear him a grudge for this, and would now and then let their cattle on to his land on purpose. One peasant even got into Pahom's wood at night and cut down five young lime trees for their bark. Pahom, passing through the wood one day, noticed something white. He came nearer and saw the stripped trunks lying on the ground, and close by stood the stumps where the trees had been. Pahom was furious.

"If he'd only cut one here and there it would have been bad enough," thought Pahom, "but the rascal has actually cut down a whole clump. If I could only find out who did this, I'd get even with him."

He racked his brains as to who it could be. Finally he decided: "It must be Simon—no one else could have done it." So he went to Simon's homestead to have a look around, but he found nothing, and only had an angry scene. However, he now felt more certain than ever that Simon had done it, and he lodged a complaint. Simon was summoned. The case was tried, and retried, and at the end of it all Simon was acquitted, there being no evidence against him. Pahom felt still more aggrieved, and let his anger loose upon the Elder and the Judges.

"You let thieves grease your palms," said he. "If you were honest folk yourselves you wouldn't let a thief go free."

So Pahom quarreled with the judges and with his neighbors. Threats to burn his hut began to be uttered. So though Pahom had more land, his place in the community was much worse than before.

About this time a rumor got about that many people were moving to new parts.

"There's no need for me to leave my land," thought Pahom. "But some of the others may leave our village and then there'd be more room for us. I'd take over their land myself and make my estate somewhat bigger. I could then live more at ease. As it is, I'm still too cramped to be comfortable."

One day Pahom was sitting at home, when a peasant, passing through the village, happened to drop in. He was allowed to stay the night, and supper was given him. Pahom had a talk with this peasant and asked him where he came from. The stranger answered that he came from beyond the Volga, where he had been working. One word led to another, and the man went on to say that many people were settling in those parts. He told how some people from his village had settled there. They had joined the community there and had had twenty-five acres per man granted them. The land was so good, he said, that the rye sown on it grew as high as a horse, and so thick that five cuts of a sickle made a sheaf. One peasant, he said, had brought nothing with him but his bare hands, and now he had six horses and two cows of his own.

Pahom's heart kindled with desire.

"Why should I suffer in this narrow hole, if one can live so well elsewhere?" he thought. "I'll sell my land and my homestead here, and with the money I'll start afresh over there and get everything new. In this crowded place one is always having trouble. But I must first go and find out all about it myself."

Toward summer he got ready and started out. He went down the Volga on a steamer to Samara, then walked another three hundred miles on foot, and at last reached the place. It was just as the stranger had said. The peasants had plenty of land: every man had twenty-five acres of communal land given him for his use, and anyone who had money could buy, besides, at a ruble-and-a-half an acre, as much good freehold land as he wanted.

Having found out all he wished to know, Pahom returned home as autumn came on, and began selling off his belongings. He sold his land at a profit, sold his homestead and all his cattle, and withdrew from membership in the village. He only waited till spring, and then started with his family for the new settlement.

IV

As soon as Pahom and his family reached their new abode, he applied for admission into the Council of a large village. He stood treat to the Elders and obtained the necessary documents. Five shares of communal land were given him for his own and his sons' use: that is to say—125 acres (not all together, but in different fields) besides the use of the communal pasture. Pahom put up the buildings he needed and bought cattle. Of the communal land alone he had three times as much as at his former home, and the land was good wheat-land. He was ten times better off than he had been. He had plenty of arable land and pasturage, and could keep as many head of cattle as he liked.

At first, in the bustle of building and settling down, Pahom was pleased with it all, but when he got used to it he began to think that even here he hadn't enough land. The first year he sowed wheat on his share of the communal land and had a good crop. He wanted to go on sowing wheat, but had not enough communal land for the purpose, and what he had already used was not available, for in those parts wheat is sown only on virgin soil or on fallow land. It is sown for one or two years, and then the land lies fallow till it is again overgrown with steppe grass. There were many who wanted such land, and there was not enough for all, so that people quarreled about it. Those who were better off wanted it for growing wheat, and those who were poor wanted it to let to dealers, so that they might raise money to pay their taxes. Pahom wanted to sow more wheat, so he rented land from a dealer for a year. He sowed much wheat and had a fine crop, but the land was too far from the village—the wheat had to be carted more than ten miles. After a time Pahom noticed that some peasant-dealers were living on separate farms and were growing wealthy, and he thought:

"If I were to buy some freehold land and have a homestead on it, it would be a different thing altogether. Then it would all be fine and close together."

The question of buying freehold land recurred to him again and again.

He went on in the same way for three years, renting land and sowing wheat. The seasons turned out well and the crops were good, so that he began to lay by money. He might have gone on living contentedly, but he grew tired of having to rent other people's land every year, and having to scramble for it. Wherever there was good land to be had, the peasants would rush for it and it was taken up at once, so that unless you were sharp about it you got none. It happened in the third year that he and a dealer together rented a piece o pasture land from some peasants, and they had already plowed it up when there was some dispute and the peasants went to law about it and things fell out so that the labor was all lost.

"If it were my own land," thought Pahom, "I should be independ ent, and there wouldn't be all this unpleasantness."

So Pahom began looking out for land which he could buy, and h came across a peasant who had bought thirteen hundred acres, bu having got into difficulties was willing to sell again cheap. Pahom bargained and haggled with him, and at last they settled the price a fifteen hundred rubles, part in cash and part to be paid later. The had all but clinched the matter when a passing dealer happened t stop at Pahom's one day to get feed for his horses. He drank tea wit Pahom, and they had a talk. The dealer said that he was just return ing from the land of the Bashkirs, far away, where he had bough thirteen thousand acres of land, all for a thousand rubles. Pahom questioned him further, and the dealer said:

"All one has to do is to make friends with the chiefs. I gave awa about one hundred rubles' worth of silk robes and carpets, besides case of tea, and I gave wine to those who would drink it; and I go the land for less than three kopecks an acre." And he showed Pahom the title deed, saying:

"The land lies near a river, and the whole steppe is virgin soil."

Pahom plied him with questions, and the dealer said:

"There's more land there than you could cover if you walked year, and it all belongs to the Bashkirs. They're as simple as sheep and land can be got almost for nothing."

"There, now," thought Pahom, "with my one thousand rubles, wh should I get only thirteen hundred acres, and saddle myself with debt besides? If I take it out there, I can get more than ten times a much for my money."

V

Pahom inquired how to get to the place, and as soon as the grai dealer had left him, he prepared to go there himself. He left his wif to look after the homestead, and started on his journey, taking his hired man with him. They stopped at a town on their way and bought a case of tea, some wine, and other presents, as the grain dealer had advised.

On and on they went until they had gone more than three hundred miles, and on the seventh day they came to a place where the Bashkirs had pitched their round tents. It was all just as the dealer had said. The people lived on the steppe, by a river, in felt-covered tents. They neither tilled the ground nor ate bread. Their cattle and horses grazed in herds on the steppe. The colts were tethered behind the tents, and the mares were driven to them twice a day. The mares were milked, and from the milk kumiss was made. It was the women who prepared the kumiss, and they also made cheese. As far as the men were concerned, drinking kumiss and tea, eating mutton, and playing on their pipes was all they cared about. They were all stout and merry, and all the summer long they never thought of doing any work. They were quite ignorant, and knew no Russian, but were good-natured enough.

As soon as they saw Pahom, they came out of their tents and gathered around their visitor. An interpreter was found, and Pahom told them he had come about some land. The Bashkirs seemed very glad; they took Pahom and led him into one of the best tents, where they made him sit on some down cushions placed on a carpet, while they sat around him. They gave him some tea and kumiss, and had a sheep killed, and gave him mutton to eat. Pahom took presents out of his cart and distributed them among the Bashkirs, and divided the tea amongst them. The Bashkirs were delighted. They talked a great deal among themselves, and then told the interpreter what to say.

"They wish to tell you," said the interpreter, "that they like you, and that it's our custom to do all we can to please a guest and to repay him for his gifts. You have given us presents, now tell us which of the things we possess please you best, that we may present them to you."

"What pleases me best here," answered Pahom, "is your land. Our land is crowded and the soil is worn out, but you have plenty of land, and it is good land. I never saw the likes of it."

The interpreter told the Bashkirs what Pahom had said. They talked among themselves for a while. Pahom could not understand what they were saying, but saw that they were much amused and heard them shout and laugh. Then they were silent and looked at Pahom while the interpreter said:

"They wish me to tell you that in return for your presents they will gladly give you as much land as you want. You have only to point it out with your hand and it is yours."

The Bashkirs talked again for a while and began to dispute. Pahom asked what they were disputing about, and the interpreter told him that some of them thought they ought to ask their Chief about the land and not act in his absence, while others thought there was no need to wait for his return.

VI

While the Bashkirs were disputing, a man in a large fox-fur cap appeared on the scene. They all became silent and rose to their feet. The interpreter said: "This is our Chief himself."

Pahom immediately fetched the best dressing gown and five pounds of tea, and offered these to the Chief. The Chief accepted them, and seated himself in the place of honor. The Bashkirs at once began telling him something. The Chief listened for a while, then made a sign with his head for them to be silent, and addressing himself to Pahom, said in Russian:

"Well, so be it. Choose whatever piece of land you like; we have plenty of it."

"How can I take as much as I like?" thought Pahom. "I must get a deed to make it secure, or else they may say: 'It is yours,' and afterward may take it away again."

"Thank you for your kind words," he said aloud. "You have much land, and I only want a little. But I should like to be sure which portion is mine. Could it not be measured and made over to me? Life and death are in God's hands. You good people give it to me, but your children might wish to take it back again."

"You are quite right," said the Chief. "We will make it over to you."

"I heard that a dealer had been here," continued Pahom, "and that you gave him a little land, too, and signed title deeds to that effect. I should like to have it done in the same way."

The Chief understood.

"Yes," replied he, "that can be done quite easily. We have a scribe, and we will go to town with you and have the deed properly sealed."

"And what will be the price?" asked Pahom.

"Our price is always the same: one thousand rubles a day."

Pahom did not understand.

"A day? What measure is that? How many acres would that be?"

"We do not know how to reckon it out," said the Chief. "We sell it by the day. As much as you can go around on your feet in a day is yours, and the price is one thousand rubles a day."

Pahom was surprised.

"But in a day you can get around a large tract of land," he said.

The Chief laughed.

"It will all be yours!" said he. "But there is one condition: If you don't return on the same day to the spot whence you started, your money is lost."

"But how am I to mark the way that I have gone?"

"Why, we shall go to any spot you like, and stay there. You must start from that spot and make your round, taking a spade with you. Wherever you think necessary, make a mark. At every turning, dig a hole and pile up the turf; then afterward we will go around with a plow from hole to hole. You may make as large a circuit as you please, but before the sun sets you must return to the place you started from. All the land you cover will be yours."

Pahom was delighted. It was decided to start early next morning. They talked a while, and after drinking some more kumiss and eating some more mutton, they had tea again, and then the night came on. They gave Pahom a feather bed to sleep on, and the Bashkirs dispersed for the night, promising to assemble the next morning at daybreak and ride out before sunrise to the appointed spot.

VII

Pahom lay on the feather bed, but could not sleep. He kept thinking about the land.

"What a large tract I'll mark off!" thought he, "I can easily do thirty-five miles in a day. The days are long now, and within a circuit of thirty-five miles what a lot of land there will be! I'll sell the poorer land, or let it to peasants, but I'll pick out the best and farm it myself. I'll buy two ox teams and hire two more laborers. About a hundred and fifty acres shall be plowland, and I'll pasture cattle on the rest."

Pahom lay awake all night, and dozed off only just before dawn. Hardly were his eyes closed when he had a dream. He thought he was lying in that same tent and heard somebody chuckling outside. He wondered who it could be, and rose and went out, and he saw the Bashkir Chief sitting in front of the tent holding his sides and rolling about with laughter. Going nearer to the Chief, Pahom asked: "What are you laughing at?" But he saw it was no longer the Chief, but the grain dealer who had recently stopped at his house and had told him about the land. Just as Pahom was going to ask: "Have you been here long?" he saw that it was not the dealer, but the peasant who had come up from the Volga long ago, to Pahom's old home. Then he saw that it was not the peasant either, but the Devil himself with hoofs and horns, sitting there and chuckling, and before him lay a man, prostrate on the ground, barefooted, with only trousers and a shirt on. And Pahom dreamed that he looked more attentively to see what sort of man it was lying there, and he saw that the man was dead, and that it was himself. Horror-struck, he awoke.

"What things one dreams about!" thought he.

Looking around he saw through the open door that the dawn was breaking.

"It's time to wake them up," thought he. "We ought to be starting."

He got up, roused his man (who was sleeping in his cart), bade him harness, and went to call the Bashkirs.

"It's time to go to the steppe to measure the land," he said.

The Bashkirs rose and assembled, and the Chief came, too. Then they began drinking kumiss again, and offered Pahom some tea, but he would not wait.

"If we are to go, let's go. It's high time," said he.

VIII

The Bashkirs got ready and they all started: some mounted on horses and some in carts. Pahom drove in his own small cart with his servant and took a spade with him. When they reached the steppe, the red dawn was beginning to kindle. They ascended a hillock (called by the Bashkirs a *shikhan*) and, dismounting from their carts and their horses, gathered in one spot. The Chief came up to Pahom and, stretching out his arm toward the plain:

"See," said he, "all this, as far as your eye can reach, is ours. You may have any part of it you like."

Pahom's eyes glistened: it was all virgin soil, as flat as the palm of your hand, as black as the seed of a poppy, and in the hollows different kinds of grasses grew breast-high.

The Chief took off his fox-fur cap, placed it on the ground, and said:

"This will be the mark. Start from here, and return here again. All the land you go around shall be yours."

Pahom took out his money and put it on the cap. Then he took off his outer coat, remaining in his sleeveless undercoat. He unfastened his girdle and tied it tight below his stomach, put a little bag of bread into the breast of his coat, and, tying a flask of water to his girdle, he drew up the tops of his boots, took the spade from his man, and stood ready to start. He considered for some moments which way he had better go—it was tempting everywhere.

"No matter," he concluded, "I'll go toward the rising sun."

He turned his face to the east, stretched himself, and waited for the sun to appear above the rim.

"I must lose no time," he thought, "and it's easier walking while it's still cool."

The sun's rays had hardly flashed above the horizon when Pahom, carrying the spade over his shoulder, went down into the steppe.

Pahom started walking neither slowly nor quickly. After having gone a thousand yards he stopped, dug a hole, and placed pieces of turf one on another to make it more visible. Then he went on; and now that he had walked off his stiffness he quickened his pace. After a while he dug another hole.

Pahom looked back. The hillock could be distinctly seen in the sunlight, with the people on it, and the glittering iron rims of the cartwheels. At a rough guess Pahom concluded that he had walked three miles. It was growing warmer; he took off his undercoat, slung it across his shoulder, and went on again. It had grown quite warm now; he looked at the sun—it was time to think of breakfast.

"The first shift is done, but there are four in a day, and it's too soon yet to turn. But I'll just take off my boots," said he to himself.

He sat down, took off his boots, stuck them into his girdle, and went on. It was easy walking now.

"I'll go on for another three miles," thought he, "and then turn to the left. This spot is so fine that it would be a pity to lose it. The further one goes, the better the land seems."

He went straight on for a while, and when he looked around, the hillock was scarcely visible and the people on it looked like black ants, and he could just see something glistening there in the sun.

"Ah," thought Pahom, "I have gone far enough in this direction; it's time to turn. Besides, I'm in a regular sweat, and very thirsty."

He stopped, dug a large hole, and heaped up pieces of turf. Next he untied his flask, had a drink, and then turned sharply to the left. He went on and on; the grass was high, and it was very hot.

Pahom began to grow tired: he looked at the sun and saw that it was noon.

"Well," he thought, "I must have a rest."

He sat down, and ate some bread and drank some water; but he did not lie down, thinking that if he did he might fall asleep. After sitting a little while, he went on again. At first he walked easily; the food had strengthened him; but it had become terribly hot and he felt sleepy. Still he went on, thinking: "An hour to suffer, a lifetime to live."

He went a long way in this direction also, and was about to turn to the left again, when he perceived a damp hollow: "It would be a pity to leave that out," he thought. "Flax would do well there." So he went on past the hollow and dug a hole on the other side of it before he made a sharp turn. Pahom looked toward the hillock. The heat made the air hazy: it seemed to be quivering, and through the haze the people on the hillock could scarcely be seen.

"Ah," thought Pahom, "I have made the sides too long; I must make this one shorter." And he went along the third side, stepping faster. He looked at the sun: it was nearly halfway to the horizon, and he had not yet done two miles of the third side of the square. He was still ten miles from the goal.

"No," he thought, "though it will make my land lopsided, I must hurry back in a straight line now. I might go too far, and as it is I have a great deal of land."

So Pahom hurriedly dug a hole and turned straight toward the hillock.

IX

Pahom went straight toward the hillock, but he now walked with difficulty. He was exhausted from the heat, his bare feet were cut and bruised, and his legs began to fail. He longed to rest, but it was impossible if he meant to get back before sunset. The sun waits for no man, and it was sinking lower and lower.

"Oh, Lord," he thought, "if only I have not blundered trying for too much! What if I am too late?"

He looked toward the hillock and at the sun. He was still far from his goal, and the sun was already near the rim of the sky.

Pahom walked on and on; it was very hard walking, but he went quicker and quicker. He pressed on, but was still far from the place. He began running, threw away his coat, his boots, his flask, and his cap, and kept only the spade which he used as a support.

"What am I to do?" he thought again. "I've grasped too much and ruined the whole affair. I can't get there before the sun sets."

And this fear made him still more breathless. Pahom kept on running; his soaking shirt and trousers stuck to him, and his mouth was parched. His breast was working like a blacksmith's bellows, his heart was beating like a hammer, and his legs were giving way as if they did not belong to him. Pahom was seized with terror lest he should die of the strain.

Though afraid of death, he could not stop.

"After having run all that way they will call me a fool if I stop now," thought he.

And he ran on and on, and drew near and heard the Bashkirs yelling and shouting to him, and their cries inflamed his heart still more. He gathered his last strength and ran on.

The sun was close to the rim of the sky and, cloaked in mist, looked large, and red as blood. Now, yes, now, it was about to set! The sun was quite low, but he was also quite near his goal. Pahom could already see the people on the hillock waving their arms to make him hurry. He could see the fox-fur cap on the ground and the money in it, and the Chief sitting on the ground holding his sides. And Pahom remembered his dream.

"There's plenty of land," thought he, "but will God let me live on it? I have lost my life, I have lost my life! Never will I reach that spot!"

Pahom looked at the sun, which had reached the earth: one side of it had already disappeared. With all his remaining strength he rushed on, bending his body forward so that his legs could hardly follow fast enough to keep him from falling. Just as he reached the hillock it suddenly grew dark. He looked up—the sun had already set!

He gave a cry: "All my labor has been in vain," thought he, and was about to stop, but he heard the Bashkirs still shouting, and remembered that though to him, from below, the sun seemed to have set, they on the hillock could still see it. He took a long breath and ran up the hillock. It was still light there. He reached the top and saw the cap. Before it sat the Chief, laughing and holding his sides. Again Pahom remembered his dream, and he uttered a cry: his legs gave way beneath him, he fell forward and reached the cap with his hands.

"Ah, that's a fine fellow!" exclaimed the Chief. "He has gained much land!"

Pahom's servant came running up and tried to raise him, but he saw that blood was flowing from his mouth. Pahom was dead.

The Bashkirs clicked their tongues to show their pity.

His servant picked up the spade and dug a grave long enough for Pahom to lie in, and buried him in it.

Six feet from his head to his heels was all he needed.

Giovanni Verga

Cavalleria Rusticana

WHEN Turiddu Macca, Nunzia's son, came back from the service, he used to strut in the square on Sundays in his *bersagliere*[1] uniform with the red cap that looked like the one worn by the fortuneteller who sets up a bench with a cage of canaries. The girls, on the way to Mass, their noses in their mantillas, eyed him longingly, and the urchins buzzed around him like flies. He had also brought a pipe with a carving of the king on horseback that seemed alive, and he lit matches on the rear of his pants, lifting his leg as if giving a kick.

But in spite of all this, *massaro* Angelo's daughter, Lola, had not shown herself at Mass or on her balcony, because she had become engaged to a certain man from Licodia,[2] a cart driver who had four Sortino[3] mules in his stable. As soon as Turiddu found out, damn it! he was going to tear that Licodian's guts from his belly, he was!—but he did nothing of the kind, and vented his rage by singing all the scornful songs he knew under the girl's window.

[1] The *Bersaglieri* are a famous Italian army corps, especially trained for quick movement and swift action against an enemy. For full dress they used to wear beautiful hats with plumes and for informal dress a red cap with hanging tassel.

[2] A large village near Vizzini, on the western slopes of the Iblei Mountains, about thirty miles inland from Syracuse.

[3] Another large village, about halfway between Syracuse and Licodia.

"Doesn't Nunzia's Turiddu have anything to do," the neighbors were saying, "that he spends his nights singing like a lonely sparrow?"

He finally ran into Lola, who was returning from a pilgrimage to Our Lady of Peril; and seeing him, she turned neither white nor red, as if it were none of her business.

"It's a lucky person who sees you!" he said.

"Oh, Turiddu, they'd told me you came back the first of the month."

"They've told me things too!" he answered. "Is it true you're going to marry Alfio, the cart driver?"

"If that's the will of God!" answered Lola, pulling the two corners of her kerchief over her chin.

"You make the will of God yourself, just as it happens to suit you! And the will of God was that I should come home from so far away to hear this fine piece of news, Lola!"

The poor devil was still trying to act brave, but his voice had grown hoarse; he walked behind the girl, swaying while the tassel of his cap danced here and there on his shoulders. She, in all honesty, was sorry to see him with such a long face, but hadn't the heart to encourage him with nice words.

"Listen, Turiddu," she told him at last, "let me catch up with my friends. What would they say in town if they saw me with you?"

"That's right," answered Turiddu, "now that you're going to marry Alfio who has four mules in his stable, you mustn't make people talk. Instead my mother, poor woman, had to sell our bay mule and that little vineyard on the highroad while I was in the service. The good old days are gone, and you don't think any more of the time when we talked together at the courtyard window; and before I went away, you gave me that handkerchief and God knows how many tears I've wept in it, going away so far that even the name of our town was lost. But now, good-by, Lola—'Let's pretend it's rained, then cleared up, and our friendship is over.' "[4]

[4] A Sicilian saying that means "Let's forget completely about everything connected with the past."

Lola married the cart driver; and every Sunday she sat on the balcony with her hands on her stomach, displaying the huge gold rings her husband had given her. Turiddu kept going up and down the little street with an air of indifference, his pipe in his mouth and his hands in his pockets, eyeing the girls; but gnawing away inside him was the fact that Lola's husband had all that gold and that she herself pretended not to notice him when he went by.

"I'll get even with her right under her eyes, the dirty bitch!" he muttered.

Across the street from Alfio lived *massaro* Cola, the winegrower, who was rich as a pig, people said, and had a daughter on his hands. Turiddu managed to get a job as field watchman at *massaro* Cola's and began to hang around the house, saying sweet words to the girl.

"Why don't you go and say these nice things to Lola?" answered Santa.

"Lola's a big Lady! Lola's married to a crowned king now!"

"I don't deserve crowned kings."

"You're worth a hundred Lolas, and I know someone who wouldn't look at Lola or her patron saint when you're around; Lola doesn't deserve to carry your shoes, she doesn't!"

"When the fox couldn't reach the grapes . . ."

"He said: how beautiful you are, my sweet little grapes!"

"Hey! watch those hands, Turiddu."

"Are you afraid I'll eat you?"

"I'm not afraid of you or your God."

"Eh! your mother was from Licodia, we know that! You've got fighting blood! Uh! I'd eat you with my eyes."

"Go ahead and eat me with your eyes, and we won't leave any crumbs; but now help me lift that bundle."

"For you I'd lift the whole house, I would!"

To avoid blushing, she threw a wooden block that she happened to have within reach, and that she missed him was a miracle.

"Let's hurry up, talk won't get us anywhere."

"If I were rich I'd try to get a wife like you, Santa."

"I won't marry a crowned king like Lola did, but I'll have my dowry too, when the Lord sends me someone."

"We know you're rich, we know it!"

"If you know it, hurry up; my father may come any minute, and I wouldn't want him to find me in the courtyard."

Her father began scowling, but the girl pretended not to notice it, because the tassel of the *bersagliere's* cap had tickled her heart and was always dancing before her eyes. When the father threw Turiddu out the door, the daughter opened the window and stood there chatting with him every evening, so that the entire neighborhood spoke of nothing else.

"I'm going crazy because of you," said Turiddu, "I'm losing my sleep and my appetite."

"Nonsense!"

"I wish I were Victor Emmanuel's son, so I could marry you!"

"Nonsense!"

"By the Holy Virgin, I could eat you like bread!"

"Nonsense!"

"On my honor!"

"Ah! For heaven's sake!"

Lola, who listened every evening, hidden behind a pot of sweet basil, and turned pale and red, one day called Turiddu:

"And so, Turiddu, old friends don't greet each other any more?"

"Well . . . ," sighed the young man, "it's a lucky person who can greet you!"

"If you want to greet me, you know where I live!" answered Lola. Turiddu went back to greet her so often that Santa noticed it and slammed the window in his face. The neighbors pointed out the *bersagliere* with a smile or a nod, when he passed. Lola's husband was making his round of the fairs with his mules.

"Sunday I want to go to confession, because I dreamed of black grapes[5] last night!" said Lola.

[5] In Sicily, an ominous dream.

"Forget it! Forget it!" begged Turiddu.

"No, now that Easter's coming, my husband would want to know why I didn't go to confession."

"Ah!" muttered *massaro* Cola's daughter Santa, while on her knees awaiting her turn at the confession box where Lola was washing her sins away. "On my soul, it's not to Rome I'll send you for penance!"

Alfio came back with his mules and loaded with money, and brought a beautiful new holiday dress as a gift for his wife.

"You're right to bring her presents," his neighbor Santa told him, "because when you're away your wife makes a cuckold of you in your own house!"

Alfio was one of those cart drivers who carry a chip on their shoulders, and hearing his wife spoken of that way, he changed color as if he had been knifed.

"Damn it!" he exclaimed. "If you haven't seen right, I won't leave you eyes to cry with, you and your whole family!"

"I'm not used to crying!" answered Santa. "I didn't even cry when with these eyes I saw Nunzia's Turiddu enter your wife's house at night."

"Fine," answered Alfio, "many thanks."

Now that the cat had come back, Turiddu didn't hang around the little street any more during the day, and drowned his ill-humor at the tavern with his friends. On Easter Eve they had a plate of sausages on the table. As Alfio came in, Turiddu understood, just from the way he fixed his eyes on him, that he had come about that business, and laid his fork on the plate.

"What can I do for you, Alfio?" he asked.

"No favors, Turiddu; I hadn't seen you for some time and wanted to talk to you—you know what about."

At first Turiddu had offered him a glass of wine, but Alfio brushed it aside with his hand. Then Turiddu stood up and said:

"Here I am, Alfio."

The cart driver threw his arms around Turiddu's neck:

"If you want to come to the cactuses of Canziria[6] tomorrow morning, we can talk about that business."

"Wait for me on the highroad at sunrise and we'll go together."

With these words they exchanged the kiss of challenge. Turiddu bit the cart driver's ear, thus making a solemn promise to be there.

His friends had abandoned the sausages in cold silence, and accompanied Turiddu home. Nunzia, poor woman, waited up for him until late every evening.

"Mother," Turiddu said to her, "remember when I went into the service, and you thought I'd never come home again? Give me a nice kiss as you did then; tomorrow morning I'm going far away."

Before daybreak he got his clasp knife, which he had hidden under the hay when he had been taken into the army, and started out for the cactuses of Canziria.

"Oh! for Christ's sake! where are you going in such a rush?" whined Lola in dismay, when her husband was about to leave.

"I'm not going far," answered Alfio, "but it'd be better for you if I would never come back."

Lola, in her nightgown, prayed at the foot of the bed, pressing to her lips the rosary Father Bernardino had brought her from the Holy Land, and recited all the Ave Marias it had beads for.

"Alfio," began Turiddu, after having gone a certain distance with his companion, who remained silent, his cap over his eyes, "I swear to God, I know I've done wrong and I'd let you kill me. But before I came here I saw my old mother who got up to see me leave, pretending she had to feed the chickens, almost as if she knew; and I swear to God I'll kill you like a dog not to make the poor old woman cry."

"That's fine," answered Alfio, taking off his jacket, "so we can really fight it out."

They were both good fighters. Turiddu was hit first, and was quick enough to take the stab in his arm; as he struck back, he struck hard and fast, and aimed at the groin.

[6] A hilly farm area near Vizzini.

"Ah, Turiddu, you really intend to kill me!"

"Yes, I told you; now that I've seen my old mother in the chicken coop, she seems to be always before my eyes."

"Open 'em well, those eyes!" shouted Alfio. "I'm going to give you a good one!"

While he was on guard, all doubled up to keep his left hand on his wound, which hurt him, and almost trailing his elbow on the ground, he quickly grabbed a handful of dust and threw it into his opponent's eyes.

"Ah!" howled Turiddu. "I'm dead."

He tried to save himself, jumping desperately backward; but Alfio caught him with another stab in the stomach and a third in the throat.

"And that's three! That's for making a cuckold of me in my own house. Now your mother will let the chickens alone."

For a while Turiddu staggered here and there among the cactuses and then fell like a log. Blood gurgled up and foamed in his throat, and he couldn't even gasp: *Ah, mamma mia!*

Nathaniel Hawthorne

Young Goodman Brown

YOUNG GOODMAN BROWN came forth at sunset into the street at Salem village; but put his head back, after crossing the threshold, to exchange a parting kiss with his young wife. And Faith, as the wife was aptly named, thrust her own pretty head into the street, letting the wind play with the pink ribbons of her cap while she called to Goodman Brown.

"Dearest heart," whispered she, softly and rather sadly, when her lips were close to his ear, "prithee put off your journey until sunrise and sleep in your own bed to-night. A lone woman is troubled with such dreams and such thoughts that she's afeared of herself sometimes. Pray tarry with me this night, dear husband, of all nights in the year."

"My love and my Faith," replied young Goodman Brown, "of all nights in the year, this one night must I tarry away from thee. My journey, as thou callest it, forth and back again, must needs be done 'twixt now and sunrise. What, my sweet wife, dost thou doubt me already, and we but three months married?"

"Then God bless you!" said Faith, with the pink ribbons; "and may you find all well when you come back."

"Amen!" cried Goodman Brown. "Say thy prayers, dear Faith, and go to bed at dusk, and no harm will come to thee."

So they parted; and the young man pursued his way until, being about to turn the corner by the meeting-house, he looked back and saw the head of Faith still peeping after him with a melancholy air, in spite of her pink ribbons.

"Poor little Faith!" thought he, for his heart smote him. "What a wretch am I to leave her on such an errand! She talks of dreams, too. Methought as she spoke there was trouble in her face, as if a dream had warned her what work is to be done to-night. But no, no; 'twould kill her to think it. Well, she's a blessed angel on earth; and after this one night I'll cling to her skirts and follow her to heaven."

With this excellent resolve for the future, Goodman Brown felt himself justified in making more haste on his present evil purpose. He had taken a dreary road, darkened by all the gloomiest trees of the forest, which barely stood aside to let the narrow path creep through, and closed immediately behind. It was all as lonely as could be; and there is this peculiarity in such a solitude, that the traveller knows not who may be concealed by the innumerable trunks and the thick boughs overheard; so that with lonely footsteps he may yet be passing through an unseen multitude.

"There may be a devilish Indian behind every tree," said Goodman Brown to himself; and he glanced fearfully behind him as he added, "What if the devil himself should be at my very elbow!"

His head being turned back, he passed a crook of the road, and, looking forward again, beheld the figure of a man, in grave and decent attire, seated at the foot of an old tree. He arose at Goodman Brown's approach and walked onward side by side with him.

"You are late, Goodman Brown," said he. "The clock of the Old South was striking as I came through Boston, and that is full fifteen minutes agone."

"Faith kept me back a while," replied the young man, with a tremor in his voice, caused by the sudden appearance of his companion, though not wholly unexpected.

It was now deep dusk in the forest, and deepest in that part of it where these two were journeying. As nearly as could be discerned, the second traveller was about fifty years old, apparently in the same rank of life as Goodman Brown, and bearing a considerable resemblance to him, though perhaps more in expression than features. Still they might have been taken for father and son. And yet, though the elder person was as simply clad as the younger, and as simple in manner too, he had an indescribable air of one who knew the world, and who would not have felt abashed at the governor's dinner table or in King William's court, were it possible that his affairs should call him thither. But the only thing about him that could be fixed upon as remarkable was his staff, which bore the likeness of a great black snake, so curiously wrought that it might almost be seen to twist and wriggle itself like a living serpent. This, of course, must have been an ocular deception, assisted by the uncertain light.

"Come, Goodman Brown," cried his fellow-traveller, "this is a dull pace for the beginning of a journey. Take my staff, if you are so soon weary."

"Friend," said the other, exchanging his slow pace for a full stop, "having kept covenant by meeting thee here, it is my purpose now to return whence I came. I have scruples touching the matter thou wot'st of."

"Sayest thou so?" replied he of the serpent, smiling apart. "Let us walk on, nevertheless, reasoning as we go; and if I convince thee not thou shalt turn back. We are but a little way in the forest yet."

"Too far! too far!" exclaimed the goodman, unconsciously resuming his walk. "My father never went into the woods on such an errand, nor his father before him. We have been a race of honest men and good Christians since the days of the martyrs; and shall I be the first of the name of Brown that ever took this path and kept"—

"Such company thou wouldst say," observed the elder person, interpreting his pause. "Well said, Goodman Brown! I have been as well acquainted with your family as with ever a one among the Puritans; and that's no trifle to say. I helped your grandfather, the constable, when he lashed the Quaker woman so smartly through the streets of Salem; and it was I that brought your father a pitch-pine knot, kindled at my own hearth, to set fire to an Indian village, in King Philip's war. They were my good friends, both; and many a pleasant walk have we had along this path, and returned merrily after midnight. I would fain be friends with you for their sake."

"If it be as thou sayest," replied Goodman Brown, "I marvel they never spoke of these matters; or, verily, I marvel not, seeing that the least rumor of the sort would have driven them from New England. We are a people of prayer, and good works to boot, and abide no such wickedness."

"Wickedness or not," said the traveller with the twisted staff, "I have a very general acquaintance here in New England. The deacons of many a church have drunk the communion wine with me; the selectmen of divers towns make me their chairman; and a majority of the Great and General Court are firm supporters of my interest. The governor and I, too—But these are state secrets."

"Can this be so?" cried Goodman Brown, with a stare of amazement at his undisturbed companion. "Howbeit, I have nothing to do with the governor and council; they have their own ways, and are no rule for a simple husbandman like me. But, were I to go on with thee, how should I meet the eye of that good old man, our minister, at Salem village? Oh, his voice would make me tremble both Sabbath day and lecture day."

Thus far the elder traveller had listened with due gravity; but now burst into a fit of irrepressible mirth, shaking himself so violently that his snake-like staff actually seemed to wriggle in sympathy.

"Ha! ha! ha!" shouted he again and again; then composing himself, "Well, go on, Goodman Brown, go on; but, prithee, don't kill me with laughing."

"Well, then, to end the matter at once," said Goodman Brown, considerably nettled, "there is my wife, Faith. It would break her dear little heart; and I'd rather break my own."

"Nay, if that be the case," answered the other, "e'en go thy ways, Goodman Brown. I would not for twenty old women like the one hobbling before us that Faith should come to any harm."

As he spoke he pointed his staff at a female figure on the path, in whom Goodman Brown recognized a very pious and exemplary dame, who had taught him his catechism in youth, and was still his moral and spiritual adviser, jointly with the minister and Deacon Gookin.

"A marvel, truly, that Goody Cloyse should be so far in the wilderness at nightfall," said he. "But with your leave, friend, I shall take a cut through the woods until we have left this Christian woman behind. Being a stranger to you, she might ask whom I was consorting with and whither I was going."

"Be it so," said his fellow-traveller. "Betake you to the woods, and let me keep the path."

Accordingly the young man turned aside, but took care to watch his companion, who advanced softly along the road until he had come within a staff's length of the old dame. She, meanwhile, was making the best of her way, with singular speed for so aged a woman, and mumbling some indistinct words—a prayer, doubtless—as she went. The traveller put forth his staff and touched her withered neck with what seemed the serpent's tail.

"The devil!" screamed the pious old lady.

"Then Goody Cloyse knows her old friend?" observed the traveller, confronting her and leaning on his writhing stick.

"Ah, forsooth, and is it your worship indeed?" cried the good dame. "Yea, truly is it, and in the very image of my old gossip, Goodman Brown, the grandfather of the silly fellow that now is. But—would your worship believe it?—my broomstick hath strangely disappeared, stolen, as I suspect, by that unhanged witch, Goody Cory, and that, too, when I was all anointed with the juice of smallage, and cinquefoil, and wolf's bane—"

"Mingled with fine wheat and the fat of a new-born babe," said the shape of old Goodman Brown.

"Ah, your worship knows the recipe," cried the old lady, cackling aloud. "So, as I was saying, being all ready for the meeting, and no horse to ride on, I made up my mind to foot it; for they tell me there is a nice young man to be taken into communion to-night. But now your good worship will lend me your arm, and we shall be there in a twinkling."

"That can hardly be," answered her friend. "I may not spare you my arm, Goody Cloyse; but here is my staff, if you will."

So saying, he threw it down at her feet, where, perhaps, it assumed life, being one of the rods which its owner had formerly lent to the Egyptian magi. Of this fact, however, Goodman Brown could not take cognizance. He had cast up his eyes in astonishment, and, looking down again, beheld neither Goody Cloyse nor the serpentine staff, but his fellow-traveller alone, who waited for him as calmly as if nothing had happened.

"That old woman taught me my catechism," said the young man; and there was a world of meaning in this simple comment.

They continued to walk onward, while the elder traveller exhorted his companion to make good speed and persevere in the path, discoursing so aptly that his arguments seemed rather to spring up in the bosom of his auditor than to be suggested by himself. As they went, he plucked a branch of maple to serve for a walking stick, and began to strip it of the twigs and little boughs, which were wet with evening dew. The moment his fingers touched them they became strangely withered and dried up as with a week's sunshine. Thus the pair proceeded, at a good free pace, until suddenly, in a gloomy hollow of the road, Goodman Brown sat himself down on the stump of a tree and refused to go any farther.

"Friend," said he, stubbornly, "my mind is made up. Not another step will I budge on this errand. What if a wretched old woman do choose to go to the devil when I thought she was going to heaven: is that any reason why I should quit my dear Faith and go after her?"

"You will think better of this by and by," said his acquaintance, composedly. "Sit here and rest yourself a while; and when you feel like moving again, there is my staff to help you along."

Without more words, he threw his companion the maple stick, and was as speedily out of sight as if he had vanished into the gloom. The young man sat a few moments by the roadside, applauding himself greatly, and thinking with how clear a conscience he should meet the minister in his morning walk, nor shrink from the eye of good old Deacon Gookin. And what calm sleep would be his that very night, which was to have been spent so wickedly, but so purely and sweetly now, in the arms of Faith! Amidst these pleasant and praiseworthy meditations, Goodman Brown heard the tramp of horses along the road, and deemed it advisable to conceal himself within the verge of the forest, conscious of the guilty purpose that had brought him thither, though now so happily turned from it.

On came the hoof tramps and the voices of the riders, two grave old voices, conversing soberly as they drew near. These mingled sounds appeared to pass along the road, within a few yards of the young man's hiding-place; but, owing doubtless to the depth of the gloom at that particular spot, neither the travellers nor their steeds were visible. Though their figures brushed the small boughs by the wayside, it could not be seen that they intercepted, even for a moment, the faint gleam from the strip of bright sky athwart which they must have passed. Goodman Brown alternately crouched and stood on tiptoe, pulling aside the branches and thrusting forth his head as far as he durst without discerning so much as a shadow. It vexed him the more, because he could have sworn, were such a thing possible, that he recognized the voices of the minister and Deacon Gookin, jogging along quietly, as they were wont to do, when bound to some ordination or ecclesiastical council. While yet within hearing, one of the riders stopped to pluck a switch.

"Of the two, reverend sir," said the voice like the deacon's, "I had rather miss an ordination dinner than to-night's meeting. They tell me that some of our community are to be here from Falmouth and beyond, and others from Connecticut and Rhode Island, besides several of the Indian powwows, who, after their fashion know almost as much deviltry as the best of us. Moreover, there is a goodly young woman to be taken into communion."

"Mighty well, Deacon Gookin!" replied the solemn old tones of the minister. "Spur up, or we shall be late. Nothing can be done, you know, until I get on the ground."

The hoofs clattered again; and the voices, talking so strangely in the empty air, passed on through the forest, where no church had ever been gathered or solitary Christian prayed. Whither, then, could these holy men be journeying so deep into the heathen wilderness? Young Goodman Brown caught hold of a tree for support, being ready to sink down on the ground, faint and overburdened with the heavy sickness of his heart. He looked up to the sky, doubting whether there really was a heaven above him. Yet there was the blue arch, and the stars brightening in it.

"With heaven above and Faith below, I will yet stand firm against the devil!" cried Goodman Brown.

While he still gazed upward into the deep arch of the firmament and had lifted his hands to pray, a cloud, though no wind was stirring, hurried across the zenith and hid the brightening stars. The blue sky was still visible, except directly overhead, where this black mass of cloud was sweeping swiftly northward. Aloft in the air, as if from the depths of the cloud, came a confused and doubtful sound of voices. Once the listener fancied that he could distinguish the accents of townspeople of his own, men and women, both pious and ungodly, many of whom he had met at the communion table, and had seen others rioting at the tavern. The next moment, so indistinct were the sounds, he doubted whether he had heard aught but the murmur of the old forest, whispering without a wind. Then came a stronger swell of those familiar tones, heard daily in the sunshine at Salem village, but never until now from a cloud of night. There was one voice, of a young woman, uttering lamentations, yet with an uncertain sorrow, and entreating for some favor, which, perhaps, it would grieve her to obtain; and all the unseen multitude, both saints and sinners, seemed to encourage her onward.

"Faith!" shouted Goodman Brown, in a voice of agony and desperation; and the echoes of the forest mocked him, crying, "Faith! Faith!" as if bewildered wretches were seeking her all through the wilderness.

The cry of grief, rage, and terror was yet piercing the night, when the unhappy husband held his breath for a response. There was a scream, drowned immediately in a louder murmur of voices, fading into far-off laughter, as the dark cloud swept away, leaving the clear and silent sky above Goodman Brown. But something fluttered lightly down through the air and caught on the branch of a tree. The young man seized it, and beheld a pink ribbon.

"My Faith is gone!" cried he, after one stupefied moment. "There is no good on earth; and sin is but a name. Come, devil; for to thee is this world given."

And, maddened with despair, so that he laughed loud and long, did Goodman Brown grasp his staff and set forth again, at such a rate that he seemed to fly along the forest path rather than to walk or run. The road grew wilder and drearier and more faintly traced, and vanished at length, leaving him in the heart of the dark wilderness, still rushing onward with the instinct that guides mortal man to evil. The whole forest was peopled with frightful sounds—the creaking of the trees, the howling of wild beasts, and the yell of Indians; while sometimes the wind tolled like a distant church bell, and sometimes gave a broad roar around the traveller, as if all Nature were laughing him to scorn. But he was himself the chief horror of the scene, and shrank not from its other horrors.

"Ha! ha! ha!" roared Goodman Brown when the wind laughed at him. "Let us hear which will laugh loudest. Think not to frighten me with your deviltry. Come witch, come wizard, come Indian powwow, come devil himself, and here comes Goodman Brown. You may as well fear him as he fear you."

In truth, all through the haunted forest there could be nothing more frightful than the figure of Goodman Brown. On he flew among the black pines, brandishing his staff with frenzied gestures, now giving vent to an inspiration of horrid blasphemy, and now shouting forth such laughter as set all the echoes of the forest laughing like demons around him. The fiend in his own shape is less hideous than when he rages in the breast of man. Thus sped the demoniac on his course, until, quivering among the trees, he saw a red light before him, as when the felled trunks and branches of a clearing have been set on fire, and throw up their lurid blaze against the sky, at the hour of midnight. He paused, in a lull of the tempest that had driven him onward, and heard the swell of what seemed a hymn, rolling solemnly from a distance with the weight of many voices. He knew the tune; it was a familiar one in the choir of the village meeting-house. The verse died heavily away, and was lengthened by a chorus, not of human voices, but of all the sounds of the benighted wilderness pealing in awful harmony together. Goodman Brown cried out, and his cry was lost to his own ear by its unison with the cry of the desert.

In the interval of silence he stole forward until the light glared full upon his eyes. At one extremity of an open space, hemmed in by the dark wall of the forest, arose a rock, bearing some rude, natural resemblance either to an altar or a pulpit, and surrounded by four blazing pines, their tops aflame, their stems untouched, like candles at an evening meeting. The mass of foliage that had overgrown the summit of the rock was all on fire, blazing high into the night and fitfully illuminating the whole field. Each pendent twig and leafy festoon was in a blaze. As the red light arose and fell, a numerous congregation alternately shone forth, then disappeared in shadow, and again grew, as it were, out of the darkness, peopling the heart of the solitary woods at once.

"A grave and dark-clad company," quoth Goodman Brown.

In truth they were such. Among them, quivering to and fro between gloom and splendor, appeared faces that would be seen next day at the council board of the province, and others which, Sabbath after Sabbath, looked devoutly heavenward, and benignantly over the crowded pews, from the holiest pulpits in the land. Some affirm that the lady of the governor was there. At least there were high dames well known to her, and wives of honored husbands, and widows, a great multitude, and ancient maidens, all of excellent repute, and fair young girls, who trembled lest their mothers should espy them. Either the sudden gleams of light flashing over the obscure field bedazzled Goodman Brown, or he recognized a score of the church members of Salem village famous for their especial sanctity. Good old Deacon Gookin had arrived, and waited at the skirts of that venerable saint, his revered pastor. But, irreverently consorting with these grave, reputable, and pious people, these elders of the church, these chaste dames and dewy virgins, there were men of dissolute lives and women of spotted fame, wretches given over to all mean and filthy vice, and suspected even of horrid crimes. It was strange to see that the good shrank not from the wicked, nor were the sinners abashed by the saints. Scattered also among their palefaced enemies were the Indian priests, or powwows, who had often scared their native forest with more hideous incantations than any known to English witchcraft.

"But where is Faith?" thought Goodman Brown; and, as hope came into his heart, he trembled.

Another verse of the hymn arose, a slow and mournful strain, such as the pious love, but joined to words which expressed all that our nature can conceive of sin, and darkly hinted at far more. Unfathomable to mere mortals is the lore of fiends. Verse after verse was sung; and still the chorus of the desert swelled between like the deepest tone of a mighty organ; and with the final peal of that dreadful anthem there came a sound, as if the roaring wind, the rushing streams, the howling beasts, and every other voice of the unconcerted wilderness were mingling and according with the voice of guilty man in homage to the prince of all. The four blazing pines threw up a loftier flame, and obscurely discovered shapes and visages of horror on the smoke wreaths above the impious assembly. At the same moment the fire on the rock shot redly forth and formed a glowing arch above its base, where now appeared a figure. With reverence be it spoken, the figure bore no slight similitude, both in garb and manner, to some grave divine of the New England churches.

"Bring forth the converts!" cried a voice that echoed through the field and rolled into the forest.

At the word, Goodman Brown stepped forth from the shadow of the trees and approached the congregation, with whom he felt a loathful brotherhood by the sympathy of all that was wicked in his heart. He could have well-nigh sworn that the shape of his own dead father beckoned him to advance, looking downward from a smoke wreath, while a woman, with dim features of despair, threw out her hand to warn him back. Was it his mother? But he had no power to retreat one step, nor to resist, even in thought, when the minister and good old Deacon Gookin seized his arms and led him to the blazing rock. Thither came also the slender form of a veiled female, led between Goody Cloyse, that pious teacher of the catechism, and Martha Carrier, who had received the devil's promise to be queen of hell. A rampant hag was she. And there stood the proselytes beneath the canopy of fire.

"Welcome, my children," said the dark figure, "to the communion of your race. Ye have found thus young your nature and your destiny. My children, look behind you!"

They turned; and flashing forth, as it were, in a sheet of flame, the fiend worshippers were seen; the smile of welcome gleamed darkly on every visage.

"There," resumed the sable form, "are all whom ye have reverenced from youth. Ye deemed them holier than yourselves, and shrank from your own sin, contrasting it with their lives of righteousness and prayerful aspirations heavenward. Yet here are they all in my worshipping assembly. This night it shall be granted you to know their secret deeds: how hoary-bearded elders of the church have whispered wanton words to the young maids of their households; how many a woman, eager for widows' weeds, has given her husband a drink at bedtime and let him sleep his last sleep in her bosom; how beardless youths have made haste to inherit their fathers' wealth: and how fair damsels—blush not, sweet ones—have dug little graves in the garden, and bidden me, the sole guest, to an infant's funeral. By the sympathy of your human hearts for sin ye shall scent out all the places—whether in church, bedchamber, street, field, or forest—where crime has been committed, and shall exult to behold the whole earth one stain of guilt, one mighty blood spot. Far more than this. It shall be yours to penetrate, in every bosom, the deep mystery of sin, the fountain of all wicked arts, and which inexhaustibly supplies more evil impulses than human power—than my power at its utmost—can make manifest in deeds. And now, my children, look upon each other."

They did so; and, by the blaze of the hell-kindled torches, the wretched man beheld his Faith, and the wife her husband, trembling before that unhallowed altar.

"Lo, there ye stand, my children," said the figure, in a deep and solemn tone, almost sad with its despairing awfulness, as if his once angelic nature could yet mourn for our miserable race. "Depending upon one another's hearts, ye had still hoped that virtue were not all a dream. Now are ye undeceived. Evil is the nature of mankind. Evil must be your only happiness. Welcome again, my children, to the communion of your race."

"Welcome," repeated the fiend worshippers, in one cry of despair and triumph.

And there they stood, the only pair, as it seemed, who were yet hesitating on the verge of wickedness in this dark world. A basin was hollowed, naturally, in the rock. Did it contain water, reddened by the lurid light? or was it blood? or, perchance, a liquid flame? Herein did the shape of evil dip his hand and prepare to lay the mark of baptism upon their foreheads, that they might be partakers of the mystery of sin, more conscious of the secret guilt of others, both in deed and thought, than they could now be of their own. The husband cast one look at his pale wife, and Faith at him. What polluted wretches would the next glance show them to each other, shuddering alike at what they disclosed and what they saw!

"Faith! Faith!" cried the husband, "look up to heaven, and resist the wicked one."

Whether Faith obeyed he knew not. Hardly had he spoken when he found himself amid calm night and solitude, listening to a roar of the wind which died heavily away through the forest. He staggered against the rock, and felt it chill and damp; while a hanging twig, that had been all on fire, besprinkled his cheek with the coldest dew.

The next morning young Goodman Brown came slowly into the street of Salem village, staring around him like a bewildered man. The good old minister was taking a walk along the graveyard to get an appetite for breakfast and meditate his sermon, and bestowed a blessing, as he passed, on Goodman Brown. He shrank from the venerable saint as if to avoid an anathema. Old Deacon Gookin was at domestic worship, and the holy words of his prayer were heard through the open window. "What God doth the wizard pray to?" quoth Goodman Brown. Goody Cloyse, that excellent old Christian, stood in the early sunshine at her own lattice, catechizing a little girl who had brought her a pint of morning's milk. Goodman Brown snatched away the child as from the grasp of the fiend himself. Turning the corner by the meeting-house, he spied the head of Faith, with the pink ribbons, gazing anxiously forth, and bursting into such joy at sight of him that she skipped along the street and almost kissed her husband before the whole village. But Goodman Brown looked sternly and sadly into her face, and passed on without a greeting.

Had Goodman Brown fallen asleep in the forest and only dreamed a wild dream of a witch-meeting?

Be it so if you will; but, alas! it was a dream of evil omen for young Goodman Brown. A stern, a sad, a darkly meditative, a distrustful, if not a desperate man did he become from the night of that fearful dream. On the Sabbath day, when the congregation were singing a holy psalm, he could not listen because an anthem of sin rushed loudly upon his ear and drowned all the blessed strain. When the minister spoke from the pulpit with power and fervid eloquence, and, with his hand on the open Bible, of the sacred truths of our religion, and of saint-like lives and triumphant deaths, and of future bliss or misery unutterable, then did Goodman Brown turn pale, dreading lest the roof should thunder down upon the gray blasphemer and his hearers. Often, awaking suddenly at midnight, he shrank from the bosom of Faith; and at morning or eventide, when the family knelt down at prayer, he scowled and muttered to himself, and gazed sternly at his wife, and turned away. And when he had lived long, and was borne to his grave a hoary corpse, followed by Faith, an aged woman, and children and grandchildren, a goodly procession, besides neighbors not a few, they carved no hopeful verse upon his tombstone, for his dying hour was gloom.

Herman Melville

Sketch Eighth

Norfolk Isle and the Chola Widow

At last they in an Island did espy
A seemely woman, sitting by the shore,
That with great sorrow and sad agony
Seemed some great misfortune to deplore,
And lowd to them for succour called evermore.

Blacke hys eye as the midnyghte sky,
Whyte hys neck as the driven snowe,
Redde hys cheek as the mornynge lyghte,
Cold he lys ynne the ground belowe;
Mie love ys dedde,
Gon to hys deathe-bedde,
All under the cactus tree.

Each lonely scene shall thee restore,
For thee the tear be duly shed;
Belov'd till life can charm no more,
And mourn'd till Pity's self be dead.

FAR to the northeast of Charles's Isle, sequestered from the rest, lies Norfolk Isle; and, however insignificant to most voyagers, to me, through sympathy, that lone island has become a spot made sacred by the strangest trials of humanity.

It was my first visit to the Encantadas. Two days had been spent ashore in hunting tortoises. There was not time to capture many; so on the third afternoon we loosed our sails. We were just in the act of getting under way, the uprooted anchor yet suspended and invisibly swaying beneath the wave, as the good ship gradually turned her heel to leave the isle behind, when the seaman who heaved with me at the windlass paused suddenly, and directed my attention to something moving on the land, not along the beach, but somewhat back, fluttering from a height.

In view of the sequel of this little story, be it here narrated how it came to pass, that an object which partly from its being so small was quite lost to every other man on board, still caught the eye of my handspike companion. The rest of the crew, myself included, merely stood up to our spikes in heaving, whereas, unwontedly exhilarated, at every turn of the ponderous windlass, my belted comrade leaped atop of it, with might and main giving a downward, thewy, perpendicular heave, his raised eye bent in cheery animation upon the slowly receding shore. Being high lifted above all others was the reason he perceived the object, otherwise unperceivable; and this elevation of his eye was owing to the elevation of his spirits; and this again—for truth must out—to a dram of Peruvian pisco, in guerdon for some kindness done, secretly administered to him that morning by our mulatto steward. Now, certainly, pisco does a deal of mischief in the world; yet seeing that, in the present case, it was the means, though indirect, of rescuing a human being from the most dreadful fate, must we not also needs admit that sometimes pisco does a deal of good?

Glancing across the water in the direction pointed out, I saw some white thing hanging from an inland rock, perhaps half a mile from the sea.

"It is a bird; a white-winged bird; perhaps a—no; it is—it is a handkerchief!"

"Aye, a handkerchief!" echoed my comrade, and with a louder shout apprised the captain.

Quickly now—like the running out and training of a great gun—the long cabin spy-glass was thrust through the mizzen-rigging from the high platform of the poop; whereupon a human figure was plainly seen upon the inland rock, eagerly waving towards us what seemed to be the handkerchief.

Our captain was a prompt, good fellow. Dropping the glass, he lustily ran forward, ordering the anchor to be dropped again; hands to stand by a boat, and lower away.

In a half-hour's time the swift boat returned. It went with six and came with seven; and the seventh was a woman.

It is not artistic heartlessness, but I wish I could but draw in crayons; for this woman was a most touching sight; and crayons, tracing softly melancholy lines, would best depict the mournful image of the dark-damasked Chola widow.

Her story was soon told, and though given in her own strange language was as quickly understood; for our captain, from long trading on the Chilian coast, was well versed in the Spanish. A *Cholo,* or half-breed Indian woman of Payta in Peru, three years gone by, with her young new-wedded husband Felipe, of pure Castilian blood, and her one only Indian brother, Truxill, Hunilla had taken passage on the main in a French whaler, commanded by a joyous man; which vessel, bound to the cruising grounds beyond the Enchanted Isles, proposed passing close by their vicinity. The object of the little party was to procure tortoise oil, a fluid which for its great purity and delicacy is held in high estimation wherever known; and it is well known all along this part of the Pacific coast. With a chest of clothes, tools, cooking utensils, a rude apparatus for trying out the oil, some casks of biscuit, and other things, not omitting two favorite dogs, of which faithful animal all the Cholos are very fond, Hunilla and her companions were safely landed at their chosen place; the Frenchman, according to the contract made ere sailing, engaged to take them off upon returning from a four months' cruise in the westward seas; which interval the three adventurers deemed quite sufficient for their purposes.

On the isle's lone beach they paid him in silver for their passage out, the stranger having declined to carry them at all except upon that condition; though willing to take every means to insure the due fulfilment of his promise. Felipe had striven hard to have this payment put off to the period of the ship's return. But in vain. Still they thought they had, in another way, ample pledge of the good faith of the Frenchman. It was arranged that the expenses of the passage home should not be payable in silver, but in tortoises; one hundred tortoises ready captured to the returning captain's hand. These the Cholos meant to secure after their own work was done, against the probable time of the Frenchman's coming back; and no doubt in prospect already felt, that in those hundred tortoises—now somewhere ranging in the isle's interior—they possessed one hundred hostages. Enough: the vessel sailed; the gazing three on shore answered the loud glee of the singing crew; and ere evening, the French craft was hull down in the distant sea, its masts three faintest lines which quickly faded from Hunilla's eye.

The stranger had given a blithesome promise, and had anchored it with oaths; but oaths and anchors equally will drag; naught else abides on fickle earth but unkept promises of joy. Contrary winds from out unstable skies, or contrary moods of his more varying mind, or shipwreck and sudden death in solitary waves; whatever was the cause, the blithe stranger never was seen again.

Yet, however dire a calamity was here in store, misgivings of it ere due time never disturbed the Cholos' busy minds, now all intent upon the toilsome matter which had brought them hither. Nay, by swift doom coming like the thief at night, ere seven weeks went by, two of the little party were removed from all anxieties of land or sea. No more they sought to gaze with feverish fear, or still more feverish hope, beyond the present's horizon line; but into the furthest future their own silent spirits sailed. By persevering labor beneath that burning sun, Felipe and Truxill had brought down to their hut many scores of tortoises, and tried out the oil, when, elated with their good success, and to reward themselves for such hard work, they, too hastily, made a catamaran, or Indian raft, much used on the Spanish main, and merrily started on a fishing trip, just without a long reef with many jagged gaps, running parallel with the shore, about half a mile from it. By some bad tide or hap, or natural negligence of joyfulness (for though they could not be heard, yet by their gestures they seemed singing at the time), forced in deep water against that iron bar, the ill-made catamaran was overset, and came all to pieces; when dashed by broad-chested swells between their broken logs and the sharp teeth of the reef, both adventurers perished before Hunilla's eyes.

Before Hunilla's eyes they sank. The real woe of this event passed before her sight as some sham tragedy on the stage. She was seated in a rude bower among the withered thickets, crowning a lofty cliff, a little back from the beach. The thickets were so disposed, that in looking upon the sea at large she peered out from among the branches as from the lattice of a high balcony. But upon the day we speak of here, the better to watch the adventure of those two hearts she loved, Hunilla had withdrawn the branches to one side, and held them so. They formed an oval frame, through which the bluely boundless sea rolled like a painted one. And there, the invisible painter painted to her view the wave-tossed and disjointed raft, its once level logs slantingly upheaved, as raking masts, and the four struggling arms undistinguishable among them; and then all subsided into smooth-flowing creamy waters, slowly drifting the splintered wreck; while first and last, no sound of any sort was heard. Death in a silent picture; a dream of the eye; such vanishing shapes as the mirage shows.

So instant was the scene, so trance-like its mild pictorial effect, so distant from her blasted bower and her common sense of things, that Hunilla gazed and gazed, nor raised a finger or a wail. But as good to sit thus dumb, in stupor staring on that dumb show, for all that otherwise might be done. With half a mile of sea between, how could her two enchanted arms aid those four fated ones? The distance long, the time one sand. After the lightning is beheld, what fool shall stay the thunder-bolt? Felipe's body was washed ashore, but Truxill's never came; only his gay, braided hat of golden straw—that same sunflower thing he waved to her, pushing from the strand—and now, to the last gallant, it still saluted her. But Felipe's body floated to the marge, with one arm encirclingly outstretched. Lock-jawed in grim death, the lover-husband softly clasped his bride—true to her even in death's dream. Ah, Heaven, when man thus keeps his faith, wilt Thou be faithless who created the faithful one? But they cannot break faith who never plighted it.

It needs not to be said what nameless misery now wrapped the lonely widow. In telling her own story she passed this almost entirely over, simply recounting the event. Construe the comment of her features as you might, from her mere words little would you have weened that Hunilla was herself the heroine of her tale. But not thus did she defraud us of our tears. All hearts bled that grief could be so brave.

She but showed us her soul's lid, and the strange ciphers thereon engraved; all within, with pride's timidity, was withheld. Yet was there one exception. Holding out her small olive hand before our captain, she said in mild and slowest Spanish, "Señor, I buried him," then paused, struggled as against the writhed coilings of a snake, and cringing suddenly, leaped up, repeating in impassioned pain, "I buried him, my life, my soul!"

Doubtless it was by half-unconscious, automatic motions of her hand, that this heavy-hearted one performed the final office for Felipe, and planted a rude cross of withered sticks—no green ones might be had—at the head of that lonely grave, where rested now in lasting uncomplaint and quiet haven he whom untranquil seas had overthrown.

But some dull sense of another body that should be interred, of another cross that should hallow another grace—unmade as yet—some dull anxiety and pain touching her undiscovered brother, now haunted the oppressed Hunilla. Her hands fresh from the burial earth, she slowly went back to the beach, with unshaped purposes wandering there, her spell-bound eye bent upon the incessant waves. But they bore nothing to her but a dirge, which maddened her to think that murderers should mourn. As time went by, and these things came less dreamingly to her mind, the strong persuasions of her Romish faith, which sets peculiar store by consecrated urns, prompted her to resume in waking earnest that pious search which had but been begun as in somnambulism. Day after day, week after week, she trod the cindery beach, till at length a double motive edged every eager glance. With equal longing she now looked for the living and the dead; the brother and the captain; alike vanished, never to return. Little accurate note of time had Hunilla taken under such emotions as were hers, and little, outside herself, served for calendar or dial. As to poor Crusoe in the self-same sea, no saint's bell pealed forth the lapse of week or month; each day went by unchallenged; no chanticleer announced those sultry dawns, no lowing herds those poisonous nights. All wonted and steadily recurring sounds, human, or humanized by sweet fellowship with man, but one stirred that torrid trance—the cry of dogs; save which naught but the rolling sea invaded it, an all-pervading monotone; and to the widow that was the least loved voice she could have heard.

No wonder that as her thoughts now wandered to the unreturning ship, and were beaten back again, the hope against hope so struggled in her soul, that at length she desperately said, "Not yet, not yet; my foolish heart runs on too fast." So she forced patience for some further weeks. But to those whom earth's sure indraft draws, patience or impatience is still the same.

Hunilla now sought to settle precisely in her mind, to an hour, how long it was since the ship had sailed; and then, with the same precision, how long a space remained to pass. But this proved impossible. What present day or month it was she could not say. Time was her labyrinth, in which Hunilla was entirely lost.

And now follows—

Against my own purposes a pause descends upon me here. One knows not whether nature doth not impose some secrecy upon him who has been privy to certain things. At least, it is to be doubted whether it be good to blazon such. If some books are deemed most baneful and their sale forbid, how, then, with deadlier facts, not dreams of doting men? Those whom books will hurt will not be proof against events. Events, not books, should be forbid. But in all things man sows upon the wind, which bloweth just there whither it listeth; for ill or good, man cannot know. Often ill comes from the good, as good from ill.

When Hunilla—

Dire sight it is to see some silken beast long dally with a golden lizard ere she devour. More terrible, to see how feline Fate will sometimes dally with a human soul, and by a nameless magic make it repulse a sane despair with a hope which is but mad. Unwittingly I imp this cat-like thing, sporting with the heart of him who reads; for if he feel not, he reads in vain.

—"The ship sails this day, to-day," at last said Hunilla to herself; "this gives me certain time to stand on; without certainty I go mad. In loose ignorance I have hoped and hoped; now in firm knowledge I will but wait. Now I live and no longer perish in bewilderings. Holy Virgin, aid me! Thou wilt waft back the ship. Oh, past length of weary weeks—all to be dragged over—to buy the certainty of to-day, I freely give ye, though I tear ye from me!"

As mariners tossed in tempest on some desolate ledge patch them a boat out of the remnants of their vessel's wreck, and launch it in the self-same waves—see here Hunilla, this lone shipwrecked soul, out of treachery invoking trust. Humanity, thou strong thing. I worship thee, not in the laurelled victor, but in this vanquished one.

Truly Hunilla leaned upon a reed, a real one; no metaphor: a real Eastern reed. A piece of hollow cane, drifted from unknown isles, and found upon the beach, its once jagged ends rubbed smoothly even as by sand-paper; its golden glazing gone. Long ground between the sea and land, upper and nether stone, the unvarnished substance was filed bare, and wore another polish now, one with itself, the polish of its agony. Circular lines at intervals cut all round this surface, divided it into six panels of unequal length. In the first were scored the days, each tenth one marked by a longer and deeper notch; the second was scored for the number of sea-fowl eggs for sustenance, picked out from the rocky nests; the third, how many fish had been caught from the shore; the fourth, how many small tortoises found inland; the fifth, how many days of sun; the sixth, of clouds; which last, of the two, was the greater one. Long night of busy numbering, misery's mathematics, to weary her too-wakeful soul to sleep; yet sleep for that was none.

The panel of the days was deeply worn, the long tenth notches half effaced, as alphabets of the blind. Ten thousand times the longing widow had traced her finger over the bamboo—dull flute, which played on, gave no sound—as if counting birds flown by in air, would hasten tortoises creeping through the woods.

After the one hundred and eightieth day no further mark was seen; that last one was the faintest, as the first the deepest.

"There were more days," said our Captain; "many, many more; why did you not go on and notch them too, Hunilla?"

"Señor, ask me not."

"And meantime, did no other vessel pass the isle?"

"Nay, Señor;—but—"

"You do not speak; but *what,* Hunilla?"

"Ask me not, Señor."

"You saw ships pass, far away; you waved to them; they passed on;—was that it, Hunilla?"

"Señor, be it as you say."

Braced against her woe, Hunilla would not—durst not—trust the weakness of her tongue. Then when our Captain asked whether any whaleboats had——

But no, I will not file this thing complete for scoffing souls to quote, and call it firm proof upon their side. The half shall here remain untold. Those two unnamed events which befell Hunilla on this isle, let them abide between her and her God. In nature, as in law, it may be libelous to speak some truths.

Still, how it was that, although our vessel had lain three days anchored nigh the isle, its one human tenant should not have discovered us till just upon the point of sailing, never to revisit so lone and far a spot, this needs explaining ere the sequel come.

The place where the French captain had landed the little party was on the farther and opposite end of the isle. There too it was that they had afterwards built their hut. Nor did the widow in her solitude desert the spot where her loved ones had dwelt with her, and where the dearest of the twain now slept his last long sleep, and all her plaints awaked him not, and he of husbands the most faithful during life.

Now, high broken land rises between the opposite extremities of the isle. A ship anchored at one side is invisible from the other. Neither is the isle so small but a considerable company might wander for days through the wilderness of one side, and never be seen, or their halloos heard, by any stranger holding aloof on the other. Hence Hunilla, who naturally associated the possible coming of ships with her own part of the isle, might to the end have remained quite ignorant of the presence of our vessel, were it not for a mysterious presentiment, borne to her, so our mariners averred, by this isle's enchanted air. Nor did the widow's answer undo the thought.

"How did you come to cross the isle this morning, then, Hunilla?" said the Captain.

"Señor, something came flitting by me. It touched my cheek, my heart, Señor."

"What do you say, Hunilla?"

"I have said, Señor, something came through the air."

It was a narrow chance. For when in crossing the isle Hunilla gained the high land in the centre, she must then for the first have perceived our masts, and also marked that their sails were being loosed, perhaps even heard the echoing chorus of the windlass song. The strange ship was about to sail, and she behind. With all haste she now descends the height on the hither side, but soon loses sight of the ship among the sunken jungles at the mountain's base. She struggles on through the withered branches, which seek at every step to bar her path, till she comes to the isolated rock, still some way from the water. This she climbs, to reassure herself. The ship is still in plainest sight. But now, worn out with over-tension, Hunilla all but faints; she fears to step down from her giddy perch; she is fain to pause, there where she is, and as a last resort catches the turban from her head, unfurls and waves it over the jungles towards us.

During the telling of her story the mariners formed a voiceless circle round Hunilla and the Captain; and when at length the word was given to man the fastest boat, and pull round to the isle's thither side, to bring away Hunilla's chest and the tortoise oil, such alacrity of both cheery and sad obedience seldom before was seen. Little ado was made. Already the anchor had been recommitted to the bottom, and the ship swung calmly to it.

But Hunilla insisted upon accompanying the boat as indispensable pilot to her hidden hut. So being refreshed with the best the steward could supply, she started with us. Nor did ever any wife of the most famous admiral, in her husband's barge, receive more silent reverence of respect, than poor Hunilla from this boat's crew.

Rounding many a vitreous cape and bluff, in two hours' time we shot inside the fatal reef; wound into a secret cove, looked up along a green many-gabled lava wall, and saw the island's solitary dwelling.

It hung upon an impending cliff, sheltered on two sides by tangled thickets, and half-screened from view in front by juttings of the rude stairway, which climbed the precipice from the sea. Built of canes, it was thatched with long, mildewed grass. It seemed an abandoned hayrick, whose haymakers were now no more. The roof inclined but one way; the eaves coming to within two feet of the ground. And here was a simple apparatus to collect the dews, or rather doubly-distilled and finest winnowed rains, which, in mercy or in mockery, the night skies sometimes drop upon these blighted Encantadas. All along beneath the eave, a spotted sheet, quite weather-stained, was spread, pinned to short, upright stakes, set in the shallow sand. A small clinker, thrown into the cloth, weighed its middle down, thereby straining all moisture into a calabash placed below. This vessel supplied each drop of water ever drunk upon the isle by the Cholos. Hunilla told us the calabash would sometimes, but not often, be half filled overnight. It held six quarts, perhaps. "But," said she, "we were used to thirst. At sandy Payta, where I live, no shower from heaven ever fell; all the water there is brought on mules from the inland vales."

Tied among the thickets were some twenty moaning tortoises, supplying Hunilla's lonely larder; while hundreds of vast tableted black bucklers, like displaced, shattered tombstones of dark slate, were also scattered round. These were the skeleton backs of those great tortoises from which Felipe and Truxill had made their precious oil. Several large calabashes and two goodly kegs were filled with it. In a pot near by were the caked crusts of a quantity which had been permitted to evaporate. "They meant to have strained it off next day," said Hunilla, as she turned aside.

I forgot to mention the most singular sight of all, though the first that greeted us after landing.

Some ten small, soft-haired, ringleted dogs, of a beautiful breed, peculiar to Peru, set up a concert of glad welcomings when we gained the beach, which was responded to by Hunilla. Some of these dogs had, since her widowhood, been born upon the isle, the progeny of the two brought from Payta. Owing to the jagged steeps and pitfalls, tortuous thickets, sunken clefts and perilous intricacies of all sorts in the interior, Hunilla, admonished by the loss of one favorite among them, never allowed these delicate creatures to follow her in her occasional birds'-nests climbs and other wanderings; so that, through long habituation, they offered not to follow, when that morning she crossed the land, and her own soul was then too full of other things to heed their lingering behind. Yet, all along she had so clung to them, that, besides what moisture they lapped up at early daybreak from the small scoop-holes among the adjacent rocks, she had shared the dew of her calabash among them; never laying by any considerable store against those prolonged and utter droughts which, in some disastrous seasons, warp these isles.

Having pointed out, at our desire, what few things she would like transported to the ship—her chest, the oil, not omitting the live tortoises which she intended for a grateful present to our Captain—we immediately set to work, carrying them to the boat down the long, sloping stair of deeply-shadowed rock. While my comrades were thus employed, I looked, and Hunilla had disappeared.

It was not curiosity alone, but, it seems to me, something different mingled with it, which prompted me to drop my tortoise, and once more gaze slowly around. I remembered the husband buried by

Hunilla's hands. A narrow pathway led into a dense part of the thickets. Following it through many mazes, I came out upon a small, round, open space, deeply chambered there.

The mound rose in the middle; a bare heap of finest sand, like that unverdured heap found at the bottom of an hour-glass run out. At its head stood the cross of withered sticks; the dry, peeled bark still fraying from it; its transverse limb tied up with rope, and forlornly adroop in silent air.

Hunilla was partly prostrate upon the grave; her dark head bowed, and lost in her long, loosened Indian hair; her hands extended to the cross-foot, with a little brass crucifix clasped between; a crucifix worn featureless, like an ancient graven knocker long plied in vain. She did not see me, and I made no noise, but slid aside, and left the spot.

A few moments ere all was ready for our going, she reappeared among us. I looked into her eyes, but saw no tear. There was something which seemed strangely haughty in her air, and yet it was the air of woe. A Spanish and an Indian grief, which would not visibly lament. Pride's height in vain abased to proneness on the rack; nature's pride subduing nature's torture.

Like pages the small and silken dogs surrounded her, as she slowly descended towards the beach. She caught the two most eager creatures in her arms:—*"Tita mia! Tomotita mia!"*—and fondling them, inquired how many could we take on board.

The mate commanded the boat's crew; not a hard-hearted man, but his way of life had been such that in most things, even in the smallest, simple utility was his leading motive.

"We cannot take them all, Hunilla; our supplies are short; the winds are unreliable; we may be a good many days going to Tumbez. So take those you have, Hunilla, but no more."

She was in the boat; the oarsmen, too, were seated; all save one, who stood ready to push off and then spring himself. With the sagacity of their race, the dogs now seemed aware that they were in the very instant of being deserted upon a barren strand. The gunwales of the boat were high; its prow—presented inland—was lifted; so, owing to the water, which they seemed instinctively to shun, the dogs could not well leap into the little craft. But their busy paws hard scraped the prow, as it had been some farmer's door shutting them out from shelter in a winter storm. A clamorous agony of alarm. They did not howl, or whine; they all but spoke.

"Push off! Give way!" cried the mate. The boat gave one heavy drag and lurch, and next moment shot swiftly from the beach, turned on her heel, and sped. The dogs ran howling along the water's marge; now pausing to gaze at the flying boat, then motioning as if to leap in chase, but mysteriously withheld themselves; and again ran howling along the beach. Had they been human beings, hardly would they have more vividly inspired the sense of desolation. The oars were plied as confederate feathers of two wings. No one spoke. I looked back upon the beach, and then upon Hunilla, but her face was set in a stern dusky calm. The dogs crouching in her lap vainly licked her rigid hands. She never looked behind her, but sat motionless, till we turned a promontory of the coast and lost all sights and sounds astern. She seemed as one who, having experienced the sharpest of mortal pangs, was henceforth content to have all lesser heart-strings riven, one by one. To Hunilla, pain seemed so necessary, that pain in other beings, though by love and sympathy made her own, was unrepiningly to be borne. A heart of yearning in a frame of steel. A heart of earthly yearning, frozen by the frost which falleth from the sky.

The sequel is soon told. After a long passage, vexed by calms and baffling winds, we made the little port of Tumbez in Peru, there to recruit the ship. Payta was not very distant. Our captain sold the tortoise oil to a Tumbez merchant; and adding to the silver a contribution from all hands, gave it to our silent passenger, who knew not what the mariners had done.

The last seen of lone Hunilla she was passing into Payta town, riding upon a small gray ass; and before her on the ass's shoulders, she eyed the jointed workings of the beast's armorial cross.

Theodore Dreiser

The Lost Phœbe

THEY lived together in a part of the country which was not so prosperous as it had once been, about three miles from one of those small towns that, instead of increasing in population, is steadily decreasing. The territory was not very thickly settled; perhaps a house every other mile or so, with large areas of corn- and wheat-land and fallow fields that at odd seasons had been sown to timothy and clover. Their particular house was part log and part frame, the log portion being the old original home of Henry's grandfather. The new portion, of now rain-beaten, time-worn slabs, through which the wind squeaked in the chinks at times, and which several overshadowing elms and a butternut-tree made picturesque and reminiscently pathetic, but a little damp, was erected by Henry when he was twenty-one and just married.

That was forty-eight years before. The furniture inside, like the house outside, was old and mildewy and reminiscent of an earlier day. You have seen the what-not of cherry wood, perhaps, with spiral legs and fluted top. It was there. The old-fashioned four poster bed, with its ball-like protuberances and deep curving incisions, was there also, a sadly alienated descendant of an early Jacobean ancestor. The bureau of cherry was also high and wide and solidly built, but faded-looking, and with a musty odor. The rag carpet that underlay all these sturdy examples of enduring furniture was a weak, faded, lead-and-pink-colored affair woven by Phœbe Ann's own hands, when she was fifteen years younger than she was when she died. The creaky wooden loom on which it had been done now stood like a dusty, bony skeleton, along with a broken rocking-chair, a worm-eaten clothespress—Heaven knows how old—a lime-stained bench that had once been used to keep flowers on outside the door, and other decrepit factors of household utility, in an east room that was a lean-to against this so-called main portion. All sorts of other broken-down furniture were about this place; an antiquated clothes-horse, cracked in two of its ribs; a broken mirror in an old cherry frame, which had fallen from a nail and cracked itself three days before their youngest son, Jerry, died; an extension hat-rack, which once had had porcelain knobs on the ends of its pegs; and a sewing-machine, long since outdone in its clumsy mechanism by rivals of a newer generation.

The orchard to the east of the house was full of gnarled old apple-trees, worm-eaten as to trunks and branches, and fully ornamented with green and white lichens, so that it had a sad, greenish-white, silvery effect in moonlight. The low outhouses, which had once housed chickens, a horse or two, a cow, and several pigs, were covered with patches of moss as to their roof, and the sides had been free of paint for so long that they were blackish gray as to color, and a little spongy. The picket-fence in front, with its gate squeaky and askew, and the side fences of the stake-and-rider type were in an equally run-down condition. As a matter of fact, they had aged synchronously with the persons who lived here, old Henry Reifsneider and his wife Phœbe Ann.

They had lived here, these two, ever since their marriage, forty-eight years before, and Henry had lived here before that from his childhood up. His father and mother, well along in years when he was a boy, had invited him to bring his wife here when he had first fallen in love and decided to marry; and he had done so. His father and mother were the companions of himself and his wife for ten years after they were married, when both died; and then Henry and Phœbe were left with their five children growing lustily apace. But all sorts of things had happened since then. Of the seven children, all told, that had been born to them, three had died; one girl had gone to Kansas; one boy had gone to Sioux Falls, never even to be heard of after; another boy had gone to Washington; and the last girl lived five counties away in the same State, but was so burdened with cares of her own that she rarely gave them a thought. Time and a commonplace home life that had never been attractive had weaned them thoroughly, so that, wherever they were, they gave little thought as to how it might be with their father and mother.

Old Henry Reifsneider and his wife Phœbe were a loving couple. You perhaps know how it is with simple natures that fasten themselves like lichens on the stones of circumstance and weather their days to a crumbling conclusion. The great world sounds widely, but it has no call for them. They have no soaring intellect. The orchard, the meadow, the corn-field, the pig-pen, and the chicken-lot measure the range of their human activities. When the wheat is headed it is reaped and threshed; when the corn is browned and frosted it is cut and shocked; when the timothy is in full head it is cut, and the hay-cock erected. After that comes winter, with the hauling of grain to market, the sawing and splitting of wood, the simple chores of fire-building, meal-getting, occasional repairing, and visiting. Beyond these and the changes of weather—the snows, the rains, and the fair days—there are no immediate, significant things. All the rest of life is a far-off, clamorous phantasmagoria, flickering like Northern lights in the night, and sounding as faintly as cow-bells tinkling in the distance.

Old Henry and his wife Phœbe were as fond of each other as it is possible for two old people to be who have nothing else in this life to be fond of. He was a thin old man, seventy when she died, a queer, crotchety person with coarse gray-black hair and beard, quite straggly and unkempt. He looked at you out of dull, fishy, watery eyes that had deep-brown crow's-feet at the sides. His clothes, like the clothes of many farmers, were aged and angular and baggy, standing out at the pockets, not fitting about the neck, protuberant and worn at elbow and knee. Phœbe Ann was thin and shapeless, a very umbrella of a woman, clad in shabby black, and with a black bonnet for her best wear. As time had passed, and they had only themselves to look after, their movements had become slower and slower, their activities fewer and fewer. The annual keep of pigs had been reduced from five to one grunting porker, and the single horse which Henry now retained was a sleepy animal, not over-nourished and not very clean. The chickens, of which formerly there was a large flock, had almost disappeared, owing to ferrets, foxes, and the lack of proper care, which produces disease. The former healthy garden was now a straggling memory of itself, and the vines and flower-beds that formerly ornamented the windows and dooryard had now become choking thickets. A will had been made which divided the small tax-eaten property equally among the remaining four, so that it was really of no interest to any of them. Yet these two lived together in peace and sympathy, only that now and then old Henry would become unduly cranky, complaining almost invariably that something had been neglected or mislaid which was of no importance at all.

"Phœbe, where's my corn-knife? You ain't never minded to let my things alone no more."

"Now you hush, Henry," his wife would caution him in a cracked and squeaky voice. "If you don't, I'll leave yuh. I'll git up and walk out of here some day, and then where would y' be? Y' ain't got anybody but me to look after yuh, so yuh just behave yourself. Your corn-knife's on the mantel where it's allus been unless you've gone an' put it summers else."

Old Henry, who knew his wife would never leave him in any circumstances, used to speculate at times as to what he would do if she were to die. That was the one leaving that he really feared. As he climbed on the chair at night to wind the old, long-pendulumed, double-weighted clock, or went finally to the front and the back door to see that they were safely shut in, it was a comfort to know that Phœbe was there, properly ensconced on her side of the bed, and that if he stirred restlessly in the night, she would be there to ask what he wanted.

"Now, Henry, do lie still! You're as restless as a chicken."

"Well, I can't sleep, Phœbe."

"Well, yuh needn't roll so, anyhow. Yuh kin let me sleep."

This usually reduced him to a state of somnolent ease. If she wanted a pail of water, it was a grumbling pleasure for him to get it; and if she did rise first to build the fires, he saw that the wood was cut and placed within easy reach. They divided this simple world nicely between them.

As the years had gone on, however, fewer and fewer people had called. They were well-known for a distance of as much as ten square miles as old Mr. and Mrs. Reifsneider, honest, moderately Christian, but too old to be really interesting any longer. The writing of letters had become an almost impossible burden too difficult to continue or even negotiate via others, although an occasional letter still did arrive from the daughter in Pemberton County. Now and then some old friend stopped with a pie or cake or a roasted chicken or duck, or merely to see that they were well; but even these kindly minded visits were no longer frequent.

One day in the early spring of her sixty-fourth year Mrs. Reifsneider took sick, and from a low fever passed into some indefinable ailment which, because of her age, was no longer curable. Old Henry drove to Swinnerton, the neighboring town, and procured a doctor. Some friends called, and the immediate care of her was taken off his hands. Then one chill spring night she died, and old Henry, in a fog of sorrow and uncertainty, followed her body to the nearest graveyard, an unattractive space with a few pines growing in it. Although he might have gone to the daughter in Pemberton or sent for her, it was really too much trouble and he was too weary and fixed. It was suggested to him at once by one friend and another that he come to stay with them awhile, but he did not see fit. He was so old and so fixed in his notions and so accustomed to the exact surroundings he had known all his days, that he could not think of leaving. He wanted to remain near where they had put his Phœbe; and the fact that he would have to live alone did not trouble him in the least. The living children were notified and the care of him offered if he would leave, but he would not.

"I kin make a shift for myself," he continually announced to old Dr. Morrow, who had attended his wife in this case. "I kin cook a little, and, besides, it don't take much more'n coffee an' bread in the mornin's to satisfy me. I'll get along now well enough. Yuh just let me be." And after many pleadings and proffers of advice, with supplies of coffee and bacon and baked bread duly offered and accepted, he was left to himself. For a while he sat idly outside his door brooding in the spring sun. He tried to revive his interest in farming, and to keep himself busy and free from thought by looking after the fields, which of late had been much neglected. It was a gloomy thing to come in of an evening, however, or in the afternoon and find no shadow of Phœbe where everything suggested her. By degrees he put a few of her things away. At night he sat beside his lamp and read in the papers that were left him occasionally or in a Bible that he had neglected for years, but he could get little solace from these things. Mostly he held his hand over his mouth and looked at the floor as he sat and thought of what had become of her, and how soon he himself would die. He made a great business of making his coffee in the morning and frying himself a little bacon at night; but his appetite was gone. The shell in which he had been housed so long seemed vacant, and its shadows were suggestive of immedicable griefs. So he lived quite dolefully for five long months, and then a change began.

It was one night, after he had looked after the front and the back door, wound the clock, blown out the light, and gone through all the selfsame motions that he had indulged in for years, that he went to bed not so much to sleep as to think. It was a moonlight night. The green-lichen-covered orchard just outside and to be seen from his bed where he now lay was a silvery affair, sweetly spectral. The moon shone through the east windows, throwing the pattern of the panes on the wooden floor, and making the old furniture, to which he was accustomed, stand out dimly in the room. As usual he had been thinking of Phœbe and the years when they had been young together, and of the children who had gone, and the poor shift he was making of his present days. The house was coming to be in a very bad state indeed. The bed-clothes were in disorder and not clean, for he made a wretched shift of washing. It was a terror to him. The roof leaked, causing things, some of them, to remain damp for weeks at a time, but he was getting into that brooding state where he would accept anything rather than exert himself. He preferred to pace slowly to and fro or to sit and think.

By twelve o'clock of this particular night he was asleep, however, and by two had waked again. The moon by this time had shifted to a position on the western side of the house, and it now shone in through the windows of the living-room and those of the kitchen beyond. A certain combination of furniture—a chair near a table, with his coat on it, the half-open kitchen door casting a shadow, and the position of a lamp near a paper—gave him an exact representation of Phœbe leaning over the table as he had often seen her do in life. It gave him a great start. Could it be she—or her ghost? He had scarcely ever believed in spirits; and still——He looked at her fixedly in the feeble half-light, his old hair tingling oddly at the roots, and then sat up. The figure did not move. He put his thin legs out of the bed and sat looking at her, wondering if this could really be Phœbe. They had talked of ghosts often in their lifetime, of apparitions and omens; but they had never agreed that such things could be. It had never been a part of his wife's creed that she could have a spirit that could return to walk the earth. Her after-world was quite a different affair, a vague heaven, no less, from which the righteous did not trouble to return. Yet here she was now, bending over the table in her black skirt and gray shawl, her pale profile outlined against the moonlight.

"Phœbe," he called, thrilling from head to toe and putting out one bony hand, "have yuh come back?"

The figure did not stir, and he arose and walked uncertainly to the door, looking at it fixedly the while. As he drew near, however, the apparition resolved itself into its primal content—his old coat over the high-backed chair, the lamp by the paper, the half-open door.

"Well," he said to himself, his mouth open, "I thought shore I saw her." And he ran his hand strangely and vaguely through his hair, the while his nervous tension relaxed. Vanished as it had, it gave him the idea that she might return.

Another night, because of this first illusion, and because his mind was now constantly on her and he was old, he looked out of the window that was nearest his bed and commanded a hen-coop and pig-pen and a part of the wagon-shed, and there, a faint mist exuding from the damp of the ground, he thought he saw her again. It was one of those little wisps of mist, one of those faint exhalations of the earth that rise in a cool night after a warm day, and flicker like small white cypresses of fog before they disappear. In life it had been a custom of hers to cross this lot from her kitchen door to the pig-pen to throw in any scrap that was left from her cooking, and here she was again. He sat up and watched it strangely, doubtfully, because of his previous experience, but inclined, because of the nervous titillation that passed over his body, to believe that spirits really were, and that Phœbe, who would be concerned because of his lonely state, must be thinking about him, and hence returning. What other way would she have? How otherwise could she express herself? It would be within the province of her charity so to do, and like her loving interest in him. He quivered and watched it eagerly; but, a faint breath of air stirring, it wound away toward the fence and disappeared.

A third night, as he was actually dreaming, some ten days later, she came to his bedside and put her hand on his head.

"Poor Henry!" she said. "It's too bad."

He roused out of his sleep, actually to see her, he thought, moving from his bed-room into the one living-room, her figure a shadowy mass of black. The weak straining of his eyes caused little points of light to flicker about the outlines of her form. He arose, greatly astonished, walked the floor in the cool room, convinced that Phœbe was coming back to him. If he only thought sufficiently, if he made it perfectly clear by his feeling that he needed her greatly, she would come back, this kindly wife, and tell him what to do. She would perhaps be with him much of the time, in the night, anyhow; and that would make him less lonely, this state more endurable.

In age and with the feeble it is not such a far cry from the subtleties of illusion to actual hallucination, and in due time this transition was made for Henry. Night after night he waited, expecting her return. Once in his weird mood he thought he saw a pale light moving about the room, and another time he thought he saw her walking in the orchard after dark. It was one morning when the details of his lonely state were virtually unendurable that he woke with the thought that she was not dead. How he had arrived at this conclusion it is hard to say. His mind had gone. In its place was a fixed illusion. He and Phœbe had had a senseless quarrel. He had reproached her for not leaving his pipe where he was accustomed to find it, and she had left. It was an aberrated fulfillment of her old jesting threat that if he did not behave himself she would leave him.

"I guess I could find yuh ag'in," he had always said. But her cackling threat had always been.

"Yuh'll not find me if I ever leave yuh. I guess I kin git some place where yuh can't find me."

This morning when he arose he did not think to build the fire in the customary way or to grind his coffee and cut his bread, as was his wont, but solely to meditate as to where he should search for her and how he should induce her to come back. Recently the one horse had been dispensed with because he found it cumbersome and beyond his needs. He took down his soft crush hat after he had dressed himself, a new glint of interest and determination in his eye, and taking his black crook cane from behind the door, where he had always placed it, started out briskly to look for her among the nearest neighbors. His old shoes clumped soundly in the dust as he walked, and his gray-black locks, now grown rather long, straggled out in a dramatic fringe or halo from under his hat. His short coat stirred busily as he walked, and his hands and face were peaked and pale.

"Why, hello, Henry! Where're yuh goin' this mornin'?" inquired Farmer Dodge, who, hauling a load of wheat to market, encountered him on the public road. He had not seen the aged farmer in months, not since his wife's death, and he wondered now, seeing him looking so spry.

"Yuh ain't seen Phœbe, have yuh?" inquired the old man, looking up quizzically.

"Phœbe who?" inquired Farmer Dodge, not for the moment connecting the name with Henry's dead wife.

"Why, my wife Phœbe, o'course. Who do yuh s'pose I mean?" He stared up with a pathetic sharpness of glance from under his shaggy, gray eyebrows.

"Wall, I'll swan, Henry, yuh ain't jokin', are yuh?" said the solid Dodge, a pursy man, with a smooth, hard, red face. "It can't be your wife yuh're talkin' about. She's dead."

"Dead! Shucks!" retorted the demented Reifsneider. "She left me early this mornin', while I was sleepin'. She allus got up to build the fire, but she's gone now. We had a little spat last night, an' I guess that's the reason. But I guess I kin find her. She's gone over to Matilda Race's; that's where she's gone."

He started briskly up the road, leaving the amazed Dodge to stare in wonder after him.

"Well, I'll be switched!" he said aloud to himself. "He's clean out'n his head. That poor old feller's been livin' down there till he's gone outen his mind. I'll have to notify the authorities." And he flicked his whip with great enthusiasm. "Geddap!" he said, and was off.

Reifsneider met no one else in this poorly populated region until he reached the whitewashed fence of Matilda Race and her husband three miles away. He had passed several other houses en route, but these not being within the range of his illusion were not considered. His wife, who had known Matilda well, must be here. He opened the picket-gate which guarded the walk, and stamped briskly up to the door.

"Why, Mr. Reifsneider," exclaimed old Matilda herself, a stout woman, looking out of the door in answer to his knock, "what brings yuh here this mornin'?"

"Is Phœbe here?" he demanded eagerly.

"Phœbe who? What Phœbe?" replied Mrs. Race, curious as to this sudden development of energy on his part.

"Why, my Phœbe, o'course, My wife Phœbe. Who do yuh s'pose? Ain't she here now?"

"Lawsy me!" exclaimed Mrs. Race, opening her mouth. "Yuh pore man! So you're clean out'n your mind now. Yuh come right in and sit down. I'll git yuh a cup o' coffee. O' course your wife ain't here; but yuh come in an' sit down. I'll find her fer yuh after a while. I know where she is."

The old farmer's eyes softened, and he entered. He was so thin and pale a specimen, pantalooned and patriarchal, that he aroused Mrs. Race's extremest sympathy as he took off his hat and laid it on his knees quite softly and mildly.

"We had a quarrel last night, an' she left me," he volunteered.

"Laws! laws!" sighed Mrs. Race, there being no one present with whom to share her astonishment as she went to her kitchen. "The pore man! Now somebody's just got to look after him. He can't be allowed to run around the country this way lookin' for his dead wife. It's turrible."

She boiled him a pot of coffee and brought in some of her new-baked bread and fresh butter. She set out some of her best jam and put a couple of eggs to boil, lying whole-heartedly the while.

"Now yuh stay right there, Uncle Henry, till Jake comes in, an' I'll send him to look for Phœbe. I think it's more'n likely she's over to Swinnerton with some o' her friends. Anyhow, we'll find out. Now yuh just drink this coffee an' eat this bread. Yuh must be tired. Yuh've had a long walk this mornin'." Her idea was to take counsel with Jake, "her man," and perhaps have him notify the authorities.

She bustled about, meditating on the uncertainties of life, while old Reifsneider thrummed on the rim of his hat with his pale fingers and later ate abstractedly of what she offered. His mind was on his wife, however, and since she was not here, or did not appear, it wandered vaguely away to a family by the name of Murray, miles away in another direction. He decided after a time that he would not wait for Jake Race to hunt his wife but would seek her for himself. He must be on, and urge her to come back.

"Well, I'll be goin'," he said, getting up and looking strangely about him. "I guess she didn't come here after all. She went over to the Murrays', I guess. I'll not wait any longer, Mis' Race. There's lot to do over to the house to-day." And out he marched in the face of her protests taking to the dusty road again in the warm spring sun, his cane striking the earth as he went.

It was two hours later that this pale figure of a man appeared in the Murrays' doorway, dusty, perspiring, eager. He had tramped all of five miles, and it was noon. An amazed husband and wife of sixty heard his strange query, and realized also that he was mad. They begged him to stay to dinner, intending to notify the authorities later and see what could be done; but though he stayed to partake of a little something, he did not stay long, and was off again to another distant farmhouse, his idea of many things to do and his need of Phœbe impelling him. So it went for that day and the next and the next, the circle of his inquiry ever widening.

The process by which a character assumes the significance of being peculiar, his antics weird, yet harmless, in such a community is often involute and pathetic. This day, as has been said, saw Reifsneider at other doors, eagerly asking his unnatural question, and leaving a trail of amazement, sympathy, and pity in his wake. Although the authorities were informed—the county sheriff, no less—it was not deemed advisable to take him into custody; for when those who knew old Henry, and had for so long, reflected on the condition of the county insane asylum, a place which, because of the poverty of the district, was of staggering aberration and sickening environment, it was decided to let him remain at large; for, strange to relate, it was found on investigation that at night he returned peaceably enough to his lonesome domicile there to discover whether his wife had returned, and to brood in loneliness until the morning. Who would lock up a thin, eager, seeking old man with iron-gray hair and an attitude of kindly, innocent inquiry, particularly when he was well known for a past of only kindly servitude and reliability? Those who had known him best rather agreed that he should be allowed to roam at large. He could do no harm. There were many who were willing to help him as to food, old clothes, the odds and ends of his daily life—at least at first. His figure after a time became not so much a common-place as an accepted curiosity, and the replies, "Why, no, Henry; I ain't see her," or "No, Henry; she ain't been here to-day," more customary.

For several years thereafter then he was an odd figure in the sun and rain, on dusty roads and muddy ones, encountered occasionally in strange and unexpected places, pursuing his endless search. Undernourishment, after a time, although the neighbors and those who knew his history gladly contributed from their store, affected his body; for he walked much and ate little. The longer he roamed the public highway in this manner, the deeper became his strange hallucination; and finding it harder and harder to return from his more and more distant pilgrimages, he finally began taking a few utensils with him from his home, making a small package of them, in order that he might not be compelled to return. In an old tin coffee-pot of large size he placed a small tin cup, a knife, fork, and spoon, some salt and pepper, and to the outside of it, by a string forced through a pierced hole, he fastened a plate, which could be released, and which was his woodland table. It was no trouble for him to secure the little food that he needed, and with a strange, almost religious dignity, he had no hesitation in asking for that much. By degrees his hair became longer and longer, his once black hat became an earthen brown, and his clothes threadbare and dusty.

For all of three years he walked, and none knew how wide were his perambulations, nor how he survived the storms and cold. They could not see him, with homely rural understanding and forethought, sheltering himself in hay-cocks, or by the sides of cattle, whose warm bodies protected him from the cold, and whose dull understandings were not opposed to his harmless presence. Overhanging rocks and trees kept him at times from the rain, and a friendly hay-loft or corn-crib was not above his humble consideration.

The involute progression of hallucination is strange. From asking at doors and being constantly rebuffed or denied, he finally came to the conclusion that although his Phœbe might not be in any of the houses at the doors of which he inquired, she might nevertheless be within the sound of his voice. And so, from patient inquiry, he began to call sad, occasional cries, that ever and anon waked the quiet landscapes and ragged hill regions, and set to echoing his thin "O-o-o Phœbe! O-o-o Phœbe!" It had a pathetic, albeit insane, ring, and many a farmer or plowboy came to know it even from afar and say, "There goes old Reifsneider."

Another thing that puzzled him greatly after a time and after many hundreds of inquiries was, when he no longer had any particular dooryard in view and no special inquiry to make, which way to go. These cross-roads, which occasionally led in four or even six directions, came after a time to puzzle him. But to solve this knotty problem, which became more and more of a puzzle, there came to his aid another hallucination. Phœbe's spirit or some power of the air or wind or nature would tell him. If he stood at the center of the parting of the ways, closed his eyes, turned thrice about, and called "O-o-o Phœbe!" twice, and then threw his cane straight before him, that would surely indicate which way to go for Phœbe, or one of these mystic powers would surely govern its direction and fall! In whichever direction it went, even though, as was not infrequently the case, it took him back along the path he had already come, or across fields, he was not so far gone in his mind but that he gave himself ample time to search before he called again. Also the hallucination seemed to persist that at some time he would surely find her. There were hours when his feet were sore, and his limbs weary, when he would stop in the heat to wipe his seamed brow, or in the cold to beat his arms. Sometimes, after throwing away his cane, and finding it indicating the direction from which he had just come, he would shake his head wearily and philosophically, as if contemplating the unbelievable or an untoward fate, and then start briskly off. His strange figure came finally to be known in the farthest reaches of three or four counties. Old Reifsneider was a pathetic character. His fame was wide.

Near a little town called Watersville, in Green County, perhaps four miles from that minor center of human activity, there was a place or precipice locally known as the Red Cliff, a sheer wall of red sandstone, perhaps a hundred feet high, which raised its sharp face for half a mile or more above the fruitful cornfields and orchards that lay beneath, and which was surmounted by a thick grove of trees. The slope that slowly led up to it from the opposite side was covered by a rank growth of beech, hickory, and ash, through which threaded a number of wagon-tracks crossing at various angles. In fair weather it had become old Reifsneider's habit, so inured was he by now to the open, to make his bed in some such patch of trees as this to fry his bacon or boil his eggs at the foot of some tree before laying himself down for the night. Occasionally, so light and inconsequential was his sleep, he would walk at night. More often, the moonlight or some sudden wind stirring in the trees or a reconnoitering animal arousing him, he would sit up and think, or pursue his quest in the moonlight or the dark, a strange, unnatural, half wild, half savage-looking but utterly harmless creature, calling at lonely road crossings, staring at dark and shuttered houses, and wondering where, where Phœbe could really be.

That particular lull that comes in the systole-diastole of this earthly ball at two o'clock in the morning invariably aroused him, and though he might not go any farther he would sit up and contemplate the darkness or the stars, wondering. Sometimes in the strange processes of his mind he would fancy that he saw moving among the trees the figure of his lost wife, and then he would get up to follow, taking his utensils, always on a string, and his cane. If she seemed to evade him too easily he would run, or plead, or, suddenly losing track of the fancied figure, stand awed or disappointed, grieving for the moment over the almost insurmountable difficulties of his search.

It was in the seventh year of these hopeless peregrinations, in the dawn of a similar springtime to that in which his wife had died, that he came at last one night to the vicinity of this selfsame patch that crowned the rise to the Red Cliff. His far-flung cane, used as a divining-rod at the last cross-roads, had brought him hither. He had walked many, many miles. It was after ten o'clock at night, and he was very weary. Long wandering and little eating had left him but a shadow of his former self. It was a question now not so much of physical strength but of spiritual endurance which kept him up. He had scarcely eaten this day, and now exhausted he set himself down in the dark to rest and possibly to sleep.

Curiously on this occasion a strange suggestion of the presence of his wife surrounded him. It would not be long now, he counseled with himself, although the long months had brought him nothing, until he should see her, talk to her. He fell asleep after a time, his head on his knees. At midnight the moon began to rise, and at two in the morning, his wakeful hour, was a large silver disk shining through the trees to the east. He opened his eyes when the radiance became strong, making a silver pattern at his feet and lighting the woods with strange lusters and silvery, shadowy forms. As usual, his old notion that his wife must be near occurred to him on this occasion, and he looked about him with a speculative, anticipatory eye. What was it that moved in the distant shadows along the path by which he had entered—a pale, flickering will-o'-the-wisp that bobbed gracefully among the trees and riveted his expectant gaze? Moonlight and shadows combined to give it a strange form and a stranger reality, this fluttering of bogfire or dancing of wandering fireflies. Was it truly his lost Phœbe? By a circuitous route it passed about him, and in his fevered state he fancied that he could see the very eyes of her, not as she was when he last saw her in the black dress and shawl but now a strangely younger Phœbe, gayer, sweeter, the one whom he had known years before as a girl. Old Reifsneider got up. He had been expecting and dreaming of this hour all these years, and now as he saw the feeble light dancing lightly before him he peered at it questioningly, one thin hand in his gray hair.

Of a sudden there came to him now for the first time in many years the full charm of her girlish figure as he had known it in boyhood, the pleasing, sympathetic smile, the brown hair, the blue sash she had once worn about her waist at a picnic, her gay, graceful movements. He walked around the base of the tree, straining with his eyes, forgetting for once his cane and utensils, and following eagerly after. On she moved before him, a will-o'-the-wisp of the spring, a little flame above her head, and it seemed as though among the small saplings of ash and beech and the thick trunks of hickory and elm that she signaled with a young, a lightsome hand.

"O Phœbe! Phœbe!" he called. "Have yuh really come? Have yuh really answered me?" And hurrying faster, he fell once, scrambling lamely to his feet, only to see the light in the distance dancing illusively on. On and on he hurried until he was fairly running, brushing his ragged arms against the trees, striking his hands and face against impeding twigs. His hat was gone, his lungs were breathless, his reason quite astray, when coming to the edge of the cliff he saw her below among a silvery bed of apple-trees now blooming in the spring.

"O Phœbe!" he called. "O Phœbe! Oh, no, don't leave me!" And feeling the lure of a world where love was young and Phœbe as this vision presented her, a delightful epitome of their quondam youth, he gave a gay cry of "Oh, wait, Phœbe!" and leaped.

Some farmer-boys, reconnoitering this region of bounty and prospect some few days afterward, found first the tin utensils tied together under the tree where he had left them, and then later at the foot of the cliff, pale, broken, but elate, a molded smile of peace and delight upon his lips, his body. His old hat was discovered lying under some low-growing saplings the twigs of which had held it back. No one of all the simple population knew how eagerly and joyously he had found his lost mate.

Sherwood Anderson

The Egg

MY FATHER was, I am sure, intended by nature to be a cheerful, kindly man. Until he was thirty-four years old he worked as a farmhand for a man named Thomas Butterworth whose place lay near the town of Bidwell, Ohio. He had then a horse of his own, and on Saturday evenings drove into town to spend a few hours in social intercourse with other farmhands. In town he drank several glasses of beer and stood about in Ben Head's saloon—crowded on Saturday evenings with visiting farmhands. Songs were sung and glasses thumped on the bar. At ten o'clock father drove home along a lonely country road, made his horse comfortable for the night, and himself went to bed, quite happy in his position in life. He had at that time no notion of trying to rise in the world.

It was in the spring of his thirty-fifth year that father married my mother, then a country school-teacher, and in the following spring I came wriggling and crying into the world. Something happened to the two people. They became ambitious. The American passion for getting up in the world took possession of them.

It may have been that mother was responsible. Being a schoolteacher she had no doubt read books and magazines. She had, I presume, read of how Garfield, Lincoln, and other Americans rose from poverty to fame and greatness, and as I lay beside her—in the days of her lying-in—she may have dreamed that I would some day rule men and cities. At any rate she induced father to give up his place as a farmhand, sell his horse, and embark on an independent enterprise of his own. She was a tall silent woman with a long nose and troubled gray eyes. For herself she wanted nothing. For father and myself she was incurably ambitious.

The first venture into which the two people went turned out badly. They rented ten acres of poor stony land on Grigg's Road, eight miles from Bidwell, and launched into chicken-raising. I grew into boyhood on the place and got my first impressions of life there. From the beginning they were impressions of disaster, and if, in my turn, I am a gloomy man inclined to see the darker side of life, I attribute it to the fact that what should have been for me the happy joyous days of childhood were spent on a chicken farm.

One unversed in such matters can have no notion of the many and tragic things that can happen to a chicken. It is born out of an egg, lives for a few weeks as a tiny fluffy thing such as you will see pictured on Easter cards, then becomes hideously naked, eats quantities of corn and meal bought by the sweat of your father's brow, gets diseases called pip, cholera, and other names, stands looking with stupid eyes at the sun, becomes sick and dies. A few hens and now and then a rooster, intended to serve God's mysterious ends, struggle through to maturity. The hens lay eggs out of which come other chickens and the dreadful cycle is thus made complete. It is all unbelievably complex. Most philosophers must have been raised on chicken farms. One hopes for so much from a chicken and is so dreadfully disillusioned. Small chickens, just setting out on the journey of life, look so bright and alert and they are in fact so dreadfully stupid. They are so much like people they mix one up in one's judgments of life. If disease does not kill them, they wait until your expectations are thoroughly aroused and then walk under the wheels of a wagon—to go squashed and dead back to their maker. Vermin infest their youth, and fortunes must be spent for curative powders. In later life I have seen how a literature has been built up on the subject of fortunes to be made out of the raising of chickens. It is intended to be read by the gods who have just eaten of the tree of the knowledge of good and evil. It is a hopeful literature and declares that much may be done by simple ambitious people who own a few hens. Do not be led astray by it. It was not written for you. Go hunt for gold on the frozen hills of Alaska, put your faith in the honesty of a politician, believe if you will that the world is daily growing better and that good will triumph over evil, but do not read and believe the literature that is written concerning the hen. It was not written for you.

I, however, digress. My tale does not primarily concern itself with the hen. If correctly told it will center on the egg. For ten years my father and mother struggled to make our chicken farm pay and then they gave up that struggle and began another. They moved into the town of Bidwell, Ohio, and embarked in the restaurant business. After ten years of worry with incubators that did not hatch, and with tiny—and in their own way lovely—balls of fluff that passed on into semi-naked pullethood and from that into dead henhood, we threw all aside and, packing our belongings on a wagon, drove down Grigg's Road toward Bidwell, a tiny caravan of hope looking for a new place from which to start on our upward journey through life.

We must have been a sad-looking lot, not, I fancy, unlike refugees fleeing from a battlefield. Mother and I walked in the road. The wagon that contained our goods had been borrowed for the day from Mr. Albert Griggs, a neighbor. Out of its sides stuck the legs of cheap chairs, and at the back of the pile of beds, tables, and boxes filled with kitchen utensils was a crate of live chickens, and on top of that the baby carriage in which I had been wheeled about in my infancy. Why we stuck to the baby carriage I don't know. It was unlikely other children would be born and the wheels were broken. People who have few possessions cling tightly to those they have. That is one of the facts that make life so discouraging.

Father rode on top of the wagon. He was then a bald-headed man of forty-five, a little fat, and from long association with mother and the chickens he had become habitually silent and discouraged. All during our ten years on the chicken farm he had worked as a laborer on neighboring farms and most of the money he had earned had been spent for remedies to cure chicken diseases, on Wilmer's White Wonder Cholera Cure or Professor Bidlow's Egg Producer or some other preparations that mother found advertised in the poultry papers. There were two little patches of hair on father's head just above his ears. I remember that as a child I used to sit looking at him when he had gone to sleep in a chair before the stove on Sunday afternoons in the winter. I had at that time already begun to read books and have notions of my own, and the bald path that led over the top of his head was, I fancied, something like a broad road, such a road as Caesar might have made on which to lead his legions out of Rome and into the wonders of an unknown world. The tufts of hair that grew above father's ears were, I thought, like forests. I fell into a half-sleeping, half-walking state and dreamed I was a tiny thing going along the road into a far beautiful place where there were no chicken farms and where life was a happy eggless affair.

One might write a book concerning our flight from the chicken farm into town. Mother and I walked the entire eight miles—she to be sure that nothing fell from the wagon and I to see the wonders of the world. On the seat of the wagon beside father was his greatest treasure. I will tell you of that.

On a chicken farm, where hundreds and even thousands of chickens come out of eggs, surprising things sometimes happen. Grotesques are born out of eggs as out of people. The accident does not often occur—perhaps once in a thousand births. A chicken is, you see, born that has four legs, two pairs of wings, two heads, or what not. The things do not live. They go quickly back to the hand of their maker that has for a moment trembled. The fact that the poor little things could not live was one of the tragedies of life to father. He had some sort of notion that if he could but bring into henhood or roosterhood a five-legged hen or a two-headed rooster his fortune would be made. He dreamed of taking the wonder about the county fairs and of growing rich by exhibiting it to other farmhands.

At any rate, he saved all the little monstrous things that had been born on our chicken farm. They were preserved in alcohol and put each in its own glass bottle. These he had carefully put into a box, and on our journey into town it was carried on the wagon seat beside him. He drove the horses with one hand and with the other clung to the box. When we got to our destination, the box was taken down at once and the bottles removed. All during our days as keepers of a restaurant in the town of Bidwell, Ohio, the grotesques in their little glass bottles sat on a shelf back of the counter. Mother sometimes protested, but father was a rock on the subject of his treasure. The grotesques were, he declared, valuable. People, he said, liked to look at strange and wonderful things.

Did I say that we embarked in the restaurant business in the town of Bidwell, Ohio? I exaggerated a little. The town itself lay at the foot of a low hill and on the shore of a small river. The railroad did not run through the town and the station was a mile away to the north at a place called Pickleville. There had been a cider mill and pickle factory at the station, but before the time of our coming they had both gone out of business. In the morning and in the evening busses came down to the station along a road called Turner's Pike from the hotel on the main street of Bidwell. Our going to the out-of-the-way place to embark in the restaurant business was mother's idea. She talked of it for a year and then one day went off and rented an empty store building opposite the railroad station. It was her idea that the restaurant would be profitable. Traveling men, she said, would be always waiting around to take trains out of town and town people would come to the station to await incoming trains. They would come to the restaurant to buy pieces of pie and drink coffee. Now that I am older I know that she had another motive in going. She was ambitious for me. She wanted me to rise in the world, to get into a town school and become a man of the towns.

At Pickleville father and mother worked hard, as they always had done. At first there was the necessity of putting our place into shape to be a restaurant. That took a month. Father built a shelf on which he put tins of vegetables. He painted a sign on which he put his name in large red letters. Below his name was the sharp command—"EAT

HERE"—that was so seldom obeyed. A showcase was bought and filled with cigars and tobacco. Mother scrubbed the floor and the walls of the room. I went to school in the town and was glad to be away from the farm from the presence of the discouraged, sad-looking chickens. Still I was not very joyous. In the evening I walked home from school along Turner's Pike and remembered the children I had seen playing in the town school yard. A troop of little girls had gone hopping about and singing. I tried that. Down along the frozen road I went hopping solemnly on one leg. "Hippity Hop To The Barber Shop," I sang shrilly. Then I stopped and looked doubtfully about. I was afraid of being seen in my gay mood. It must have seemed to me that I was doing a thing that should not be done by one who, like myself, had been raised on a chicken farm where death was a daily visitor.

Mother decided that our restaurant should remain open at night. At ten in the evening a passenger train went north past our door followed by a local freight. The freight crew had switching to do in Pickleville, and when the work was done they came to our restaurant for hot coffee and food. Sometimes one of them ordered a fried egg. In the morning at four they returned north-bound and again visited us. A little trade began to grow up. Mother slept at night and during the day tended the restaurant and fed our boarders while father slept. He slept in the same bed mother had occupied during the night and I went off to the town of Bidwell and to school. During the long nights, while mother and I slept, father cooked meats that were to go into sandwiches for the lunch baskets of our boarders. Then an idea in regard to getting up in the world came into his head. The American spirit took hold of him. He also became ambitious.

In the long nights when there was little to do, father had time to think. That was his undoing. He decided that he had in the past been an unsuccessful man because he had not been cheerful enough and that in the future he would adopt a cheerful outlook on life. In the early morning he came upstairs and got into bed with mother. She woke and the two talked. From my bed in the corner I listened.

It was father's idea that both he and mother should try to entertain the people who came to eat at our restaurant. I cannot now remember his words, but he gave the impression of one about to become in some obscure way a kind of public entertainer. When people, particularly young people from the town of Bidwell, came into our place, as on very rare occasions they did, bright entertaining conversation was to be made. From father's words I gathered that something of the jolly innkeeper effect was to be sought. Mother must have been doubtful from the first, but she said nothing discouraging. It was father's notion that a passion for the company of himself and mother would spring up in the breasts of the younger people of the town of Bidwell. In the evening bright happy groups would come singing down Turner's Pike. They would troop shouting with joy and laughter into our place. There would be song and festivity. I do not mean to give the impression that father spoke so elaborately of the matter. He was, as I have said, an uncommunicative man. "They want some place to go. I tell you they want some place to go," he said over and over. That was as far as he got. My own imagination has filled in the blanks.

For two or three weeks this notion of father's invaded our house. We did not talk much, but in our daily lives tried earnestly to make smiles take the place of glum looks. Mother smiled at the boarders and I, catching the infection, smiled at our cat. Father became a little feverish in his anxiety to please. There was, no doubt, lurking somewhere in him, a touch of the spirit of the showman. He did not waste much of his ammunition on the railroad men he served at night, but seemed to be waiting for a young man or woman from Bidwell to come in to show what he could do. On the counter in the restaurant there was a wire basket kept always filled with eggs, and it must have been before his eyes when the idea of being entertaining was born in his brain. There was something pre-natal about the way eggs kept themselves connected with the development of his idea. At any rate, an egg ruined his new impulse in life. Late one night I was awakened by a roar of anger coming from father's throat. Both mother and I sat upright in our beds. With trembling hands she lighted a lamp that stood on a table by her head. Downstairs the front door of our restaurant went shut with a bang and in a few minutes father tramped up the stairs. He held an egg in his hand and his hand trembled as though he were having a chill. There was a half-insane light in his eyes. As he stood glaring at us I was sure he intended throwing the egg at either mother or me. Then he laid it gently on the table beside the lamp and dropped on his knees beside mother's bed. He began to cry like a boy, and I, carried away by his grief, cried with him. The two of us filled the little upstairs room with our wailing voices. It is ridiculous, but of the picture we made I can remember only the fact that mother's hand continually stroked the bald path that ran across the top of his head. I have forgotten what mother said to him and how she induced him to tell her of what had happened downstairs. His explanation also has gone out of my mind. I remember only my own grief and fright and the shiny path over father's head glowing in the lamplight as he knelt by the bed.

As to what happened downstairs. For some unexplainable reason I know the story as well as though I had been a witness to my father's discomfiture. One in time gets to know many unexplainable things. On that evening young Joe Kane, son of a merchant of Bidwell, came to Pickleville to meet his father, who was expected on the ten-o'clock evening train from the South. The train was three hours late and Joe came into our place to loaf about and to wait for its arrival. The local freight train came in and the freight crew were fed. Joe was left alone in the restaurant with father.

From the moment he came into our place the Bidwell young man must have been puzzled by my father's actions. It was his notion that father was angry at him for hanging around. He noticed that the restaurant-keeper was apparently disturbed by his presence and he thought of going out. However, it began to rain and he did not fancy the long walk to town and back. He bought a five-cent cigar and ordered a cup of coffee. He had a newspaper in his pocket and took it out and began to read. "I'm waiting for the evening train. It's late," he said apologetically.

For a long time father, whom Joe Kane had never seen before, remained silently gazing at his visitor. He was no doubt suffering from an attack of stage fright. As so often happens in life he had thought so much and so often of the situation that now confronted him that he was somewhat nervous in its presence.

For one thing, he did not know what to do with his hands. He thrust one of them nervously over the counter and shook hands with Joe Kane. "How-de-do," he said. Joe Kane put his newspaper down and stared at him. Father's eyes lighted on the basket of eggs that sat on the counter and he began to talk. "Well," he began hesitatingly, "well, you have heard of Christopher Columbus, eh?" He seemed to be angry. "That Christopher Columbus was a cheat," he declared emphatically. "He talked of making an egg stand on its end. He talked, he did, and then he went and broke the end of the egg."

My father seemed to his visitor to be beside himself at the duplicity of Christopher Columbus. He muttered and swore. He declared it was wrong to teach children that Christopher Columbus was a great man when, after all, he cheated at the critical moment. He had declared he would make an egg stand on end and then, when his bluff had been called, he had done a trick. Still grumbling at Columbus, father took an egg from the basket on the counter and began to walk up and down. He rolled the egg between the palms of his hands. He smiled genially. He began to mumble words regarding the effect to be produced on an egg by the electricity that comes out of the human body. He declared that, without breaking its shell and by virtue of rolling it back and forth in his hands, he could stand the egg on its end. He explained that the warmth of his hands and the gentle rolling movement he gave the egg created a new center of gravity, and Joe Kane was mildly interested. "I have handled thousands of eggs," father said. "No one knows more about eggs than I do."

He stood the egg on the counter and it fell on its side. He tried the trick again and again, each time rolling the egg between the palms of his hands and saying the words regarding the wonders of electricity and the laws of gravity. When after a half-hour's effort he did succeed in making the egg stand for a moment, he looked up to find that his visitor was no longer watching. By the time he had succeeded in calling Joe Kane's attention to the success of his effort, the egg had again rolled over and lay on its side.

Afire with the showman's passion and at the same time a good deal disconcerted by the failure of his first effort, father now took the bottles containing the poultry monstrosities down from their place on the shelf and began to show them to his visitor. "How would you like to have seven legs and two heads like this fellow?" he asked, exhibiting the most remarkable of his treasures. A cheerful smile played over his face. He reached over the counter and tried to slap Joe Kane on the shoulder as he had seen men do in Ben Head's saloon when he was a young farmhand and drove to town on Saturday evenings. His visitor was made a little ill by the sight of the body of the terribly deformed bird floating in the alcohol in the bottle and got up to go. Coming from behind the counter, father took hold of the young man's arm and led him back to his seat. He grew a little angry and for a moment had to turn his face away and force himself to smile. Then he put the bottles back on the shelf. In an outburst of generosity he fairly compelled Joe Kane to have a fresh cup of coffee and another cigar at his expense. Then he took a pan and filling it with vinegar, taken from a jug that sat beneath the counter, he declared himself about to do a new trick. "I will heat this egg in this pan of vinegar," he said. "Then I will put it through the neck of a bottle without breaking the shell. When the egg is inside the bottle it will resume its normal shape and the shell will become hard again. Then I will give the bottle with the egg in it to you. You can take it about with you wherever you go. People will want to know how you got the egg in the bottle. Don't tell them. Keep them guessing. That is the way to have fun with this trick."

Father grinned and winked at his visitor. Joe Kane decided that the man who confronted him was mildly insane but harmless. He drank the cup of coffee that had been given him and began to read his paper again. When the egg had been heated in vinegar, father carried it on a spoon to the counter and going into a back room got an empty bottle. He was angry because his visitor did not watch him as he began to do his trick, but nevertheless went cheerfully to work. For a long time he struggled, trying to get the egg to go through the neck of the bottle. He put the pan of vinegar back on the stove, intending to reheat the egg, then picked it up and burned his fingers. After a second bath in the hot vinegar, the shell of the egg had been softened a little, but not enough for his purpose. He worked and worked and a spirit of desperate determination took possession of him. When he thought that at last the trick was about to be consummated, the delayed train came in at the station and Joe Kane started to go nonchalantly out at the door. Father made a last desperate effort to conquer the egg and make it do the thing that would establish his reputation as one who knew how to entertain guests who came into his restaurant. He worried the egg. He attempted to be somewhat rough with it. He swore and the sweat stood out on his forehead. The egg broke under his hand. When the contents spurted over his clothes, Joe Kane, who had stopped at the door, turned and laughed.

A roar of anger rose from my father's throat. He danced and shouted a string of inarticulate words. Grabbing another egg from the basket on the counter, he threw it, just missing the head of the young man as he dodged through the door and escaped.

Father came upstairs to mother and me with an egg in his hand. I do not know what he intended to do. I imagine he had some idea of destroying it, of destroying all eggs, and that he intended to let mother and me see him begin. When, however, he got into the presence of mother, something happened to him. He laid the egg gently on the table and dropped on his knees by the bed as I have already explained. He later decided to close the restaurant for the night and to come upstairs and get into bed. When he did so, he blew out the light and after much muttered conversation both he and mother went to sleep. I suppose I went to sleep also, but my sleep was troubled. I awoke at dawn and for a long time looked at the egg that lay on the table. I wondered why eggs had to be and why from the egg came the hen who again laid the egg. The question got into my blood. It has stayed there, I imagine, because I am the son of my father. At any rate, the problem remains unsolved in my mind. And that, I conclude, is but another evidence of the complete and final triumph of the egg—at least as far as my family is concerned.

William Faulkner

Red Leaves

I

THE TWO INDIANS crossed the plantation toward the slave quarters. Neat with whitewash, of baked soft brick, the two rows of houses in which lived the slaves belonging to the clan, faced one another across the mild shade of the lane marked and scored with naked feet and with a few homemade toys mute in the dust. There was no sign of life.

"I know what we will find," the first Indian said.

"What we will not find," the second said. Although it was noon, the lane was vacant, the doors of the cabins empty and quiet; no cooking smoke rose from any of the chinked and plastered chimneys.

"Yes. It happened like this when the father of him who is now the Man died."

"You mean, of him who was the Man."

"Yao."

The first Indian's name was Three Basket. He was perhaps sixty. They were both squat men, a little solid, burgherlike; paunchy, with big heads, big, broad, dust-colored faces of a certain blurred serenity like carved heads on a ruined wall in Siam or Sumatra, looming out of a mist. The sun had done it, the violent sun, the violent shade. Their hair looked like sedge grass on burnt-over land. Clamped through one ear Three Basket wore an enameled snuffbox.

"I have said all the time that this is not the good way. In the old days there were no quarters, no Negroes. A man's time was his own then. He had time. Now he must spend most of it finding work for them who prefer sweating to do."

"They are like horses and dogs."

"They are like nothing in this sensible world. Nothing contents them save sweat. They are worse than the white people."

"It is not as though the Man himself had to find work for them to do."

"You said it. I do not like slavery. It is not the good way. In the old days, there was the good way. But not now."

"You do not remember the old way either."

"I have listened to them who do. And I have tried this way. Man was not made to sweat."

"That's so. See what it has done to their flesh."

"Yes. Black. It has a bitter taste, too."

"You have eaten of it?"

"Once. I was young then, and more hardy in the appetite than now. Now it is different with me."

"Yes. They are too valuable to eat now."

"There is a bitter taste to the flesh which I do not like."

"They are too valuable to eat, anyway, when the white men will give horses for them."

They entered the lane. The mute, meager toys—the fetish-shaped objects made of wood and rags and feathers—lay in the dust about the patinaed doorsteps, among bones and broken gourd dishes. But there was no sound from any cabin, no face in any door; had not been since yesterday, when Issetibbeha died. But they already knew what they would find.

It was in the central cabin, a house a little larger than the others, where at certain phases of the moon the Negroes would gather to begin their ceremonies before removing after nightfall to the creek bottom, where they kept the drums. In this room they kept the minor accessories, the cryptic ornaments, the ceremonial records which consisted of sticks daubed with red clay in symbols. It had a hearth in the center of the floor, beneath a hole in the roof, with a few cold wood ashes and a suspended iron pot. The window shutters were closed; when the two Indians entered, after the abashless sunlight they could distinguish nothing with the eyes save a movement, shadow, out of which eyeballs rolled, so that the place appeared to be full of Negroes. The two Indians stood in the doorway.

"Yao," Basket said. "I said this is not the good way."

"I don't think I want to be here," the second said.

"That is black man's fear which you smell. It does not smell as ours does."

"I don't think I want to be here."

"Your fear has an odor too."

"Maybe it is Issetibbeha which we smell."

"Yao. He knows. He knows what we will find here. He knew when he died what we should find here today." Out of the rank twilight of the room the eyes, the smell, of Negroes rolled about them. "I am Three Basket, whom you know," Basket said into the room. "We are come from the Man. He whom we seek is gone?" The Negroes said nothing. The smell of them, of their bodies, seemed to ebb and flux in the still hot air. They seemed to be musing as one upon something remote, inscrutable. They were like a single octopus. They were like the roots of a huge tree uncovered, the earth broken momentarily upon the writhen, thick, fetid tangle of its lightless and outraged life. "Come," Basket said. "You know our errand. Is he whom we seek gone?"

"They are thinking something," the second said. "I do not want to be here."

"They are knowing something," Basket said.

"They are hiding him, you think?"

"No. He is gone. He has been gone since last night. It happened like this before, when the grandfather of him who is now the Man died. It took us three days to catch him. For three days Doom lay above the ground, saying 'I see my horse and my dog. But I do not see my slave. What have you done with him that you will not permit me to lie quiet?' "

"They do not like to die."

"Yao. They cling. It makes trouble for us, always. A people without honor and without decorum. Always a trouble."

"I do not like it here."

"Nor do I. But then, they are savages; they cannot be expected to regard usage. That is why I say that this way is a bad way."

"Yao. They cling. They would even rather work in the sun than to enter the earth with a chief. But he is gone."

The Negroes had said nothing, made no sound. The white eyeballs rolled, wild, subdued; the smell was rank, violent. "Yes, they fear," the second said. "What shall we do now?"

"Let us go and talk with the Man."

"Will Moketubbe listen?"

"What can he do? He will not like to. But he is the Man now."

"Yao. He is the Man. He can wear the shoes with the red heels all the time now." They turned and went out. There was no door in the door frame. There were no doors in any of the cabins.

"He did that anyway," Basket said.

"Behind Issetibbeha's back. But now they are his shoes, since he is the Man."

"Yao. Issetibbeha did not like it. I have heard. I know that he said to Moketubbe: 'When you are the Man, the shoes will be yours. But until then, they are my shoes.' But now Moketubbe is the Man; he can wear them."

"Yao," the second said. "He is the Man now. He used to wear the shoes behind Issetibbeha's back, and it was not known if Issetibbeha knew this or not. And then Issetibbeha became dead, who was not old, and the shoes are Moketubbe's, since he is the Man now. What do you think of that?"

"I don't think about it," Basket said. "Do you?"

"No," the second said.

"Good," Basket said. "You are wise."

II

The house sat on a knoll, surrounded by oak trees. The front of it was one story in height, composed of the deck house of a steamboat which had gone ashore and which Doom, Issetibbeha's father, had dismantled with his slaves and hauled on cypress rollers twelve miles home overland. It took them five months. His house consisted at the time of one brick wall. He set the steamboat broadside on to the wall, where now the chipped and flaked gilding of the rococo cornices arched in faint splendor above the gilt lettering of the stateroom names above the jalousied doors.

Doom had been born merely a subchief, a Mingo, one of three children on the mother's side of the family. He made a journey—he was a young man then and New Orleans was a European city—from north Mississippi to New Orleans by keel boat, where he met the Chevalier Sœur Blonde de Vitry, a man whose social position, on its face, was as equivocal as Doom's own. In New Orleans, among the gamblers and cutthroats of the river front, Doom, under the tutelage of his patron, passed as the chief, the Man, the hereditary owner of that land which belonged to the male side of the family; it was the Chevalier de Vitry who called him *du homme,* and hence Doom.

They were seen everywhere together—the Indian, the squat man with a bold, inscrutable, underbred face, and the Parisian, the expatriate, the friend, it was said, of Carondelet and the intimate of General Wilkinson. Then they disappeared, the two of them, vanishing from their old equivocal haunts and leaving behind them the legend of the sums which Doom was believed to have won, and some tale about a young woman, daughter of a fairly well-to-do West Indian family, the son and brother of whom sought Doom with a pistol about his old haunts for some time after his disappearance.

Six months later the young woman herself disappeared, boarding the St. Louis packet, which put in one night at a wood landing on the north Mississippi side, where the woman, accompanied by a Negro maid, got off. Four Indians met her with a horse and wagon, and they traveled for three days, slowly, since she was already big with child, to the plantation, where she found that Doom was now chief. He never told her how he accomplished it, save that his uncle and his cousin had died suddenly. At that time the house consisted of a brick wall built by shiftless slaves, against which was propped a thatched lean-to divided into rooms and littered with bones and refuse, set in the center of ten thousand acres of matchless parklike forest where deer grazed like domestic cattle. Doom and the woman were married there a short time before Issetibbeha was born, by a combination itinerant minister and slave trader who arrived on a mule, to the saddle of which was lashed a cotton umbrella and a three-gallon demijohn of whisky. After that, Doom began to acquire more slaves and to cultivate some of his land, as the white people did. But he never had enough for them to do. In utter idleness the majority of them led lives transplanted whole out of African jungles, save on the occasions when, entertaining guests, Doom coursed them with dogs.

When Doom died, Issetibbeha, his son, was nineteen. He became proprietor of the land and of the quintupled herd of blacks for which he had no use at all. Though the title of Man rested with him, there was a hierarchy of cousins and uncles who ruled the clan and who finally gathered in squatting conclave over the Negro question, squatting profoundly beneath the golden names above the doors of the steamboat.

"We cannot eat them," one said.

"Why not?"

"There are too many of them."

"That's true," a third said. "Once we started, we should have to eat them all. And that much flesh diet is not good for man."

"Perhaps they will be like deer flesh. That cannot hurt you."

"We might kill a few of them and not eat them," Issetibbeha said.

They looked at him for a while. "What for?" one said.

"That is true," a second said. "We cannot do that. They are too valuable; remember all the bother they have caused us, finding things for them to do. We must do as the white men do."

"How is that?" Issetibbeha said.

"Raise more Negroes by clearing more land to make corn to feed them, then sell them. We will clear the land and plant it with food and raise Negroes and sell them to the white men for money."

"But what will we do with this money?" a third said.

They thought for a while.

"We will see," the first said. They squatted, profound, grave.

"It means work," the third said.

"Let the Negroes do it," the first said.

"Yao. Let them. To sweat is bad. It is damp. It opens the pores."

"And then the night air enters."

"Yao. Let the Negroes do it. They appear to like sweating."

So they cleared the land with the Negroes and planted it in grain. Up to that time the slaves had lived in a huge pen with a lean-to roof over one corner, like a pen for pigs. But now they began to build quarters, cabins, putting the young Negroes in the cabins in pairs to mate; five years later Issetibbeha sold forty head to a Memphis trader, and he took the money and went abroad upon it, his maternal uncle from New Orleans conducting the trip. At that time the Chevalier Sœur Blonde de Vitry was an old man in Paris, in a toupee and a corset, with a careful toothless old face fixed in a grimace quizzical and profoundly tragic. He borrowed three hundred dollars from Issetibbeha and in return he introduced him into certain circles; a year later Issetibbeha returned home with a gilt bed, a pair of girandoles by whose light it was said that Pompadour arranged her hair while Louis smirked at his mirrored face across her powdered shoulder, and a pair of slippers with red heels. They were too small for him, since he had not worn shoes at all until he reached New Orleans on his way abroad.

He brought the slippers home in tissue paper and kept them in the remaining pocket of a pair of saddlebags filled with cedar shavings, save when he took them out on occasion for his son, Moketubbe, to play with. At three years of age Moketubbe had a broad, flat, Mongolian face that appeared to exist in a complete and unfathomable lethargy, until confronted by the slippers.

Moketubbe's mother was a comely girl whom Issetibbeha had seen one day working in her shift in a melon patch. He stopped and watched her for a while—the broad, solid thighs, the sound back, the serene face. He was on his way to the creek to fish that day, but he didn't go any farther; perhaps while he stood there watching the unaware girl he may have remembered his own mother, the city woman, the fugitive with her fans and laces and her Negro blood, and all the tawdry shabbiness of that sorry affair. Within the year Moketubbe was born; even at three he could not get his feet into the slippers. Watching him in the still, hot afternoons as he struggled with the slippers with a certain monstrous repudiation of fact, Issetibbeha laughed quietly to himself. He laughed at Moketubbe and the shoes for several years, because Moketubbe did not give up trying to put them on until he was sixteen. Then he quit. Or Issetibbeha thought he had. But he had merely quit trying in Issetibbeha's presence. Issetibbeha's newest wife told him that Moketubbe had stolen and hidden the shoes. Issetibbeha quit laughing then, and he sent the woman away, so that he was alone. "Yao," he said. "I too like being alive, it seems." He sent for Moketubbe. "I give them to you," he said.

Moketubbe was twenty-five then, unmarried. Issetibbeha was not tall, but he was taller by six inches than his son and almost a hundred pounds lighter. Moketubbe was already diseased with flesh, with a pale, broad, inert face and dropsical hands and feet. "They are yours now," Issetibbeha said, watching him. Moketubbe had looked at him once when he entered, a glance brief, discreet, veiled.

"Thanks," he said.

Issetibbeha looked at him. He could never tell if Moketubbe saw anything, looked at anything. "Why will it not be the same if I give the slippers to you?"

"Thanks," Moketubbe said. Issetibbeha was using snuff at the time; a white man had shown him how to put the powder into his lip and scour it against his teeth with a twig of gum or of alphea.

"Well," he said, "a man cannot live forever." He looked at his son, then his gaze went blank in turn, unseeing, and he mused for an instant. You could not tell what he was thinking, save that he said half aloud: "Yao. But Doom's uncle had no shoes with red heels."

He looked at his son again, fat, inert. "Beneath all that, a man might think of doing anything and it not be known until too late." He sat in a splint chair hammocked with deer thongs. "He cannot even get them on; he and I are both frustrated by the same gross meat which he wears. He cannot even get them on. But is that my fault?"

He lived for five years longer, then he died. He was sick one night, and though the doctor came in a skunk-skin vest and burned sticks, he died before noon.

That was yesterday; the grave was dug, and for twelve hours now the People had been coming in wagons and carriages and on horseback and afoot, to eat the baked dog and the succotash and the yams cooked in ashes and to attend the funeral.

III

"It will be three days," Basket said, as he and the other Indian returned to the house. "It will be three days and the food will not be enough; I have seen it before."

The second Indian's name was Louis Berry. "He will smell too, in this weather."

"Yao. They are nothing but a trouble and a care."

"Maybe it will not take three days."

"They run far. Yao. We will smell this Man before he enters the earth. You watch and see if I am not right."

They approached the house.

"He can wear the shoes now," Berry said. "He can wear them now in man's sight."

"He cannot wear them for a while yet," Basket said. Berry looked at him. "He will lead the hunt."

"Moketubbe?" Berry said. "Do you think he will? A man to whom even talking is travail?"

"What else can he do? It is his own father who will soon begin to smell."

"That is true," Berry said. "There is even yet a price he must pay for the shoes. Yao. He has truly bought them. What do you think?"

"What do you think?"

"What do you think?"

"I think nothing."

"Nor do I. Issetibbeha will not need the shoes now. Let Moketubbe have them; Issetibbeha will not care."

"Yao. Man must die."

"Yao. Let him; there is still the Man."

The bark roof of the porch was supported by peeled cypress poles, high above the texas of the steamboat, shading an unfloored banquette where on the trodden earth mules and horses were tethered in bad weather. On the forward end of the steamboat's deck sat an old man and two women. One of the women was dressing a fowl, the other was shelling corn. The old man was talking. He was barefoot, in a long linen frock coat and a beaver hat.

"This world is going to the dogs," he said. "It is being ruined by white men. We got along fine for years and years, before the white men foisted their Negroes upon us. In the old days the old men sat in the shade and ate stewed deer's flesh and corn and smoked tobacco and talked of honor and grave affairs; now what do we do? Even the old wear themselves into the grave taking care of them that like sweating." When Basket and Berry crossed the deck he ceased and looked up at them. His eyes were querulous, bleared; his face was myriad with tiny wrinkles. "He is fled also," he said.

"Yes," Berry said, "he is gone."

"I knew it. I told them so. It will take three weeks, like when Doom died. You watch and see."

"It was three days, not three weeks," Berry said.

"Were you there?"

"No," Berry said. "But I have heard."

"Well, I was there," the old man said. "For three whole weeks, through the swamps and the briers—" They went on and left him talking.

What had been the saloon of the steamboat was now a shell, rotting slowly; the polished mahogany, the carving glinting momentarily and fading through the mold in figures cabalistic and profound; the gutted windows were like cataracted eyes. It contained a few sacks of seed or grain, and the fore part of the running gear of a barouche, to the axle of which two C-springs rusted in graceful curves, supporting nothing. In one corner a fox cub ran steadily and soundlessly up and down a willow cage; three scrawny gamecocks moved in the dust, and the place was pocked and marked with their dried droppings.

They passed through the brick wall and entered a big room of chinked logs. It contained the hinder part of the barouche, and the dismantled body lying on its side, the window slatted over with willow withes, through which protruded the heads, the still, beady, outraged eyes and frayed combs of still more game chickens. It was floored with packed clay; in one corner leaned a crude plow and two hand-hewn boat paddles. From the ceiling, suspended by four deer thongs, hung the gilt bed which Issetibbeha had fetched from Paris. It had neither mattress nor springs, the frame crisscrossed now by a neat hammocking of thongs.

Issetibbeha had tried to have his newest wife, the young one, sleep in the bed. He was congenitally short of breath himself, and he passed the nights half reclining in his splint chair. He would see her to bed and, later, wakeful, sleeping as he did but three or four hours a night, he would sit in the darkness and simulate slumber and listen to her sneak infinitesimally from the gilt and ribboned bed, to lie on a quilt pallet on the floor until just before daylight. Then she would enter the bed quietly again and in turn simulate slumber, while in the darkness beside her Issetibbeha quietly laughed and laughed.

The girandoles were lashed by thongs to two sticks propped in a corner where a ten-gallon whisky keg lay also. There was a clay hearth; facing it, in the splint chair, Moketubbe sat. He was maybe an inch better than five feet tall, and he weighed two hundred and fifty pounds. He wore a broadcloth coat and no shirt, his round, smooth copper balloon of belly swelling above the bottom piece of a suit of linen underwear. On his feet were the slippers with the red heels. Behind his chair stood a stripling with a punkah-like fan made of fringed paper. Moketubbe sat motionless, with his broad, yellow face with its closed eyes and flat nostrils, his flipperlike arms extended. On his face was an expression profound, tragic, and inert. He did not open his eyes when Basket and Berry came in.

"He has worn them since daylight?" Basket said.

"Since daylight," the stripling said. The fan did not cease. "You can see."

"Yao," Basket said. "We can see." Moketubbe did not move. He looked like an effigy, like a Malay god in frock coat, drawers, naked chest, the trivial scarlet-heeled shoes.

"I wouldn't disturb him, if I were you," the stripling said.

"Not if I were you," Basket said. He and Berry squatted. The stripling moved the fan steadily. "O Man," Basket said, "listen." Moketubbe did not move. "He is gone," Basket said.

"I told you so," the stripling said. "I knew he would flee. I told you."

"Yao," Basket said. "You are not the first to tell us afterward what we should have known before. Why is it that some of you wise men took no steps yesterday to prevent this?"

"He does not wish to die," Berry said.

"Why should he not wish it?" Basket said.

"Because he must die some day is no reason," the stripling said. "That would not convince me either, old man."

"Hold your tongue," Berry said.

"For twenty years," Basket said, "while others of his race sweat in the fields, he served the Man in the shade. Why should he not wish to die, since he did not wish to sweat?"

"And it will be quick," Berry said. "It will not take long."

"Catch him and tell him that," the stripling said.

"Hush," Berry said. They squatted, watching Moketubbe's face. He might have been dead himself. It was as though he were cased so in flesh that even breathing took place too deep within him to show.

"Listen, O Man," Basket said. "Issetibbeha is dead. He waits. His dog and his horse we have. But his slave has fled. The one who held the pot for him, who ate of his food, from his dish, is fled. Issetibbeha waits."

"Yao," Berry said.

"This is not the first time," Basket said. "This happened when Doom, thy grandfather, lay waiting at the door of the earth. He lay waiting three days, saying, 'Where is my Negro?' And Issetibbeha, thy father, answered, 'I will find him. Rest; I will bring him to you so that you may begin the journey.' "

"Yao," Berry said.

Moketubbe had not moved, had not opened his eyes.

"For three days Issetibbeha hunted in the bottom," Basket said. "He did not ever return home for food, until the Negro was with him; then he said to Doom, his father, 'Here is thy dog, thy horse, thy Negro; rest.' Issetibbeha, who is dead since yesterday, said it. And now Issetibbeha's Negro is fled. His horse and his dog wait with him, but his Negro is fled."

"Yao," Berry said.

Moketubbe had not moved. His eyes were closed; upon his supine monstrous shape there was a colossal inertia, something profoundly immobile, beyond and impervious to flesh. They watched his face, squatting.

"When thy father was newly the Man, this happened," Basket said. "And it was Issetibbeha who brought back the slave to where his father waited to enter the earth." Moketubbe's face had not moved, his eyes had not moved. After a while Basket said, "Remove the shoes."

The stripling removed the shoes. Moketubbe began to pant, his bare chest moving deep, as though he were rising from beyond his unfathomed flesh back into life, like up from the water, the sea. But his eyes had not opened yet.

Berry said, "He will lead the hunt."

"Yao," Basket said. "He is the Man. He will lead the hunt."

IV

All that day the Negro, Issetibbeha's body servant, hidden in the barn, watched Issetibbeha's dying. He was forty, a Guinea man. He had a flat nose, a close, small head; the inside corners of his eyes showed red a little, and his prominent gums were a pale bluish red above his square, broad teeth. He had been taken at fourteen by a trader off Kamerun, before his teeth had been filed. He had been Issetibbeha's body servant for twenty-three years.

On the day before, the day on which Issetibbeha lay sick, he returned to the quarters at dusk. In that unhurried hour the smoke of the cooking fires blew slowly across the street from door to door, carrying into the opposite one the smell of the identical meat and bread. The women tended them; the men were gathered at the head of the lane, watching him as he came down the slope from the house, putting his naked feet down carefully in a strange dusk. To the waiting men his eyeballs were a little luminous.

"Issetibbeha is not dead yet," the headman said.

"Not dead," the body servant said. "Who not dead?"

In the dusk they had faces like his, the different ages, the thoughts sealed inscrutable behind faces like the death masks of apes. The smell of the fires, the cooking, blew sharp and slow across the strange dusk, as from another world, above the lane and the pickaninnies naked in the dust.

"If he lives past sundown, he will live until daybreak," one said.

"Who says?"

"Talk says."

"Yao. Talk says. We know but one thing." They looked at the body servant as he stood among them, his eyeballs a little luminous. He was breathing slow and deep. His chest was bare; he was sweating a little. "He knows. He knows it."

"Let us let the drums talk."

"Yao. Let the drums tell it."

The drums began after dark. They kept them hidden in the creek bottom. They were made of hollowed cypress knees, and the Negroes kept them hidden; why, none knew. They were buried in the mud on the bank of a slough; a lad of fourteen guarded them. He was undersized, and a mute; he squatted in the mud there all day, clouded over with mosquitoes, naked save for the mud with which he coated himself against the mosquitoes, and about his neck a fiber bag containing a pig's rib to which black shreds of flesh still adhered, and two scaly barks on a wire. He slobbered onto his clutched knees, drooling; now and then Indians came noiselessly out of the bushes behind him and stood there and contemplated him for a while and went away, and he never knew it.

From the loft of the stable where he lay hidden until dark and after, the Negro could hear the drums. They were three miles away, but he could hear them as though they were in the barn itself below him, thudding and thudding. It was as though he could see the fire too, and the black limbs turning into and out of the flames in copper gleams. Only there would be no fire. There would be no more light there than where he lay in the dusty loft, with the whispering arpeggios of rat feet along the warm and immemorial ax-squared rafters. The only fire there would be the smudge against mosquitoes where the women with nursing children crouched, their heavy sluggish breasts nippled full and smooth into the mouths of men children; contemplative, oblivious of the drumming, since a fire would signify life.

There was a fire in the steamboat, where Issetibbeha lay dying among his wives, beneath the lashed girandoles and the suspended bed. He could see the smoke, and just before sunset he saw the doctor come out, in a waistcoat made of skunk skins, and set fire to two clay-daubed sticks at the bows of the boat deck. "So he is not dead yet," the Negro said into the whispering gloom of the loft, answering himself; he could hear the two voices, himself and himself:

"Who not dead?"

"You are dead."

"Yao, I am dead," he said quietly. He wished to be where the drums were. He imagined himself springing out of the bushes, leaping among the drums on his bare, lean, greasy, invisible limbs. But he could not do that, because man leaped past life, into where death was; he dashed into death and did not die, because when death took a man, it took him just this side of the end of living. It was when death overran him from behind, still in life. The thin whisper of rat feet died in fainting gusts along the rafters. Once he had eaten rat. He was a boy then, but just come to America. They had lived ninety days in a three-foot-high 'tween-deck in tropic latitudes, hearing from topside the drunken New England captain intoning aloud from a book which he did not recognize for ten years afterward to be the Bible. Squatting in the stable so, he had watched the rat, civilized, by association with man reft of its inherent cunning of limb and eye; he had caught it without difficulty, with scarce a movement of his hand, and he ate it slowly, wondering how any of the rats had escaped so long. At that time he was still wearing the single white garment which the trader, a deacon in the Unitarian church, had given him, and he spoke then only his native tongue.

He was naked now, save for a pair of dungaree pants bought by Indians from white men, and an amulet slung on a thong about his hips. The amulet consisted of one half of a mother-of-pearl lorgnon which Issetibbeha had brought back from Paris, and the skull of a cottonmouth moccasin He had killed the snake himself and eaten it, save the poison head. He lay in the loft, watching the house, the steamboat, listening to the drums, thinking of himself among the drums.

He lay there all night. The next morning he saw the doctor come out, in his skunk vest, and get on his mule and ride away, and he became quite still and watched the final dust from beneath the mule's delicate feet die away, and then he found that he was still breathing and it seemed strange to him that he still breathed air, still needed air. Then he lay and watched quietly, waiting to move, his eyeballs a little luminous, but with a quiet light, and his breathing light and regular, and saw Louis Berry come out and look at the sky. It was good light then, and already five Indians squatted in their Sunday clothes along the steamboat deck; by noon there were twenty-five there. That afternoon they dug the trench in which the meat would be baked, and the yams; by that time there were almost a hundred guests—decorous, quiet, patient in their stiff European finery—and he watched Berry lead Issetibbeha's mare from the stable and tie her to a tree, and then he watched Berry emerge from the house with the old hound which lay beside Issetibbeha's chair. He tied the hound to the tree too, and it sat there, looking gravely about at the faces. Then it began to howl. It was still howling at sundown, when the Negro climbed down the back wall of the barn and entered the spring branch, where it was already dusk. He began to run then. He could hear the hound howling behind him, and near the spring, already running, he passed another Negro. The two men, the one motionless and the other running, looked for an instant at each other as though across an actual boundary between two different worlds. He ran on into full darkness, mouth closed, fists doubled, his broad nostrils bellowing steadily.

He ran on in the darkness. He knew the country well, because he had hunted it often with Issetibbeha, following on his mule the course of the fox or the cat beside Issetibbeha's mare; he knew it as well as did the men who would pursue him. He saw them for the first time shortly before sunset of the second day. He had run thirty miles then, up the creek bottom, before doubling back; lying in a pawpaw thicket he saw the pursuit for the first time. There were two of them, in shirts and straw hats, carrying their neatly rolled trousers under their arms, and they had no weapons. They were middle-aged, paunchy, and they could not have moved very fast anyway; it would be twelve hours before they could return to where he lay watching them. "So I will have until midnight to rest," he said. He was near enough to the plantation to smell the cooking fires, and he thought how he ought to be hungry, since he had not eaten in thirty hours. "But it is more important to rest," he told himself. He continued to tell himself that, lying in the pawpaw thicket, because the effort of resting, the need and the haste to rest, made his heart thud the same as the running had done. It was as though he had forgot how to rest, as though the six hours were not long enough to do it in, to remember again how to do it.

As soon as dark came he moved again. He had thought to keep going steadily and quietly through the night, since there was nowhere for him to go, but as soon as he moved he began to run at top speed, breasting his panting chest, his broad-flaring nostrils through the choked and whipping darkness. He ran for an hour, lost by then, without direction, when suddenly he stopped, and after a time his thudding heart unraveled from the sound of the drums. By the sound they were not two miles away; he followed the sound until he could smell the smudge fire and taste the acrid smoke. When he stood among them the drums did not cease; only the headman came to him where he stood in the drifting smudge, panting, his nostrils flaring and pulsing, the hushed glare of his ceaseless eyeballs in his mud-daubed face as though they were worked from lungs.

"We have expected thee," the headman said. "Go, now."

"Go?"

"Eat, and go. The dead may not consort with the living; thou knowest that."

"Yao. I know that." They did not look at one another. The drums had not ceased.

"Wilt thou eat?" the headman said.

"I am not hungry. I caught a rabbit this afternoon, and ate while I lay hidden."

"Take some cooked meat with thee, then."

He accepted the cooked meat, wrapped in leaves, and entered the creek bottom again; after a while the sound of the drums ceased. He walked steadily until daybreak. "I have twelve hours," he said. "Maybe more, since the trail was followed by night." He squatted and ate the meat and wiped his hands on his thighs. Then he rose and removed the dungaree pants and squatted again beside a slough and coated himself with mud—face, arms, body and legs—and squatted again, clasping his knees, his head bowed. When it was light enough to see, he moved back into the swamp and squatted again and went to sleep so. He did not dream at all. It was well that he moved, for, waking suddenly in broad daylight and the high sun, he saw the two Indians. They still carried their neatly rolled trousers; they stood opposite the place where he lay hidden, paunchy, thick, soft-looking, a little ludicrous in their straw hats and shirt tails.

"This is wearying work," one said.

"I'd rather be at home in the shade myself," the other said. "But there is the Man waiting at the door to the earth."

"Yao." They looked quietly about; stooping, one of them removed from his shirt tail a clot of cockleburs. "Damn that Negro," he said.

"Yao. When have they ever been anything but a trial and a care to us?"

In the early afternoon, from the top of a tree, the Negro looked down into the plantation. He could see Issetibbeha's body in a hammock between the two trees where the horse and the dog were tethered, and the concourse about the steamboat was filled with wagons and horses and mules, with carts and saddle-horses, while in bright clumps the women and the smaller children and the old men squatted about the long trench where the smoke from the barbecuing meat blew slow and thick. The men and the big boys would all be down there in the creek bottom behind him, on the trail, their Sunday clothes rolled carefully up and wedged into tree crotches. There was a clump of men near the door to the house, to the saloon of the steamboat, though, and he watched them, and after a while he saw them bring Moketubbe out in a litter made of buckskin and persimmon poles; high hidden in his leafed nook the Negro, the quarry, looked quietly down upon his irrevocable doom with an expression as profound as Moketubbe's own. "Yao," he said quietly. "He will go then. That man whose body has been dead for fifteen years, he will go also."

In the middle of the afternoon he came face to face with an Indian. They were both on a footlog across a slough—the Negro gaunt, lean, hard, tireless and desperate; the Indian thick, soft-looking, the apparent embodiment of the ultimate and the supreme reluctance and inertia. The Indian made no move, no sound; he stood on the log and watched the Negro plunge into the slough and swim ashore and crash away into the undergrowth.

Just before sunset he lay behind a down log. Up the log in slow procession moved a line of ants. He caught them and ate them slowly, with a kind of detachment, like that of a dinner guest eating salted nuts from a dish. They too had a salt taste, engendering a salivary reaction out of all proportion. He ate them slowly, watching the unbroken line move up the log and into oblivious doom with a steady and terrific undeviation. He had eaten nothing else all day; in his caked mud mask his eyes rolled in reddened rims. At sunset, creeping along the creek bank toward where he had spotted a frog, a cottonmouth moccasin slashed him suddenly across the forearm with a thick, sluggish blow. It struck clumsily, leaving two long slashes across his arm like two razor slashes, and half sprawled with its own momentum and rage, it appeared for the moment utterly helpless with its own awkwardness and choleric anger. "Olé, grandfather," the Negro said. He touched its head and watched it slash him again across his arm, and again, with thick, raking, awkward blows. "It's that I do not wish to die," he said. Then he said it again—"It's that I do not wish to die"—in a quiet tone, of slow and low amaze, as though it were something that, until the words had said themselves, he found that he had not known, or had not known the depth and extent of his desire.

V

Moketubbe took the slippers with him. He could not wear them very long while in motion, not even in the litter where he was slung reclining, so they rested upon a square of fawnskin upon his lap—the cracked, frail slippers a little shapeless now, with their scaled patent-leather surfaces and buckleless tongues and scarlet heels, lying upon the supine obese shape just barely alive, carried through swamp and briar by swinging relays of men who bore steadily all day long the crime and its object, on the business of the slain. To Moketubbe it must have been as though, himself immortal, he were being carried rapidly through hell by doomed spirits which, alive, had contemplated his disaster, and, dead, were oblivious partners to his damnation.

After resting for a while, the litter propped in the center of the squatting circle and Moketubbe motionless in it, with closed eyes and his face at once peaceful for the instant and filled with inescapable foreknowledge, he could wear the slippers for a while. The stripling put them on him, forcing his big, tender, dropsical feet into them; whereupon into his face came again that expression tragic, passive and profoundly attentive, which dyspeptics wear. Then they went on. He made no move, no sound, inert in the rhythmic litter out of some reserve of inertia, or maybe of some kingly virtue such as courage or fortitude. After a time they set the litter down and looked at him, at the yellow face like that of an idol, beaded over with sweat. Then Three Basket or Had-Two-Fathers would say: "Take them off. Honor has been served." They would remove the shoes. Moketubbe's face would not alter, but only then would his breathing become perceptible, going in and out of his pale lips with a faint ah-ah-ah sound, and they would squat again while the couriers and the runners came up.

"Not yet?"

"Not yet. He is going east. By sunset he will reach Mouth of Tippah. Then he will turn back. We may take him tomorrow."

"Let us hope so. It will not be too soon."

"Yao. It has been three days now."

"When Doom died, it took only three days."

"But that was an old man. This one is young."

"Yao. A good race. If he is taken tomorrow, I will win a horse."

"May you win it."

"Yao. This work is not pleasant."

That was the day on which the food gave out at the plantation. The guests returned home and came back the next day with more food, enough for a week longer. On that day Issetibbeha began to smell; they could smell him for a long way up and down the bottom when it got hot toward noon and the wind blew. But they didn't capture the Negro on that day, nor on the next. It was about dusk on the sixth day when the couriers came up to the litter; they had found blood. "He has injured himself."

"Not bad, I hope," Basket said. "We cannot send with Issetibbeha one who will be of no service to him."

"Nor whom Issetibbeha himself will have to nurse and care for," Berry said.

"We do not know," the courier said. "He has hidden himself. He has crept back into the swamp. We have left pickets."

They trotted with the litter now. The place where the Negro had crept into the swamp was an hour away. In the hurry and excitement they had forgotten that Moketubbe still wore the slippers; when they reached the place Moketubbe had fainted. They removed the slippers and brought him to.

With dark, they formed a circle about the swamp. They squatted, clouded over with gnats and mosquitoes; the evening star burned low and close down the west, and the constellations began to wheel overhead. "We will give him time," they said. "Tomorrow is just another name for today."

"Yao. Let him have time." Then they ceased, and gazed as one into the darkness where the swamp lay. After a while the noise ceased, and soon the courier came out of the darkness.

"He tried to break out."

"But you turned him back?"

"He turned back. We feared for a moment, the three of us. We could smell him creeping in the darkness, and we could smell something else, which we did not know. That was why we feared, until he told us. He said to slay him there, since it would be dark and he would not have to see the face when it came. But it was not that which we smelled; he told us what it was. A snake had struck him. That was two days ago. The arm swelled, and it smelled bad. But it was not that which we smelled then, because the swelling had gone down and his arm was no larger than that of a child. He showed us. We felt the arm, all of us did; it was no larger than that of a child. He said to give him a hatchet so he could chop the arm off. But tomorrow is today also."

"Yao. Tomorrow is today."

"We feared for a while. Then he went back into the swamp."

"That is good."

"Yao. We feared. Shall I tell the Man?"

"I will see," Basket said. He went away. The courier squatted, telling again about the Negro. Basket returned. "The Man says that it is good. Return to your post."

The courier crept away. They squatted about the litter; now and then they slept. Sometime after midnight the Negro waked them. He began to shout and talk to himself, his voice coming sharp and sudden out of the darkness, then he fell silent. Dawn came; a white crane flapped slowly across the jonquil sky. Basket was awake. "Let us go now," he said. "It is today."

Two Indians entered the swamp, their movements noisy. Before they reached the Negro they stopped, because he began to sing. They could see him, naked and mud-caked, sitting on a log, singing. They squatted silently a short distance away, until he finished. He was chanting something in his own language, his face lifted to the rising sun. His voice was clear, full, with a quality wild and sad. "Let him have time," the Indians said, squatting, patient, waiting. He ceased and they approached. He looked back and up at them through the cracked mud mask. His eyes were bloodshot, his lips cracked upon his square short teeth. The mask of mud appeared to be loose on his face, as if he might have lost flesh since he put it there; he held his left arm close to his breast. From the elbow down it was caked and shapeless with black mud. They could smell him, a rank smell. He watched them quietly until one touched him on the arm. "Come," the Indian said. "You ran well. Do not be ashamed."

VI

As they neared the plantation in the tainted bright morning, the Negro's eyes began to roll a little, like those of a horse. The smoke from the cooking pit blew low along the earth and upon the squatting and waiting guests about the yard and upon the steamboat deck, in their bright, stiff, harsh finery; the women, the children, the old men. They had sent couriers along the bottom, and another on ahead, and Issetibbeha's body had already been removed to where the grave waited, along with the horse and the dog, though they could still smell him in death about the house where he had lived in life. The guests were beginning to move toward the grave when the bearers of Moketubbe's litter mounted the slope.

The Negro was the tallest there, his high, close, mud-caked head looming above them all. He was breathing hard, as though the desperate effort of the six suspended and desperate days had catapulted upon him at once; although they walked slowly, his naked scarred chest rose and fell above the close-clutched left arm. He looked this way and that continuously, as if he were not seeing, as though sight never quite caught up with the looking. His mouth was open a little upon his big white teeth; he began to pant. The already moving guests halted, pausing, looking back, some with pieces of meat in their hands, as the Negro looked about at their faces with his wild, restrained, unceasing eyes.

"Will you eat first?" Basket said. He had to say it twice.

"Yes," the Negro said. "That's it. I want to eat."

The throng had begun to press back toward the center; the word passed to the outermost: "He will eat first."

They reached the steamboat. "Sit down," Basket said. The Negro sat on the edge of the deck. He was still panting, his chest rising and falling, his head ceaseless with its white eyeballs, turning from side to side. It was as if the inability to see came from within, from hopelessness, not from absence of vision. They brought food and watched quietly as he tried to eat it. He put the food into his mouth and chewed it, but chewing, the half-masticated matter began to emerge from the corners of his mouth and to drool down his chin, onto his chest, and after a while he stopped chewing and sat there, naked, covered with dried mud, the plate on his knees, and his mouth filled with a mass of chewed food, open, his eyes wide and unceasing, panting and panting. They watched him, patient, implacable, waiting.

"Come," Basket said at last.

"It's water I want," the Negro said. "I want water."

The well was a little way down the slope toward the quarters. The slope lay dappled with the shadows of noon, of that peaceful hour when, Issetibbeha napping in his chair and waiting for the noon meal and the long afternoon to sleep in, the Negro, the body servant, would be free. He would sit in the kitchen door then, talking with the women who prepared the food. Beyond the kitchen the lane between the quarters would be quiet, peaceful, with the women talking to one another across the lane and the smoke of the dinner fires blowing upon the pickaninnies like ebony toys in the dust.

"Come," Basket said.

The Negro walked among them, taller than any. The guests were moving on toward where Issetibbeha and the horse and the dog waited. The Negro walked with his high ceaseless head, his panting chest. "Come," Basket said. "You wanted water."

"Yes," the Negro said. "Yes." He looked back at the house, then down to the quarters, where today no fire burned, no face showed in any door, no pickaninny in the dust, panting. "It struck me here, raking me across this arm; once, twice, three times. I said, 'Olé, Grandfather.' "

"Come now," Basket said. The Negro was still going through the motion of walking, his knee action high, his head high, as though he were on a treadmill. His eyeballs had a wild, restrained glare, like those of a horse. "You wanted water," Basket said. "Here it is "

There was a gourd in the well. They dipped it full and gave it to the Negro, and they watched him try to drink. His eyes had not ceased as he tilted the gourd slowly against his caked face. They could watch his throat working and the bright water cascading from either side of the gourd, down his chin and breast. Then the water stopped. "Come," Basket said.

"Wait," the Negro said. He dipped the gourd again and tilted it against his face, beneath his ceaseless eyes. Again they watched his throat working and the unswallowed water sheathing broken and myriad down his chin, channeling his caked chest. They waited, patient, grave, decorous, implacable; clansman and guest and kin. Then the water ceased, though still the empty gourd tilted higher and higher, and still his black throat aped the vain motion of his frustrated swallowing. A piece of water-loosened mud carried away from his chest and broke at his muddy feet, and in the empty gourd they could hear his breath: ah-ah-ah.

"Come," Basket said, taking the gourd from the Negro and hanging it back in the well.

Luigi Pirandello

The Soft Touch of Grass

THEY went into the next room, where he was sleeping in a big chair, to ask if he wanted to look at her for the last time before the lid was put on the coffin.

"It's dark. What time is it?" he asked.

It was nine-thirty in the morning, but the day was overcast and the light dim. The funeral had been set for ten o'clock.

Signor Pardi stared up at them with dull eyes. It hardly seemed possible that he could have slept so long and well all night. He was still numb with sleep and the sorrow of these last days. He would have liked to cover his face with his hands to shut out the faces of his neighbors grouped about his chair in the thin light; but sleep had weighted his body like lead, and although there was a tingling in his toes urging him to rise, it quickly went away. Should he still give way to his grief? He happened to say aloud, "Always . . ." but he said it like someone settling himself under the covers to go back to sleep. They all looked at him questioningly. Always what?

Always dark, even in the daytime, he had wanted to say, but it made no sense. The day after her death, the day of her funeral, he would always remember this wan light and his deep sleep, too, with her lying dead in the next room. Perhaps the windows . . .

"The windows?"

Yes, they were still closed. They had not been opened during the night, and the warm glow of those big dripping candles lingered. The bed had been taken away, and she was there in her padded casket, rigid and ashen against the creamy satin.

No. Enough. He had seen her.

He closed his eyes, for they burned from all the crying he had done these past few days. Enough. He had slept, and everything had been washed away with that sleep. Now he was relaxed, with a sense of sorrowful emptiness. Let the casket be closed and carried away with all it held of his past life.

But since she was still there . . .

He jumped to his feet and tottered. They caught him and, with eyes still closed, he allowed himself to be led to the open casket. When he opened his eyes and saw her, he called her by name, her name that lived for him alone, the name in which he saw her and knew her in all the fullness of the life they had shared together. He glared resentfully at the others daring to stare at her lying still in death. What did they know about her? They could not even imagine what it meant to him to be deprived of her. He felt like screaming, and it must have been apparent, for his son hurried over to take him away. He was quick to see the meaning of this and felt a chill as though he were stripped bare. For shame—those foolish ideas up to the very last, even after his night-long sleep. Now they must hurry so as not to keep the friends waiting who had come to follow the coffin to the church.

"Come on, Papa. Be reasonable."

With angry, piteous eyes, the bereaved man turned back to his big chair.

Reasonable, yes; it was useless to cry out the anguish that welled within him and that could never be expressed by words or deeds. For a husband who is left a widower at a certain age, a man still yearning for his wife, can the loss be the same as that of a son for whom—at a certain point—it is almost timely to be left an orphan? Timely, since he was on the point of getting married and would, as soon as the three months' mourning were passed, now that he had the added excuse that it was better for both of them to have a woman to look after the house.

"Pardi! Pardi!" they shouted from the entrance hall.

His chill became more intense when he understood clearly for the first time that they were not calling him but his son. From now on their surname would belong more to his son than to him. And he, like a fool, had gone in there to cry out the living name of his mate, like a profanation. For shame! Yes, useless, foolish ideas, he now realized, after that long sleep which had washed him clean of everything.

Now the one vital thing to keep him going was his curiosity as to how their new home would be arranged. Where, for example, were they going to have him sleep? The big double bed had been removed. Would he have a small bed? he wondered. Yes, probably his son's single bed. Now he would have the small bed. And his son would soon be lying in a big bed, his wife beside him within arm's reach. He, alone, in his little bed, would stretch out his arms into thin air.

He felt torpid, perplexed, with a sensation of emptiness inside and all around him. His body was numb from sitting so long. If he tried now to get up, he felt sure that he would rise light as a feather in all that emptiness, now that his life was reduced to nothing. There was hardly any difference between himself and the big chair. Yet that chair appeared secure on its four legs, whereas he no longer knew where his feet and legs belonged nor what to do with his hands. What did he care about his life? He did not care particularly about the lives of others, either. Yet, as he was still alive, he must go on. Begin again—some sort of life which he could not yet conceive and which he certainly would never have contemplated if things had not changed in his own world. Now, deposed like this all of a sudden, not old and yet no longer young . . .

He smiled and shrugged his shoulders. For his son, all at once, he had become a child. But after all, as everyone knows, fathers are children to their grown sons who are full of worldly ambition and have successfully outdistanced them in positions of importance. They keep their fathers in idleness to repay all they have received when they themselves were small, and their fathers in turn become young again.

The single bed . . .

But they did not even give him the little room where his son had slept. Instead, they said, he would feel more independent in another, almost hidden on the courtyard; he would feel free there to do as he liked. They refurnished it with all the best pieces, so it would not occur to anyone that it had once been a servant's room. After the marriage, all the front rooms were pretentiously decorated and newly furnished, even to the luxury of carpets. Not a trace remained of the way the old house had looked. Even with his own furniture relegated to that little dark room, out of the mainstream of the young people's existence, he did not feel at home. Yet, oddly enough, he did not resent the disregard he seemed to have reaped along with the old furniture, because he admired the new rooms and was satisfied with his son's success.

But there was another deeper reason, not too clear as yet, a promise of another life, all shining and colorful, which was erasing the memory of the old one. He even drew a secret hope from it that a new life might begin for him, too. Unconsciously, he sensed the luminous opening of a door at his back whence he might escape at the right moment, easy enough now that no one bothered about him, leaving him as if on holiday in the sanctuary of his little room "to do as he pleased." He felt lighter than air. His eyes had a gleam in them that colored everything, leading him from marvel to marvel, as though he really were a child again. He had the eyes of a child—lively and open wide on a world which was still new.

He took the habit of going out early in the morning to begin his holiday which was to last as long as his life lasted. Relieved of all responsibilities, he agreed to pay his son so much every month out of his pension for his maintenance. It was very little. Though he needed nothing, his son thought he should keep some money for himself to satisfy any need he might have. But need for what? He was satisfied now just to look on at life.

Having shaken off the weight of experience, he no longer knew how to get along with oldsters. He avoided them. And the younger people considered him too old, so he went to the park where the children played.

That was how he started his new life—in the meadow among the children in the grass. What an exhilarating scent the grass had, and so fresh where it grew thick and high. The children played hide-and-seek there. The constant trickle of some hidden stream outpurled the rustle of the leaves. Forgetting their game, the children pulled off their shoes and stockings. What a delicious feeling to sink into all that freshness of soft new grass with bare feet!

He took off one shoe and was stealthily removing the other when a young girl appeared before him, her face flaming. "You pig!" she cried, her eyes flashing.

Her dress was caught up in front on a bush, and she quickly pulled it down over her legs, because he was looking up at her from where he sat on the ground.

He was stunned. What had she imagined? Already she had disappeared. He had wanted to enjoy the children's innocent fun. Bending down, he put his two hands over his hard, bare feet. What had she seen wrong? Was he too old to share a child's delight in going barefoot in the grass? Must one immediately think evil because he was old? Ah, he knew that he could change in a flash from being a child to becoming a man again, if he must. He was still a man, after all, but he didn't want to think about it. He refused to think about it. It was really as a child that he had taken off his shoes. How wrong it was of that wretched girl to insult him like that! He threw himself face down on the grass. All his grief, his loss, his daily loneliness had brought about this gesture, interpreted now in the light of vulgar malice. His gorge rose in disgust and bitterness. Stupid girl! If he had wanted that—even his son admitted he might have "some desires"—he had plenty of money in his pocket for such needs.

Indignant, he pulled himself upright. Shamefacedly, with trembling hands, he put on his shoes again. All the blood had gone to his head, and the pulse now beat hot behind his eyes. Yes, he knew where to go for that. He knew.

Calmer now, he got up and went back to the house. In the welter of furniture which seemed to have been placed there on purpose to drive him mad, he threw himself on the bed and turned his face to the wall.

Jean-Paul Sartre

The Wall

THEY pushed us into a big white room and I began to blink because the light hurt my eyes. Then I saw a table and four men behind the table, civilians, looking over the papers. They had bunched another group of prisoners in the back and we had to cross the whole room to join them. There were several I knew and some others who must have been foreigners. The two in front of me were blond with round skulls; they looked alike. I supposed they were French. The smaller one kept hitching up his pants; nerves.

It lasted about three hours; I was dizzy and my head felt empty; but the room was well heated and I found that pleasant enough: for the past twenty-four hours we hadn't stopped shivering. The guards brought the prisoners up to the table, one after the other. The four men asked each one his name and occupation. Most of the time they didn't go any further—or they would simply ask a question here and there: "Did you have anything to do with the sabotage of munitions?" Or "Where were you the morning of the 9th and what were you doing?" They didn't listen to the answers or at least didn't seem to. They were quiet for a moment and then, looking straight in front of them, began to write. They asked Tom if it were true he was in the International Brigade; Tom couldn't tell them otherwise because of the papers they found in his coat. They didn't ask Juan anything but they wrote for a long time after he told them his name.

"My brother José is the anarchist," Juan said, "you know he isn't here any more. I don't belong to any party, I never had anything to do with politics."

They didn't answer. Juan went on, "I haven't done anything. I don't want to pay for somebody else."

His lips trembled. A guard shut him up and took him away. It was my turn.

"Your name is Pablo Ibbieta?"

"Yes."

The man looked at the papers and asked me, "Where's Ramon Gris?"

"I don't know."

"You hid him in your house from the 6th to the 19th."

"No."

They wrote for a minute and then the guards took me out. In the corridor Tom and Juan were waiting between two guards. We started walking. Tom asked one of the guards, "So?"

"So what?" the guard said.

"Was that the cross-examination or the sentence?"

"Sentence," the guard said.

"What are they going to do with us?"

The guard answered dryly, "Sentence will be read in your cell."

As a matter of fact, our cell was one of the hospital cellars. It was terrifically cold there because of the drafts. We shivered all night and it wasn't much better during the day. I had spent the previous five days in a cell in a monastery, a sort of hole in the wall that must have dated from the middle ages: since there were a lot of prisoners and not much room, they locked us up anywhere. I didn't miss my cell; I hadn't suffered too much from the cold but I was alone; after a long time it gets irritating. In the cellar I had company. Juan hardly ever spoke: he was afraid and he was too young to have anything to say. But Tom was a good talker and he knew Spanish well.

There was a bench in the cellar and four mats. When they took us back we sat and waited in silence. After a long moment, Tom said, "We're screwed."

"I think so too," I said, "but I don't think they'll do anything to the kid."

"They don't have a thing against him," said Tom. "He's the brother of a militiaman and that's all."

I looked at Juan: he didn't seem to hear. Tom went on, "You know what they do in Saragossa? They lay the men down on the road and run over them with trucks. A Moroccan deserter told us that. They said it was to save ammunition."

"It doesn't save gas," I said.

I was annoyed at Tom: he shouldn't have said that.

"Then there's officers walking along the road," he went on, "supervising it all. They stick their hands in their pockets and smoke cigarettes. You think they finish off the guys? Hell no. They let them scream. Sometimes for an hour. The Moroccan said he damned near puked the first time."

"I don't believe they'll do that here." I said. "Unless they're really short on ammunition."

Day was coming in through four airholes and a round opening they had made in the ceiling, on the left, and you could see the sky through it. Through this hole, usually closed by a trap, they unloaded coal into the cellar. Just below the hole there was a big pile of coal dust; it had been used to heat the hospital but since the beginning of the war the patients were evacuated and the coal stayed there, unused; sometimes it even got rained on because they had forgotten to close the trap.

Tom began to shiver. "Good Jesus Christ I'm cold," he said. "Here it goes again."

He got up and began to do exercises. At each movement his shirt opened on his chest, white and hairy. He lay on his back, raised his legs in the air and bicycled. I saw his great rump trembling. Tom was husky but he had too much fat. I thought how rifle bullets or the sharp points of bayonets would soon be sunk into this mass of tender flesh as in a lump of butter. It wouldn't have made me feel like that if he'd been thin.

I wasn't exactly cold, but I couldn't feel my arms and shoulders any more. Sometimes I had the impression I was missing something and began to look around for my coat and then suddenly remembered they hadn't given me a coat. It was rather uncomfortable. They took our clothes and gave them to their soldiers, leaving us only our shirts —and those canvas pants that hospital patients wear in the middle of summer. After a while Tom got up and sat next to me, breathing heavily.

"Warmer?"

"Good Christ, no. But I'm out of wind."

Around eight o'clock in the evening a major came in with two *falangistas*. He had a sheet of paper in his hand. He asked the guard, "What are the names of those three?"

"Steinbock, Ibbieta and Mirbal," the guard said.

The major put on his eyeglasses and scanned the list: Steinbock . . . Steinbock . . . Oh yes . . . You are sentenced to death. You will be shot tomorrow morning." He went on looking. "The other two as well."

"That's not possible," Juan said. "Not me."

The major looked at him amazed. "What's your name?"

"Juan Mirbal," he said.

"Well, your name is there," said the major. "You're sentenced."

"I didn't do anything," Juan said.

The major shrugged his shoulders and turned to Tom and me.

"You're Basque?"

"Nobody is Basque."

He looked annoyed. "They told me there were three Basques. I'm not going to waste my time running after them. Then naturally you don't want a priest?"

We didn't even answer.

He said, "A Belgian doctor is coming shortly. He is authorized to spend the night with you." He made a military salute and left.

"What did I tell you," Tom said. "We get it."

"Yes," I said, "it's a rotten deal for the kid."

I said that to be decent but I didn't like the kid. His face was too thin and fear and suffering had disfigured it, twisting all his features. Three days before he had been a smart sort of kid, not too bad; but now he looked like an old fairy and I thought how he'd never be young again, even if they were to let him go. It wouldn't have been too hard to have a little pity for him but pity disgusts me, or rather it horrifies me. He hadn't said anything more but he had turned grey; his face and hands were both grey. He sat down again and looked at the ground with round eyes. Tom was good hearted, he wanted to take his arm, but the kid tore himself away violently and made a face.

"Let him alone," I said in a low voice, "you can see he's going to blubber."

Tom obeyed regretfully; he would have liked to comfort the kid, it would have passed his time and he wouldn't have been tempted to think about himself. But it annoyed me: I'd never thought about death because I never had any reason to, but now the reason was here and there was nothing to do but think about it.

Tom began to talk. "So you think you've knocked guys off, do you?" he asked me. I didn't answer. He began explaining to me that he had knocked off six since the beginning of August; he didn't realize the situation and I could tell he didn't *want* to realize it. I hadn't quite realized it myself, I wondered if it hurt much, I thought of bullets, I imagined their burning hail through my body. All that was beside the real question; but I was calm: we had all night to understand. After a while Tom stopped talking and I watched him out of the corner of my eye: I saw he too had turned grey and he looked rotten; I told myself "Now it starts." It was almost dark, a dim glow filtered through the airholes and the pile of coal and made a big stain beneath the spot of sky; I could already see a star through the hole in the ceiling: the night would be pure and icy.

The door opened and two guards came in, followed by a blonde man in a tan uniform. He saluted us. "I am the doctor," he said. "I have authorization to help you in these trying hours."

He had an agreeable and distinguished voice. I said, "What do you want here?"

"I am at your disposal. I shall do all I can to make your last moments less difficult."

"What did you come here for? There are others, the hospital's full of them."

"I was sent here," he answered with a vague look. "Ah! Would you like to smoke?" he added hurriedly, "I have cigarettes and even cigars."

He offered us English cigarettes and *puros,* but we refused. I looked him in the eyes and he seemed irritated. I said to him, "You aren't here on an errand of mercy. Besides, I know you. I saw you with the fascists in the barracks yard the day I was arrested."

I was going to continue, but something surprising suddenly happened to me; the presence of this doctor no longer interested me. Generally when I'm on somebody I don't let go. But the desire to talk left me completely; I shrugged and turned my eyes away. A little later I raised my head; he was watching me curiously. The guards were sitting on a mat. Pedro, the tall one, was twiddling his thumbs, the other shook his head from time to time to keep from falling asleep.

"Do you want a light?" Pedro suddenly asked the doctor. The other nodded "Yes": I think he was about as smart as a log, but he surely wasn't bad. Looking in his cold blue eyes it seemed to me that his only sin was lack of imagination. Pedro went out and came back with an oil lamp which he set on the corner of the bench. It gave a bad light but it was better than nothing: they had left us in the dark the night before. For a long time I watched the circle of light the lamp made on the ceiling. I was fascinated. Then suddenly I woke up, the circle of light disappeared and I felt myself crushed under an enormous weight. It was not the thought of death, or fear; it was nameless. My cheeks burned and my head ached.

I shook myself and looked at my two friends. Tom had hidden his face in his hands. I could only see the fat white nape of his neck. Little Juan was the worst, his mouth was open and his nostrils trembled. The doctor went and put his hand on his shoulder as if to comfort him: but his eyes stayed cold. Then I saw the Belgian's hand drop stealthily along Juan's arm, down to the wrist. Juan paid no attention. The Belgian took his wrist between three fingers, distractedly, the same time drawing away a little and turning his back to me. But I leaned backward and saw him take a watch from his pocket and look at it for a moment, never letting go of the wrist. After a minute he let the hand fall inert and went and leaned his back against the wall, then, as if he suddenly remembered something very important which had to be jotted down on the spot, he took a notebook from his pocket and wrote a few lines. "Bastard," I thought angrily, "let him come and take my pulse. I'll shove my fist in his rotten face."

He didn't come but I felt him watching me. I raised my head and returned his look. Impersonally, he said to me, "Doesn't it seem cold to you here?" He looked cold, he was blue.

"I'm not cold," I told him.

He never took his hard eyes off me. Suddenly I understood and my hands went to my face: I was drenched in sweat. In this cellar, in the midst of winter, in the midst of drafts, I was sweating. I ran my hands through my hair, gummed together with perspiration; at the same time I saw my shirt was damp and sticking to my skin: I had been dripping for an hour and hadn't felt it. But that swine of a Belgian hadn't missed a thing; he had seen the drops rolling down my cheeks and thought: this is the manifestation of an almost pathological state of terror; and he had felt normal and proud of being alive because he was cold. I wanted to stand up and smash his face but no sooner had I made the slightest gesture than my rage and shame were wiped out; I fell back on the bench with indifference.

I satisfied myself by rubbing my neck with my handkerchief because now I felt the sweat dropping from my hair onto my neck and it was unpleasant. I soon gave up rubbing, it was useless; my handkerchief was already soaked and I was still sweating. My buttocks were sweating too and my damp trousers were glued to the bench.

Suddenly Juan spoke. "You're a doctor?"

"Yes," the Belgian said.

"Does it hurt . . . very long?"

"Huh? When . . . ? Oh, no," the Belgian said paternally. "Not at all. It's over quickly." He acted as though he were calming a cash customer.

"But I . . . they told me . . . sometimes they have to fire twice."

"Sometimes," the Belgian said, nodding. "It may happen that the first volley reaches no vital organs."

"Then they have to reload their rifles and aim all over again?" He thought for a moment and then added hoarsely, "That takes time!"

He had a terrible fear of suffering, it was all he thought about: it was his age. I never thought much about it and it wasn't fear of suffering that made me sweat.

I got up and walked to the pile of coal dust. Tom jumped up and threw me a hateful look: I had annoyed him because my shoes squeaked. I wondered if my face looked as frightened as his: I saw he was sweating too. The sky was superb, no light filtered into the dark corner and I had only to raise my head to see the Big Dipper. But it wasn't like it had been: the night before I could see a great piece of sky from my monastery cell and each hour of the day brought me a different memory. Morning, when the sky was a hard, light blue, I thought of beaches on the Atlantic; at noon I saw the sun and I remembered a bar in Seville where I drank *manzanilla* and ate olives and anchovies; afternoons I was in the shade and I thought of the deep shadow which spreads over half a bull-ring leaving the other half shimmering in sunlight; it was really hard to see the whole world reflected in the sky like that. But now I could watch the sky as much as I pleased, it no longer evoked anything in me. I liked that better. I came back and sat near Tom. A long moment passed.

Tom began speaking in a low voice. He had to talk, without that he wouldn't have been able to recognize himself in his own mind. I thought he was talking to me but he wasn't looking at me. He was undoubtedly afraid to see me as I was, grey and sweating: we were alike and worse than mirrors of each other. He watched the Belgian the living.

"Do you understand?" he said. "I don't understand."

I began to speak in a low voice too. I watched the Belgian. "Why? What's the matter?"

"Something is going to happen to us that I can't understand."

There was a strange smell about Tom. It seemed to me I was more sensitive than usual to odors. I grinned. "You'll understand in a while."

"It isn't clear," he said obstinately. "I want to be brave but at least I have to know. . . Listen, they're going to take us into the courtyard. Good. They're going to stand up in front of us. How many?"

"I don't know. Five or eight. Not more."

"All right. There'll be eight. Someone'll holler 'aim!' and I'll see eight rifles looking at me. I'll think how I'd like to get inside the wall, I'll push against it with my back . . . with every ounce of strength I have, but the wall will stay, like in a nightmare. I can imagine all that. If you only knew how well I can imagine it."

"All right, all right!" I said, "I can imagine it too."

"It must hurt like hell. You know, they aim at the eyes and the mouth to disfigure you," he added mechanically. "I can feel the wounds already; I've had pains in my head and in my neck for the past hour. Not real pains. Worse. This is what I'm going to feel tomorrow morning. And then what?"

I well understood what he meant but I didn't want to act as if I did. I had pains too, pains in my body like a crowd of tiny scars. I couldn't get used to it. But I was like him, I attached no importance to it. "After," I said, "you'll be pushing up the daisies."

He began to talk to himself: he never stopped watching the Belgian. The Belgian didn't seem to be listening. I knew what he had come to do; he wasn't interested in what we thought; he came to watch our bodies, bodies dying in agony while yet alive.

"It's like a nightmare," Tom was saying. "You want to think something, you always have the impression that it's all right, that you're going to understand and then it slips, it escapes you and fades away. I tell myself there will be nothing afterwards. But I don't understand what it means. Sometimes I almost can . . . and then it fades away and I start thinking about the pains again, bullets, explosions. I'm a materialist, I swear it to you; I'm not going crazy. But something's the matter. I see my corpse; that's not hard but *I'm* the one who sees it, with *my* eyes. I've got to think . . . think that I won't see anything anymore and the world will go on for the others. We aren't made to think that, Pablo. Believe me: I've already stayed up a whole night waiting for something. But this isn't the same: this will creep up behind us, Pablo, and we won't be able to prepare for it."

"Shut up," I said, "Do you want me to call a priest?"

He didn't answer. I had already noticed he had a tendency to act like a prophet and call me Pablo, speaking in a toneless voice. I didn't like that: but it seems all the Irish are that way. I had the vague impression he smelled of urine. Fundamentally, I hadn't much sympathy for Tom and I didn't see why, under the pretext of dying together, I should have any more. It would have been different with some others. With Ramon Gris, for example. But I felt alone between Tom and Juan. I liked that better, anyhow: with Ramon I might have been more deeply moved. But I was terribly hard just then and I wanted to stay hard.

He kept on chewing his words, with something like distraction. He certainly talked to keep himself from thinking. He smelled of urine like an old prostate case. Naturally, I agreed with him, I could have said everything he said: it isn't *natural* to die. And since I was going to die, nothing seemed natural to me, not this pile of coal dust, or the bench, or Pedro's ugly face. Only it didn't please me to think the same things as Tom. And I knew that, all through the night, every five minutes, we would keep on thinking things at the same time. I looked at him sideways and for the first time he seemed strange to me: he wore death on his face. My pride was wounded: for the past twenty-four hours I had lived next to Tom, I had listened to him, I had spoken to him and I knew we had nothing in common. And now we looked as much alike as twin brothers, simply because we were going to die together. Tom took my hand without looking at me.

"Pablo, I wonder . . . I wonder if it's really true that everything ends."

I took my hand away and said, "Look between your feet, you pig."

There was a big puddle between his feet and drops fell from his pants-leg.

"What is it?" he asked, frightened.

"You're pissing in your pants," I told him.

"It isn't true," he said furiously. "I'm not pissing. I don't feel anything."

The Belgian approached us. He asked with false solicitude, "Do you feel ill?"

Tom did not answer. The Belgian looked at the puddle and said nothing.

"I don't know what it is," Tom said ferociously. "But I'm not afraid. I swear I'm not afraid."

The Belgian did not answer. Tom got up and went to piss in a corner. He came back buttoning his fly, and sat down without a word. The Belgian was taking notes.

All three of us watched him because he was alive. He had the motions of a living human being, the cares of a living human being; he shivered in the cellar the way the living are supposed to shiver; he had an obedient, well-fed body. The rest of us hardly felt ours—not in the same way anyhow. I wanted to feel my pants between my legs but I didn't dare; I watched the Belgian, balancing on his legs, master of his muscles, someone who could think about tomorrow. There we were, three bloodless shadows; we watched him and we sucked his life like vampires.

Finally he went over to little Juan. Did he want to feel his neck for some professional motive or was he obeying an impulse of charity? If he was acting by charity it was only time during the whole night.

He caressed Juan's head and neck. The kid let himself be handled, his eyes never leaving him, then suddenly, he seized the hand and looked at it strangely. He held the Belgian's hand between his own two hands and there was nothing pleasant about them, two grey pincers gripping his fat and reddish hand. I suspected what was going to happen and Tom must have suspected it too: but the Belgian didn't see a thing, he smiled paternally. After a moment the kid brought the fat red hand to his mouth and tried to bite it. The Belgian pulled away quickly and stumbled back against the wall. For a second he looked at us with horror, he must have suddenly understood that we were not men like him. I began to laugh and one of the guards jumped up. The other was asleep, his wide-open eyes were blank.

I felt relaxed and over-excited at the same time. I didn't want to think any more about what would happen at dawn, or death. It made no sense. I only found words or emptiness. But as soon as I tried to think of anything else I saw rifle barrels pointing at me. I lived my execution twenty times perhaps; once I even thought it was for good: I must have slept a minute. They were dragging me to the wall and I was struggling; I was asking for mercy. I woke up with a start and looked at the Belgian: I was afraid I might have cried out in my sleep. But he was stroking his moustache, he hadn't noticed anything. If I had wanted to, I think I could have slept a while; I had been awake for forty-eight hours. I was at the end of my rope.

But I didn't want to lose two hours of life: they would come to wake me up at dawn, I would follow them, stupified with sleep and I would have croaked without so much as an "Oof!"; I didn't want that, I didn't want to die like an animal, I wanted to understand. Then I was afraid of having nightmares. I got up, walked back and forth, and, to change my ideas, I began to think about my past life. A crowd of memories came back to me pell-mell. There were good and bad ones—or at least I called them that *before*. There were faces and incidents. I saw the face of a little *novillero* who was gored in Valencia during the *Feria,* the face of one of my uncles, the face of Ramon Gris. I remembered my whole life: how I was out of work for three months in 1926, how I almost starved to death. I remembered a night I spent on a bench in Granada: I hadn't eaten for three days. I was angry, I didn't want to die. That made me smile. How madly I ran after happiness, after women, after liberty. Why? I wanted to free Spain, I admired Pi y Margall, I joined the anarchist movement, I spoke at public meetings: I took everything as seriously as if I were immortal.

At that moment I felt that I had my whole life in front of me and I thought, "It's a damned lie." It was worth nothing because it was finished. I wondered how I'd been able to walk, to laugh with the girls: I wouldn't have moved so much as my little finger if I had only imagined I would die like this. My life was in front of me, shut, closed, like a bag and yet everything inside of it was unfinished. For an instant I tried to judge it. I wanted to tell myself, this is a beautiful life. But I couldn't pass judgment on it; it was only a sketch; I had spent my time counterfeiting eternity, I had understood nothing. I missed nothing: there were so many things I could have missed, the taste of *manzanilla* or the baths I took in summer in a little creek near Cadiz; but death had disenchanted everything.

The Belgian suddenly had a bright idea. "My friends," he told us, "I will undertake—if the military administration will allow it—to send a message for you, a souvenir to those who love you . . ."

Tom mumbled, "I don't have anybody."

I said nothing. Tom waited an instant then looked at me with curiosity. "You don't have anything to say to Concha?"

"No."

I hated this tender complicity: it was my own fault, I had talked about Concha the night before, I should have controlled myself. I was with her for a year. Last night I would have given an arm to see her again for five minutes. That was why I talked about her, it was stronger than I was. Now I had no more desire to see her, I had nothing more to say to her. I would not even have wanted to hold her in my arms: my body filled me with horror because it was grey and sweating—and I wasn't sure that her body didn't fill me with horror. Concha would cry when she found out I was dead, she would have no taste for life for months afterwards. But I was still the one who was going to die. I thought of her soft, beautiful eyes. When she looked at me something passed from her to me. But I knew it was over: if she looked at me *now* the look would stay in her eyes, it wouldn't reach me. I was alone.

Tom was alone too but not in the same way. Sitting cross-legged, he had begun to stare at the bench with a sort of smile, he looked amazed. He put out his hand and touched the wood cautiously as if he were afraid of breaking something, then drew back his hand quickly and shuddered. If I had been Tom I wouldn't have amused myself by touching the bench; this was some more Irish nonsense, but I too found that objects had a funny look: they were more obliterated, less dense than usual. It was enough for me to look at the bench, the lamp, the pile of coal dust, to feel that I was going to die. Naturally I couldn't think clearly about my death but I saw it everywhere, on things, in the way things fell back and kept their distance, discreetly, as people who speak quietly at the bedside of a dying man. It was *his* death which Tom had just touched on the bench.

In the state I was in, if someone had come and told me I could go home quietly, that they would leave me my life whole, it would have left me cold: several hours or several years of waiting is all the same when you have lost the illusion of being eternal. I clung to nothing, in a way I was calm. But it was a horrible calm—because of my body; my body, I saw with its eyes, I heard with its ears, but it was no longer me; it sweated and trembled by itself and I didn't recognise it anymore. I had to touch it and look at it to find out what was happening, as if it were the body of someone else. At times I could still feel it, I felt sinkings and fallings, as when you're in a plane taking a nosedive, or I felt my heart beating. But that didn't reassure me. Everything that came from my body was all cockeyed. Most of the time it was quiet and I felt no more than a sort of weight, a filthy presence against me; I had the impression of being tied to an enormous vermin. Once I felt my pants and I felt they were damp; I didn't know whether it was sweat or urine, but I went to piss on the coal pile as a precaution.

The Belgian took out his watch, looked at it. He said, "It is three thirty."

Bastard! He must have done it on purpose. Tom jumped; we hadn't noticed time was running out; night surrounded us like a shapeless, sombre mass, I couldn't even remember that it had begun.

Little Juan began to cry. He wrung his hands, pleaded, "I don't want to die. I don't want to die."

He ran across the whole cellar waving his arms in the air, then fell sobbing on one of the mats. Tom watched him with mournful eyes, without the slightest desire to console him. Because it wasn't worth the trouble: the kid made more noise than we did, but he was less touched: he was like a sick man who defends himself against his illness by fever. It's much more serious when there isn't any fever.

He wept: I could clearly see he was pitying himself; he wasn't thinking about death. For one second, one single second, I wanted to weep myself, to weep with pity for myself. But the opposite happened: I glanced at the kid, I saw his thin sobbing shoulders and I felt inhuman: I could pity neither the others nor myself. I said to myself, "I want to die cleanly."

Tom had got up, he placed himself just under the round opening and began to watch for daylight. I was determined to die cleanly and I only thought of that. But ever since the doctor told us the time, I felt time flying, flowing away drop by drop.

"Yes."

It was still dark when I heard Tom's voice: "Do you hear them?"

Men were marching in the courtyard.

"What the hell are they doing? They can't shoot in the dark."

After a while we heard no more. I said to Tom, "It's day."

Pedro got up, yawning, and came to blow out the lamp. He said to his buddy, "Cold as hell."

The cellar was all grey. We heard shots in the distance.

"It's starting," I told Tom. "They must do it in the court in the rear."

Tom asked the doctor for a cigarette. I didn't want one: I didn't want cigarettes or alcohol. From that moment on they didn't stop firing.

"Do you realise what's happening?" Tom said.

He wanted to add something but kept quiet, watching the door. The door opened and a lieutenant came in with four soldiers. Tom dropped his cigarette.

"Steinbock?"

Tom didn't answer. Pedro pointed him out.

"Juan Mirbal?"

"On the mat."

"Get up," the lieutenant said.

Juan did not move. Two soldiers took him under the arms and set him on his feet. But he fell as soon as they released him.

The soldiers hesitated.

"He's not the first sick one," said the lieutenant. "You two carry him; they'll fix it up down there."

He turned to Tom. "Let's go."

Tom went out between two soldiers. Two others followed, carrying the kid by the armpits. He hadn't fainted; his eyes were wide open and tears ran down his cheeks. When I wanted to go out the lieutenant stopped me.

"You Ibbieta?"

"Yes."

"You wait here; they'll come for you later."

They left. The Belgian and the two jailers left too, I was alone. I did not understand what was happening to me but I would have liked it better if they had gotten it over with right away. I heard shots at almost regular intervals; I shook with each one of them. I wanted to scream and tear out my hair. But I gritted my teeth and pushed my hands in my pockets because I wanted to stay clean.

After an hour they came to get me and led me to the first floor, to a small room that smelt of cigars and where the heat was stifling. There were two officers sitting smoking in the armchairs, papers on their knees.

"You're Ibbieta?"

"Yes."

"Where is Ramon Gris?"

"I don't know."

The one questioning me was short and fat. His eyes were hard behind his glasses. He said to me, "Come here."

I went to him. He got up and took my arms, staring at me with a look that should have pushed me into the earth. At the same time he pinched my biceps with all his might. It wasn't to hurt me, it was only a game; he wanted to dominate me. He also thought he had to blow his stinking breath square in my face. We stayed for a moment like that, and I almost felt like laughing. It takes a lot to intimidate a man who is going to die; it didn't work. He pushed me back violently and sat down again. He said, "It's his life against yours. You can have yours if you tell us where he is."

These men dolled up with their riding crops and boots were still going to die. A little later than I, but not too much. They busied themselves looking for names in their crumpled papers, they ran after other men to imprison or suppress them; they had opinions on the future of Spain and on other subjects. Their little activities seemed shocking and burlesqued to me; I couldn't put myself in their place, I thought they were insane. The little man was still looking at me, whipping his boots with the riding crop. All his gestures were calculated to give him the look of a live and ferocious beast.

"So? You understand?"

"I don't know where Gris is," I answered. "I thought he was in Madrid."

The other officer raised his pale hand indolently. This indolence was also calculated. I saw through all their little schemes and I was stupefied to find there were men who amused themselves that way.

"You have a quarter of an hour to think it over," he said slowly. "Take him to the laundry, bring him back in fifteen minutes. If he still refuses he will be executed on the spot."

They knew what they were doing: I had passed the night in waiting; then they had made me wait an hour in the cellar while they shot Tom and Juan and now they were locking me up in the laundry; they must have prepared their game the night before. They told themselves that nerves eventually wear out and they hoped to get me that way.

They were badly mistaken. In the laundry I sat on a stool because I felt very weak and I began to think. But not about their proposition. Of course I knew where Gris was; he was hiding with his cousins, four kilometers from the city. I also knew that I would not reveal his hiding place unless they tortured me (but they didn't seem to be thinking about that). All that was perfectly regulated, definite and in no way interested me. Only I would have liked to understand the reasons for my conduct. I would rather die than give up Gris. Why? I didn't like Ramon Gris any more. My friendship for him had died a little while before dawn at the same time as my love for Concha, at the same time as my desire to live. Undoubtedly I thought highly of him: he was tough. But it was not for this reason that I consented to die in his place; his life had no more value than mine; no life had value. They were going to slap a man up against a wall and shoot at him till he died, whether it was I or Gris or somebody else made no difference. I knew he was more useful than I to the cause of Spain but I thought to hell with Spain and anarchy; nothing was important. Yet I was there, I could save my skin and give up Gris and I refused to do it. I found that somehow comic; it was obstinacy. I thought, "I must be stubborn!" And a droll sort of gaiety spread over me.

They came for me and brought me back to the two officers. A rat ran out from under my feet and that amused me. I turned to one of the *falangistas* and said, "Did you see the rat?"

He didn't answer. He was very sober, he took himself seriously. I wanted to laugh but I held myself back because I was afraid that once I got started I wouldn't be able to stop. The *falangista* had a moustache. I said to him again, "You ought to shave off your moustache, idiot." I thought it funny that he would let the hairs of his living being invade his face. He kicked me without great conviction and I kept quiet.

"Well," said the fat officer, "have you thought about it?"

I looked at them with curiosity, as insects of a very rare species. I told them, "I know where he is. He is hidden in the cemetery. In a vault or in the gravediggers' shack."

It was a farce. I wanted to see them stand up, buckle their belts and give orders busily.

They jumped to their feet. "Let's go, Molés. Go get fifteen men from Lieutenant Lopez. You," the little fat man said, "I'll let you off if you're telling the truth, but it'll cost you plenty if you're making monkeys out of us."

They left in a great clatter and I waited peacefully under the guard of *falangistas*. From time to time I smiled, thinking about the spectacle they would make. I felt stunned and malicious. I imagined them lifting up tombstones, opening the doors of the vaults one by one. I represented this situation to myself as if I had been someone else: this prisoner obstinately playing the hero, these grim *falangistas* with their moustaches and their men in uniform running among the graves; it was irresistibly funny. After half an hour the little fat man came back alone. I thought he came to give the orders to execute me. The others must have stayed in the cemetery.

The officer looked at me. He didn't look at all sheepish. "Take him into the big courtyard with the others," he said. "After the military operations a regular court will decide what happens to him."

"Then they're not . . . not going to shoot me?"

"Not now, anyway. What happens afterwards is none of my business."

I still didn't understand. I asked, "But why? . . ."

He shrugged his shoulders without answering and the soldiers took me away. In the big courtyard there were about a hundred prisoners, women, children and a few old men. I began walking around the central grass-plot, I was stupefied. At noon they let us eat in the mess hall. Two or three people questioned me. I must have known them, but I didn't answer: I didn't even know where I was.

Around evening they pushed about ten new prisoners into the court. I recognized Garcia, the baker. He said, "What damned luck you have! I didn't think I'd see you alive."

"They sentenced me to death," I said, "and then they changed their minds. I don't know why."

"They arrested me at two o'clock," Garcia said.

"Why?" Garcia had nothing to do with politics.

"I don't know," he said. "They arrest everybody who doesn't think the way they do." He lowered his voice. "They got Gris."

I began to tremble. "When?"

"This morning. He messed it up. He left his cousin's on Tuesday because they had an argument. There were plenty of people to hide him but he didn't want to owe anything to anybody. He said, 'I'd go and hide in Ibbieta's place, but they got him, so I'll go hide in the cemetery.' "

"In the cemetery?"

"Yes. What a fool. Of course they went by there this morning, that was sure to happen. They found him in the gravediggers' shack. He shot at them and they got him."

"In the cemetery!"

Everything began to spin and I found myself sitting on the ground: I laughed so hard I cried.

Walter Van Tilburg Clark

Hook

HOOK, the hawks' child, was hatched in a dry spring among the oaks beside the seasonal river, and was struck from the nest early. In the drouth his single-willed parents had to extend their hunting ground by more than twice, for the ground creatures upon which they fed died and dried by the hundreds. The range became too great for them to wish to return and feed Hook, and when they had lost interest in each other they drove Hook down into the sand and brush and went back to solitary courses over the bleaching hills.

Unable to fly yet, Hook crept over the ground, challenging all large movements with recoiled head, erected, rudimentary wings, and the small rasp of his clattering beak. It was during this time of abysmal ignorance and continual fear that his eyes took on the first quality of a hawk, that of being wide, alert and challenging. He dwelt, because of his helplessness, among the rattling brush which grew between the oaks and the river. Even in his thickets and near the water, the white sun was the dominant presence. Except in the dawn, when the land wind stirred, or in the late afternoon, when the sea wind became strong enough to penetrate the half-mile inland to this turn in the river, the sun was the major force, and everything was dry and motionless under it. The brush, small plants and trees alike husbanded the little moisture at their hearts; the moving creatures waited for dark, when sometimes the sea fog came over and made a fine, soundless rain which relieved them.

The two spacious sounds of his life environed Hook at this time One was the great rustle of the slopes of yellowed wild wheat, with over it the chattering rustle of the leaves of the California oaks already as harsh and individually tremulous as in autumn. The othe was the distant whisper of the foaming edge of the Pacific, punctuate by the hollow shoring of the waves. But these Hook did not yet hear for he was attuned by fear and hunger to the small, spasmodic rus tlings of live things. Dry, shrunken, and nearly starved, and with hi plumage delayed, he snatched at beetles, dragging in the sand to catc them. When swifter and stronger birds and animals did not reac them first, which was seldom, he ate the small, silver fish left in th mud by the failing river. He watched, with nearly chattering beak the quick, thin lizards pause, very alert, and raise and lower them selves, but could not catch them because he had to raise his wings t move rapidly, which startled them.

Only one sight and sound not of his world of microscopic necessit was forced upon Hook. That was the flight of the big gulls from th beaches, which sometimes, in quealing play, came spinning back ove the foothills and the river bed. For some inherited reason, the bi ship-bodied birds did not frighten Hook, but angered him. Small an chewed-looking, with his wide, already yellowing eyes glaring up them, he would stand in an open place on the sand in the sun an spread his shaping wings and clatter his bill like shaken dice. Hoo was furious about the swift, easy passage of gulls.

His first opportunity to leave off living like a ground owl cam accidentally. He was standing in the late afternoon in the red lig under the thicket, his eyes half-filmed with drowse and the stupefa tion of starvation, when suddenly something beside him moved, an he struck, and killed a field mouse driven out of the wheat by thirst. was a poor mouse, shriveled and lice ridden, but in striking, Hoc had tasted blood, which raised nest memories and restored his nature. With started neck plumage and shining eyes, he tore and fed. When the mouse was devoured, Hook had entered hoarse adolescence. He began to seek with a conscious appetite, and to move more readily out of shelter. Impelled by the blood appetite, so glorious after his long preservation upon the flaky and bitter stuff of bugs, he ventured even into the wheat in the open sun beyond the oaks, and discovered the small trails and holes among the roots. With his belly often partially filled with flesh, he grew rapidly in strength and will. His eyes were taking on their final change, their yellow growing deeper and more opaque, their stare more constant, their challenge less desperate. Once during this transformation, he surprised a ground squirrel, and although he was ripped and wing-bitten and could not hold his prey, he was not dismayed by the conflict, but exalted. Even while the wing was still drooping and the pinions not grown back, he was excited by other ground squirrels and pursued them futilely, and was angered by their dusty escapes. He realized that his world was a great arena for killing, and felt the magnificence of it.

The two major events of Hook's young life occurred in the same day. A little after dawn he made the customary essay and succeeded in flight. A little before sunset, he made his first sustained flight of over two hundred yards, and at its termination struck and slew a great buck squirrel whose thrashing and terrified gnawing and squealing gave him a wild delight. When he had gorged on the strong meat, Hook stood upright, and in his eyes was the stare of the hawk, never flagging in intensity but never swelling beyond containment. After that the stare had only to grow more deeply challenging and more sternly controlled as his range and deadliness increased. There was no change in kind. Hook had mastered the first of the three hungers which are fused into the single, flaming will of a hawk, and he had experienced the second.

The third and consummating hunger did not awaken in Hook until the following spring, when the exultation of space had grown slow and steady in him, so that he swept freely with the wind over the miles of coastal foothills, circling, and ever in sight of the sea, and used without struggle the warm currents lifting from the slopes, and no longer desired to scream at the range of his vision, but intently sailed above his shadow swiftly climbing to meet him on the hillsides, sinking away and rippling across the brush-grown canyons.

That spring the rains were long, and Hook sat for hours, hunched and angry under their pelting, glaring into the fogs of the river valley, and killed only small, drenched things flooded up from their tunnels. But when the rains had dissipated, and there were sun and sea wind again, the game ran plentiful, the hills were thick and shining green, and the new river flooded about the boulders where battered turtles climbed up to shrink and sleep. Hook then was scorched by the third hunger. Ranging farther, often forgetting to kill and eat, he sailed for days with growing rage, and woke at night clattering on his dead tree limb, and struck and struck and struck at the porous wood of the trunk, tearing it away. After days, in the draft of a coastal canyon miles below his own hills, he came upon the acrid taint he did not know but had expected, and sailing down it, felt his neck plumes rise and his wings quiver so that he swerved unsteadily. He saw the unmated female perched upon the tall and jagged stump of a tree that had been shorn by storm, and he stooped, as if upon game. But she was older than he, and wary of the gripe of his importunity, and banked off screaming, and he screamed also at the intolerable delay.

At the head of the canyon, the screaming pursuit was crossed by another male with a great wing-spread, and the light golden in the fringe of his plumage. But his more skillful opening played him false against the ferocity of the twice-balked Hook. His rising maneuver for position was cut short by Hook's wild, upward swoop, and at the blow he raked desperately and tumbled off to the side. Dropping, Hook struck him again, struggled to clutch, but only raked and could not hold, and, diving, struck once more in passage, and then beat up, yelling triumph, and saw the crippled antagonist side-slip away, half-tumble once, as the ripped wing failed to balance, then steady and glide obliquely into the cover of brush on the canyon side. Beating hard and stationary in the wind above the bush that covered his competitor, Hook waited an instant, but when the bush was still, screamed again, and let himself go off with the current, reseeking, infuriated by the burn of his own wounds, the thin choke-thread of the acrid taint.

On a hilltop projection of stone two miles inland, he struck her down, gripping her rustling body with his talons, beating her wings down with his wings, belting her head when she whimpered or thrashed, and at last clutching her neck with his hook and, when her coy struggles had given way to stillness, succeeded.

In the early summer, Hook drove the three young ones from their nest, and went back to lone circling above his own range. He was complete.

II

Throughout that summer and the cool, growthless weather of the winter, when the gales blew in the river canyon and the ocean piled upon the shore, Hook was master of the sky and the hills of his range. His flight became a lovely and certain thing, so that he played with the treacherous currents of the air with a delicate ease surpassing that of the gulls. He could sail for hours, searching the blanched grasses below him with telescopic eyes, gaining height against the wind, descending in mile-long, gently declining swoops when he curved and rode back, and never beating either wing. At the swift passage of his shadow within their vision, gophers, ground squirrels and rabbits froze, or plunged gibbering into their tunnels beneath matted turf. Now, when he struck, he killed easily in one hard-knuckled blow. Occasionally, in sport, he soared up over the river and drove the heavy and weaponless gulls downstream again, until they would no longer venture inland.

There was nothing which Hook feared now, and his spirit was wholly belligerent, swift and sharp, like his gaze. Only the mixed smells and incomprehensible activities of the people at the Japanese farmer's home, inland of the coastwise highway and south of the bridge across Hook's river, troubled him. The smells were strong, unsatisfactory and never clear, and the people, though they behaved foolishly, constantly running in and out of their built-up holes, were large, and appeared capable, with fearless eyes looking up at him, so that he instinctively swerved aside from them. He cruised over their yard, their gardens, and their bean fields, but he would not alight close to their buildings.

But this one area of doubt did not interfere with his life. He ignored it, save to look upon it curiously as he crossed, his afternoon shadow sliding in an instant over the chicken-and-crate-cluttered yard, up the side of the unpainted barn, and then out again smoothly, just faintly, liquidly rippling over the furrows and then over the stubble of the grazing slopes. When the season was dry, and the dead earth blew on the fields, he extended his range to satisfy his great hunger, and again narrowed it when the fields were once more alive with the minute movements he could not only see but anticipate.

Four times that year he was challenged by other hawks blowing up from behind the coastal hills to scud down his slopes, but two of these he slew in mid-air, and saw hurtle down to thump on the ground and lie still while he circled, and a third, whose wing he tore, he followed closely to earth and beat to death in the grass, making the crimson jet out from its breast and neck into the pale wheat. The fourth was a strong flier and experienced fighter, and theirs was a long, running battle, with brief, rising flurries of striking and screaming, from which down and plumage soared off.

Here, for the first time, Hook felt doubts, and at moments wanted to drop away from the scoring, burning talons and the twisted hammer strokes of the strong beak, drop away shrieking, and take cover and be still. In the end, when Hook, having outmaneuvered his enemy and come above him, wholly in control, and going with the wind, tilted and plunged for the death rap, the other, in desperation, threw over on his back and struck up. Talons locked, beaks raking, they dived earthward. The earth grew and spread under them amazingly, and they were not fifty feet above it when Hook, feeling himself turning toward the underside, tore free and beat up again on heavy, wrenched wings. The other, stroking swiftly, and so close to down that he lost wing plumes to a bush, righted himself and planed up, but flew on lumberingly between the hills and did not return. Hook screamed the triumph, and made a brief pretense of pursuit, but was glad to return, slow and victorious, to his dead tree.

In all these encounters Hook was injured, but experienced only the fighter's pride and exultation from the sting of wounds received in successful combat. And in each of them he learned new skill. Each time the wounds healed quickly, and left him a more dangerous bird.

In the next spring, when the rains and the night chants of the little frogs were past, the third hunger returned upon Hook with a new violence. In his quest, he came into the taint of a young hen. Others too were drawn by the unnerving perfume, but only one of them, the same with which Hook had fought his great battle, was a worthy competitor. This hunter drove off two, while two others, game but neophytes, were glad enough that Hook's impatience would not permit him to follow and kill. Then the battle between the two champions fled inland, and was a tactical marvel, but Hook lodged the neck-breaking blow, and struck again as they dropped past the treetops. The blood had already begun to pool on the gray, fallen foliage as Hook flapped up between branches, too spent to cry his victory. Yet his hunger would not let him rest until, late in the second day, he drove the female to ground, among the laurels of a strange river canyon.

When the two fledglings of this second brood had been driven from the nest, and Hook had returned to his own range, he was not only complete, but supreme. He slept without concealment on his bare limb, and did not open his eyes when, in the night, the heavy-billed cranes coughed in the shadows below him.

III

The turning point of Hook's career came that autumn, when the brush in the canyons rustled dryly and the hills, mowed close by the cattle, smoked under the wind as if burning. One midafternoon, when the black clouds were torn on the rim of the sea and the surf flowered white and high on the rocks, raining in over the low cliffs, Hook rode the wind diagonally across the river mouth. His great eyes, focused for small things stirring in the dust and leaves, overlooked so large and slow a movement as that of the Japanese farmer rising from the brush and lifting the two black eyes of his shotgun. Too late Hook saw and, startled, swerved, but wrongly. The surf muffled the reports, and nearly without sound, Hook felt the minute whips of the first shot, and the astounding, breath-breaking blow of the second.

Beating his good wing, tasting the blood that quickly swelled into his beak, he tumbled off with the wind and struck into the thickets on the far side of the river mouth. The branches tore him. Wild with rage, he thrust up and clattered his beak, challenging, but when he had fallen over twice, he knew that the trailing wing would not carry, and then heard the boots of the hunter among the stones in the river bed and, seeing him loom at the edge of the bushes, crept back among the thickest brush and was still. When he saw the boots stand before him, he reared back, lifting his good wing and cocking his head for the serpent-like blow, his beak open but soundless, his great eyes hard and very shining. The boots passed on. The Japanese farmer, who believed that he had lost chickens, and who had cunningly observed Hook's flight for many afternoons, until he could plot it, did not greatly want a dead hawk.

When Hook could hear nothing but the surf and the wind in the thicket, he let the sickness and shock overcome him. The fine film of the inner lid dropped over his big eyes. His heart beat frantically, so that it made the plumage of his shot-aching breast throb. His own blood throttled his breathing. But these things were nothing compared to the lightning of pain in his left shoulder, where the shot had bunched, shattering the airy bones so the pinions trailed on the ground and could not be lifted. Yet, when a sparrow lit in the bush over him, Hook's eyes flew open again, hard and challenging, his good wing was lifted and his beak strained open. The startled sparrow darted piping out over the river.

Throughout that night, while the long clouds blew across the stars and the wind shook the bushes about him, and throughout the next day, while the clouds still blew and massed until there was no gleam of sunlight on the sand bar, Hook remained stationary, enduring his sickness. In the second evening, the rains began. First there was a long, running patter of drops upon the beach and over the dry trees and bushes. At dusk there came a heavier squall, which did not die entirely, but slacked off to a continual, spaced splashing of big drops, and then returned with the front of the storm. In long, misty curtains, gust by gust, the rain swept over the sea, beating down its heaving, and coursed up the beach. The little jets of dust ceased to rise about the drops in the fields, and the mud began to gleam. Among the boulders of the river bed, darkling pools grew slowly.

Still Hook stood behind his tree from the wind, only gentle drops reaching him, falling from the upper branches and then again from the brush. His eyes remained closed, and he could still taste his own blood in his mouth, though it had ceased to come up freshly. Out beyond him, he heard the storm changing. As rain conquered the sea, the heave of the surf became a hushed sound, often lost in the crying of the wind. Then gradually, as the night turned toward morning, the wind also was broken by the rain. The crying became fainter, the rain settled toward steadiness, and the creep of the waves could be heard again, quiet and regular upon the beach.

At dawn there was no wind and no sun, but everywhere the roaring of the vertical, relentless rain. Hook then crept among the rapid drippings of the bushes, dragging his torn sail, seeking better shelter. He stopped often and stood with the shutters of film drawn over his eyes. At midmorning he found a little cave under a ledge at the base of the sea cliff. Here, lost without branches and leaves about him, he settled to await improvement.

When, at midday of the third day, the rain stopped altogether, and the sky opened before a small, fresh wind, letting light through to glitter upon a tremulous sea, Hook was so weak that his good wing trailed also to prop him upright, and his open eyes were lusterless. But his wounds were hardened, and he felt the return of hunger.

Beyond his shelter, he heard the gulls flying in great numbers and crying their joy at the cleared air. He could even hear, from the fringe of the river, the ecstatic and unstinted bubblings and chirpings of the small birds. The grassland, he felt, would be full of the stirring anew of the close-bound life, the undrowned insects clicking as they dried out, the snakes slithering down, heads half erect, into the grasses where the mice, gophers and ground squirrels ran and stopped and chewed and licked themselves smoother and drier.

With the aid of this hunger, and on the crutches of his wings, Hook came down to stand in the sun beside his cave, whence he could watch the beach. Before him, in ellipses on tilting planes, the gulls flew. The surf was rearing again, and beginning to shelve and hiss on the sand. Through the white foam-writing it left, the long-billed pipers twinkled in bevies, escaping each wave, then racing down after it to plunge their fine drills into the minute double holes where the sand crabs bubbled. In the third row of breakers two seals lifted sleek, streaming heads and barked, and over them, trailing his spider legs, a great crane flew south. Among the stones at the foot of the cliff, small red and green crabs made a little, continuous rattling and knocking. The cliff swallows glittered and twanged on aerial forays.

The afternoon began auspiciously for Hook also. One of the two gulls which came squabbling above him dropped a freshly caught fish to the sand. Quickly Hook was upon it. Gripping it, he raised his good wing and cocked his head with open beak at the many gulls which had circled and come down at once toward the fall of the fish. The gulls sheered off, cursing raucously. Left alone on the sand, Hook devoured the fish and, after resting in the sun, withdrew again to his shelter.

IV

In the succeeding days, between rains, he foraged on the beach. He learned to kill and crack the small green crabs. Along the edge of the river mouth, he found the drowned bodies of mice and squirrels and even sparrows. Twice he managed to drive feeding gulls from their catch, charging upon them with buffeting wing and clattering beak. He grew stronger slowly, but the shot sail continued to drag. Often, at the choking thought of soaring and striking and the good, hot-blood kill, he strove to take off, but only the one wing came up, winnowing with a hiss, and drove him over onto his side in the sand. After these futile trials, he would rage and clatter. But gradually he learned to believe that he could not fly, that his life must now be that of the discharged nestling again. Denied the joy of space, without which the joy of loneliness was lost, the joy of battle and killing, the blood lust, became his whole concentration. It was his hope, as he charged feeding gulls, that they would turn and offer battle, but they never did. The sandpipers, at his approach, fled peeping, or, like a quiver of arrows shot together, streamed out over the surf in a long curve. Once, pent beyond bearing, he disgraced himself by shrieking challenge at the business-like heron which flew south every evening at the same time. The heron did not even turn his head, but flapped and glided on.

Hook's shame and anger became such that he stood awake at night. Hunger kept him awake also, for these little leavings of the gulls could not sustain his great body in its renewed violence. He became aware that the gulls slept at night in flocks on the sand, each with one leg tucked under him. He discovered also that the curlews and the pipers, often mingling, likewise slept, on the higher remnant of the bar. A sensation of evil delight filled him in the consideration of protracted striking among them.

There was only half of a sick moon in a sky of running but far-separated clouds on the night when he managed to stalk into the center of the sleeping gulls. This was light enough, but so great was his vengeful pleasure that there broke from him a shrill scream of challenge as he first struck. Without the power of flight behind it, the blow was not murderous, and this newly discovered impotence made Hook crazy, so that he screamed again and again as he struck and tore at the felled gull. He slew the one, but was twice knocked over by its heavy flounderings, and all the others rose above him, weaving and screaming, protesting in the thin moonlight. Wakened by their clamor, the wading birds also took wing, startled and plaintive. When the beach was quiet again, the flocks had settled elsewhere, beyond his pitiful range, and he was left alone beside the single kill. It was a disappointing victory. He fed with lowering spirit.

Thereafter he stalked silently. At sunset he would watch where the gulls settled along the miles of beach, and after dark he would come like a sharp shadow among them, and drive with his hook on all sides of him, till the beatings of a poorly struck victim sent the flock up. Then he would turn vindictively upon the fallen and finish them. In his best night, he killed five from one flock. But he ate only a little from one, for the vigor resulting from occasional repletion strengthened only his ire, which became so great at such a time that food revolted him. It was not the joyous, swift, controlled hunting anger of a sane hawk, but something quite different, which made him dizzy if it continued too long, and left him unsatisfied with any kill.

Then one day, when he had very nearly struck a gull while driving it from a gasping yellowfin, the gull's wing rapped against him as it broke for its running start, and, the trailing wing failing to support him, he was knocked over. He flurried awkwardly in the sand to regain his feet, but his mastery of the beach was ended. Seeing him, in clear sunlight, struggling after the chance blow, the gulls returned about him in a flashing cloud, circling and pecking on the wing. Hook's plumage showed quick little jets of irregularity here and there. He reared back, clattering and erecting the good wing, spreading the great, rusty tail for balance. His eyes shone with a little of the old pleasure. But it died, for he could reach none of them. He was forced to turn and dance awkwardly on the sand, trying to clash bills with each tormentor. They banked up quealing and returned, weaving about him in concentric and overlapping circles. His scream was lost in their clamor, and he appeared merely to be hopping clumsily with his mouth open. Again he fell sideways. Before he could right himself, he was bowled over, and a second time, and lay on his side, twisting his neck to reach them and clappering in blind fury, and was struck three times by three successive gulls, shrieking their flock triumph.

Finally he managed to roll to his breast, and to crouch with his good wing spread wide and the other stretched nearly as far, so that he extended like a gigantic moth, only his snake head, with its now silent scimitar, erect. One great eye blazed under its level brow, but where the other had been was a shallow hole from which thin blood trickled to his russet gap.

In this crouch, by short stages, stopping repeatedly to turn and drive the gulls up, Hook dragged into the river canyon and under the stiff cover of the bitter-leafed laurel. There the gulls left him, soaring up with great clatter of their valor. Till nearly sunset Hook, broken-spirited and enduring his hardening eye socket, heard them celebrating over the waves.

When his will was somewhat replenished, and his empty eye socket had stopped the twitching and vague aching which had forced him often to roll ignominiously to rub it in the dust, Hook ventured from the protective lacings of his thicket. He knew fear again, and the challenge of his remaining eye was once more strident, as in adolescence. He dared not return to the beaches, and with a new, weak hunger, the home hunger, enticing him, made his way by short hunting journeys back to the wild wheat slopes and the crisp oaks. There was in Hook an unwonted sensation now, that of the ever-neighboring possibility of death. This sensation was beginning, after his period as a mad bird on the beach, to solidify him into his last stage of life. When, during his slow homeward passage, the gulls wafted inland over him, watching the earth with curious, miserish eyes, he did not cower, but neither did he challenge, either by opened beak or by raised shoulder. He merely watched carefully, learning his first lessons in observing the world with one eye.

At first the familiar surroundings of the bend in the river and the tree with the dead limb to which he could not ascend, aggravated his humiliation, but in time, forced to live cunningly and half-starved, he lost much of his savage pride. At the first flight of a strange hawk over his realm, he was wild at his helplessness, and kept twisting his head like an owl, or spinning in the grass like a small and feathered dervish, to keep the hateful beauty of the wind-rider in sight. But in the succeeding weeks, as one after another coasted his beat, his resentment declined, and when one of the raiders, a haughty yearling, sighted his up-staring eye, and plunged and struck him dreadfully, and failed to kill him only because he dragged under a thicket in time, the second of his great hungers was gone. He had no longer the true lust to kill, no joy of battle, but only the poor desire to fill his belly.

Then truly he lived in the wheat and the brush like a ground owl, ridden with ground lice, dusty or muddy, ever half-starved, forced to sit for hours by small holes for petty and unsatisfying kills. Only once during the final months before his end did he make a kill where the breath of danger recalled his valor, and then the danger was such as a hawk with wings and eyes would scorn. Waiting beside a gopher hole, surrounded by the high, yellow grass, he saw the head emerge, and struck, and was amazed that there writhed in his clutch the neck and dusty coffin-skull of a rattlesnake. Holding his grip, Hook saw the great, thick body slither up after, the tip an erect, strident blur, and writhe on the dirt of the gopher's mound. The weight of the snake pushed Hook about, and once threw him down, and the rising and falling whine of the rattles made the moment terrible, but the vaulted mouth, gaping from the closeness of Hook's gripe, so that the pale, envenomed sabers stood out free, could not reach him. When Hook replaced the grip of his beak with the grip of his talons, and was free to strike again and again at the base of the head, the struggle was over. Hook tore and fed on the fine, watery flesh, and left the tattered armor and the long, jointed bone for the marching ants.

When the heavy rains returned, he ate well during the period of the first escapes from flooded burrows, and then well enough, in a vulture's way, on the drowned creatures. But as the rains lingered, and the burrows hung full of water, and there were no insects in the grass and no small birds sleeping in the thickets, he was constantly hungry, and finally unbearably hungry. His sodden and ground-broken plumage stood out raggedly about him, so that he looked fat, even bloated, but underneath it his skin clung to his bones. Save for his great talons and clappers, and the rain in his down, he would have been like a handful of air. He often stood for a long time under some bush or ledge, heedless of the drip, his one eye filmed over, his mind neither asleep or awake, but between. The gurgle and swirl of the brimming river, and the sound of chunks of the bank cut away to splash and dissolve in the already muddy flood, became familiar to him, and yet a torment, as if that great, ceaselessly working power of water ridiculed his fraility, within which only the faintest spark of valor still glimmered. The last two nights before the rain ended, he huddled under the floor of the bridge on the coastal highway, and heard the palpitant thunder of motors swell and roar over him. The trucks shook the bridge so that Hook, even in his famished lassitude, would sometimes open his one great eye wide and startled.

V

After the rains, when things became full again, bursting with growth and sound, the trees swelling, the thickets full of song and chatter, the fields, turning green in the sun, alive with rustling passages, and the moonlit nights strained with the song of the peepers all up and down the river and in the pools in the fields, Hook had to bear the return of the one hunger left him. At times this made him so wild that he forgot himself and screamed challenge from the open ground. The fretfulness of it spoiled his hunting, which was now entirely a matter of patience. Once he was in despair, and lashed himself through the grass and thickets, trying to rise when that virgin scent drifted for a few moments above the current of his own river. Then, breathless, his beak agape, he saw the strong suitor ride swiftly down on the wind over him, and heard afar the screaming fuss of the harsh wooing in the alders. For that moment even the battle heart beat in him again. The rim of his good eye was scarlet, and a little bead of new blood stood in the socket of the other. With beak and talon, he ripped at a fallen log, and made loam and leaves fly from about it.

But the season of love passed over to the nesting season, and Hook's love hunger, unused, shriveled in him with the others, and there remained in him only one stern quality befitting a hawk, and that the negative one, the remnant, the will to endure. He resumed his patient, plotted hunting, now along a field of the Japanese farmer, but ever within reach of the river thickets.

Growing tough and dry again as the summer advanced, inured to the family of the farmer, whom he saw daily, stooping and scraping with sticks in the ugly, open rows of their fields, where no lovely grass rustled and no life stirred save the shameless gulls, which walked at the heels of the workers, gobbling the worms and grubs as they turned up, Hook became nearly content with his shard of life. The only longing or resentment to pierce him was that which he suffered occasionally when forced to hide at the edge of the mile-long bean field from the wafted cruising and the restive, down-bent gaze of one of his own kind. For the rest, he was without flame, a snappish, dust-colored creature, fading into the grasses he trailed through, and suited to his petty ways.

At the end of that summer, for the second time in his four years, Hook underwent a drouth. The equinoctial period passed without a rain. The laurel and the rabbit-brush dropped dry leaves. The foliage of the oaks shriveled and curled. Even the night fogs in the river canyon failed. The farmer's red cattle on the hillside lowed constantly, and could not feed on the dusty stubble. Grass fires broke out along the highway, and ate fast in the wind, filling the hollows with the smell of smoke, and died in the dirt of the shorn hills. The river made no sound. Scum grew on its vestigial pools, and turtles died and stank among the rocks. The dust rode before the wind, and ascended and flowered to nothing between the hills, and every sun set was red with the dust in the air. The people in the farmer's house quarreled, and even struck one another. Birds were silent, and only the hawks flew much. The animals lay breathing hard for very long spells, and ran and crept jerkily. Their flanks were fallen in, and their eyes were red.

At first Hook gorged at the fringe of the grass fires on the multitudes of tiny things that came running and squeaking. But thereafter there were the blackened strips on the hills, and little more in the thin, crackling grass. He found mice and rats, gophers and ground-squirrels, and even rabbits, dead in the stubble and under the thickets, but so dry and fleshless that only a faint smell rose from them, even on the sunny days. He starved on them. By early December he had wearily stalked the length of the eastern foothills, hunting at night to escape the voracity of his own kind, resting often upon his wings. The queer trail of his short steps and great horned toes zigzagged in the dust and was erased by the wind at dawn. He was nearly dead, and could make no sound through the horn funnels of his clappers.

Then one night the dry wind brought him, with the familiar, lifeless dust, another familiar scent, troublesome, mingled and unclear. In his vision-dominated brain he remembered the swift circle of his flight a year past, crossing in one segment, his shadow beneath him, a yard cluttered with crates and chickens, a gray barn and then again the plowed land and the stubble. Traveling faster than he had for days, impatient of his shrunken sweep, Hook came down to the farm. In the dark wisps of cloud blown among the stars over him, but no moon, he stood outside the wire of the chicken run. The scent of fat and blooded birds reached him from the shelter, and also within the enclosure was water. At the breath of the water, Hook's gorge contracted, and his tongue quivered and clove in its groove of horn. But there was the wire. He stalked its perimeter and found no opening. He beat it with his good wing, and felt it cut but not give. He wrenched at it with his beak in many places, but could not tear it. Finally, in a fury which drove the thin blood through him, he leaped repeatedly against it, beating and clawing. He was thrown back from the last leap as from the first, but in it he had risen so high as to clutch with his beak at the top wire. While he lay on his breast on the ground, the significance of this came upon him.

Again he leapt, clawed up the wire, and, as he would have fallen, made even the dead wing bear a little. He grasped the top and tumbled within. There again he rested flat, searching the dark with quick-turning head. There was no sound or motion but the throb of his own body. Frst he drank at the chill metal trough hung for the chickens. The water was cold, and loosened his tongue and his tight throat, but it also made him drunk and dizzy, so that he had to rest again, his claws spread wide to brace him. Then he walked stiffly, to stalk down the scent. He trailed it up the runway. Then there was the stuffy, body-warm air, acrid with droppings, full of soft rustlings as his talons clicked on the board floor. The thick, white shapes showed faintly in the darkness. Hook struck quickly, driving a hen to the floor with one blow, its neck broken and stretched out stringily. He leaped the still pulsing body, and tore it. The rich, streaming blood was overpowering to his dried senses, his starved, leathery body. After a few swallows, the flesh choked him. In his rage, he struck down another hen. The urge to kill took him again, as in those nights on the beach. He could let nothing go. Balked of feeding, he was compelled to slaughter. Clattering, he struck again and again. The henhouse was suddenly filled with the squawking and helpless rushing and buffeting of the terrified, brainless fowls.

Hook reveled in mastery. Here was game big enough to offer weight against a strike, and yet unable to soar away from his blows. Turning in the midst of the turmoil, cannily, his fury caught at the perfect pitch, he struck unceasingly. When the hens finally discovered the outlet, and streamed into the yard, to run around the fence, beating and squawking, Hook followed them, scraping down the incline, clumsy and joyous. In the yard, the cock, a bird as large as he, and much heavier, found him out and gave valiant battle. In the dark, and both earthbound, there was little skill, but blow upon blow, and only chance parry. The still squawking hens pressed into one corner of the yard. While the duel went on, a dog, excited by the sustained scuffling, began to bark. He continued to bark, running back and forth along the fence on one side. A light flashed on in an uncurtained window of the farmhouse, and streamed whitely over the crates littering the ground.

Enthralled by his old battle joy, Hook knew only the burly cock before him. Now, in the farthest reach of the window light, they could see each other dimly. The Japanese farmer, with his gun and lantern, was already at the gate when the finish came. The great cock leapt to jab with his spurs and, toppling forward with extended neck as he fell, was struck and extinguished. Blood had loosened Hook's throat.

Shrilly he cried his triumph. It was a thin and exhausted cry, but within him as good as when he shrilled in mid-air over the plummeting descent of a fine foe in his best spring.

The light from the lantern partially blinded Hook. He first turned and ran directly from it, into the corner where the hens were huddled. They fled apart before his charge. He essayed the fence, and on the second try, in his desperation, was out. But in the open dust, the dog was on him, circling, dashing in, snapping. The farmer, who at first had not fired because of the chickens, now did not fire because of the dog, and, when he saw that the hawk was unable to fly, relinquished the sport to the dog, holding the lantern up in order to see better. The light showed his own flat, broad, dark face as sunken also, the cheekbones very prominent, and showed the torn-off sleeves of his shirt and the holes in the knees of his overalls. His wife, in a stained wrapper, and barefooted, heavy black hair hanging around a young, passionless face, joined him hesitantly, but watched, fascinated and a little horrified. His son joined them too, encouraging the dog, but quickly grew silent. Courageous and cruel death, however it may afterward sicken the one who has watched it, is impossible to look away from.

In the circle of the light, Hook turned to keep the dog in front of him. His one eye gleamed with malevolence. The dog was an Airedale, and large. Each time he pounced, Hook stood ground, raising his good wing, the pinions newly torn by the fence, opening his beak soundlessly, and, at the closest approach, hissed furiously, and at once struck. Hit and ripped twice by the whetted horn, the dog recoiled more quickly from several subsequent jumps and, infuriated by his own cowardice, began to bark wildly. Hook maneuvered to watch him, keeping his head turned to avoid losing the foe on the blind side. When the dog paused, safely away, Hook watched him quietly, wing partially lowered, beak closed, but at the first move again lifted the wing and gaped. The dog whined, and the man spoke to him encouragingly. The awful sound of his voice made Hook for an instant twist his head to stare up at the immense figures behind the light. The dog again sallied, barking, and Hook's head spun back. His wing was bitten this time, and with a furious side-blow, he caught the dog's nose. The dog dropped him with a yelp, and then, smarting, came on more warily, as Hook propped himself up from the ground again between his wings. Hook's artificial strength was waning, but his heart still stood to the battle, sustained by a fear of such dimension as he had never known before, but only anticipated when the arrogant young hawk had driven him to cover. The dog, unable to find any point at which the merciless, unwinking eye was not watching him, the parted beak waiting, paused and whimpered again.

"Oh, kill the poor thing," the woman begged.

The man, though, encouraged the dog again, saying, "Sick him; sick him."

The dog rushed bodily. Unable to avoid him, Hook was bowled down, snapping and raking. He left long slashes, as from the blade of a knife, on the dog's flank, but before he could right himself and assume guard again, was caught by the good wing and dragged, clattering, and seeking to make a good stroke from his back. The man followed them to keep the light on them, and the boy went with him, wetting his lips with his tongue and keeping his fists closed tightly. The woman remained behind, but could not help watching the diminished conclusion.

In the little, palely shining arena, the dog repeated his successful maneuver three times, growling but not barking, and when Hook thrashed up from the third blow, both wings were trailing, and dark, shining streams crept on his black-fretted breast from the shoulders. The great eye flashed more furiously than it ever had in victorious battle, and the beak still gaped, but there was no more clatter. He faltered when turning to keep front; the broken wings played him false even as props. He could not rise to use his talons.

The man had tired of holding the lantern up, and put it down to rub his arm. In the low, horizontal light, the dog charged again, this time throwing the weight of his forepaws against Hook's shoulder, so that Hook was crushed as he struck. With his talons up, Hook raked at the dog's belly, but the dog conceived the finish, and furiously worried the feathered bulk. Hook's neck went limp, and between his gaping clappers came only a faint chittering, as from some small kill of his own in the grasses.

In this last conflict, however, there had been some minutes of the supreme fire of the hawk whose three hungers are perfectly fused in the one will; enough to burn off a year of shame.

Between the great sails the light body lay caved and perfectly still. The dog, smarting from his cuts, came to the master and was praised. The woman, joining them slowly, looked at the great wingspread, her husband raising the lantern that she might see it better.

"Oh, the brave bird," she said.

Paul Bowles

Under the Sky

INLAND from the sea on the dry coastal plain lay the town, open, spread out under the huge high sky. People who lived outside in the country, and even some of the more educated town-dwellers, called the town "the Inferno" because nowhere in the region was the heat so intense. No other place around was quite so shadowless and so dusty; it seemed that the clouds above shrank upwards to their farthest possible positions. Many miles above, and to all sides, they hung there in their massive patterns, remote and motionless. In the spring, during the nights, the lightning constantly jumped from one cloud to another, revealing unexpected distances between them. Then, if anyone ever looked at the sky, he was surprised to see how each flash revealed a seemingly more distant portion of the heavens to which still more clouds had receded. But people in the town seldom turned their heads upward. They knew at what time of the year the rains would come, and it was unnecessary to scan those vast regions in order to say what day that would be. When the wind had blown hard for two weeks so that the dust filled the wide empty streets, and the lightning grew brighter each night until finally there was a little thunder, they could be sure the water would soon fall.

Once a year when the lightning was in the sky Jacinto left his village in the mountains and walked down to the town, carrying with him all the things his family had made since his last trip. There were two days of walking in the sierra where it was cool; the third day the road was through the hot lands, and this was the day he preferred, because the road was flat and he could walk faster and leave the others behind. He was taller and prouder than they, and he refused to bend over in order to be able to trot uphill and downhill as they did. In the mountains he labored to keep up with them, but on the plain he strode powerfully ahead and sometimes arrived at the market before sunset.

Now he stood in the public square with a small paper parcel in his hand. He had arrived the day before. Instead of sitting in the side-street near the fountain and discussing the sales with the others from his village, he walked into the municipal garden and sat down on a concrete bench marked "1936." He looked up and down the walk. No one paid him any attention. He was barefoot, so the shoeshine boys passed him by.

Tearing open the paper packet he emptied the dried leaves into his left hand. With his right he picked out all the little round, black berries and tossed them away. Then he crushed the leaves and slowly rolled them into five thin cigarettes. This took all his attention for a half hour.

A voice beside him said: "That's pretty."

He looked up. It was a town-dweller; he had never seen him before, so he did not answer.

"All for you?" said the other in the silken town voice that Jacinto had learned to distrust.

"I bought it. I made them," said Jacinto.

"But I like *grifas* too," smiled the stranger. He was poorly dressed and had black teeth.

Jacinto covered the cigarettes completely with one big hand which he placed on the seat of the bench. The stranger pointed to a soldier sleeping on another bench near the iron bandstand.

"He wants one and I want one. You should be more careful. It's three months now for possessing marijuana. Don't you know?"

"No," said Jacinto. "I don't know." Then he slowly handed over two of the cigarettes. The man took them.

"So long," he said.

Jacinto stood up full of fury, and with the other three cigarettes still in his hand, he walked out into the plaza and down the long street that led to the station. It was nearly time for the daily train from the north. Sometimes crazy people got off, who would give a man enough money for two good meals, just for carrying a bundle into the town for them. There was a cemetery behind the roundhouse where some of the railroad employees went to smoke the weed. He remembered it from the preceding year; he had met an inspector there who had taken him to see a girl. She had proved to be ugly—one side of her face was mottled with blue and purple.

At the station the train had already arrived. The people trying to get on were fighting with those who were trying to get off. He wondered why with all those open windows everyone insisted on going through the two little doors at the ends of the cars. It would have been very simple the other way, but these people were too stupid to think of it. His defeat at the hands of the townsman still bothered him; he wanted to have a gun so he could pull it out and shout: "I am the father of all of you!" But it was not likely that he ever would have a gun.

Without approaching the platform where so many people were moving about, he stood and impassively watched the confusion. From the crowd three strange-looking people suddenly emerged. They all had very white skin and yellow hair. He knew, of course, that they were from a faraway place because everyone knows that when people look as strange as that they are from the capital or even farther. There were two women and one man, and as they approached him, he noticed that they were speaking a language which only they could understand. Each one carried a leather bag covered with small squares of colored paper stuck on at different angles. He stepped back, keeping his eyes on the face of the younger woman. He could not be sure whether he found her beautiful or revolting. Still he continued to look at her as she passed, holding on to the man's arm. The other woman noticed him, and smiled faintly as she went by.

He turned angrily and walked toward the tracks. He was angry at her stupidity—for thinking he could have enough money to pay her as much as she would surely want. He walked on until he came to the cemetery. It was empty save for the gray lizards that scurried from the path at his feet. In the farthest corner there was a small square building with a white stone woman on top. He sat in the shade of the little building and took out his cigarettes.

The train whistled; it was starting on its trip to the sea where the people eat nothing but fish and travel on top of the water. He drew in the first few breaths very slowly and deliberately, holding the smoke in his lungs until he felt it burning the edges of his soul. After a few minutes the feeling began to take shape. From the back of his head it moved down to his shoulders. It was as if he were wearing a tight metal garment. At that instant he looked at the sky and saw far above him the tiny black dots that were vultures, moving ever so slowly in circles as they surveyed the plain in the afternoon sunlight. Beyond them stood the clouds, deep and monumental. "Ay!" he sighed, shutting his eyes, and it occurred to him that this was what the dead people, who were lying on all sides of him, looked at day after day. This was all they could see—the clouds, and the vultures, which they did not need to fear, hidden safely as they were, deep in holy ground.

He continued to smoke, going deeper and deeper into delight. Finally he lay back and murmured: "Now I am dead too." When he opened his eyes it was still the same day, and the sun was very low in the sky. Some men were talking nearby. He listened; they were trainmen come to smoke, discussing wages and prices of meals. He did not believe any of the figures they so casually mentioned. They were lying to impress one another, and they did not even believe each other. He smoked half of the second cigarette, rose, stretched, and jumped over the cemetery wall, going back to the station by a roundabout path in order not to have to speak to the trainmen. Those people, when they smoked, always wanted more and more company; they would never let a fellow smoker go quietly on his way.

He went to the cantina by the station, and standing in the street, watched the railway employees playing billiards inside. As night approached, the lightning became increasingly visible. He walked up the long street toward the center of town. Men were playing marimbas in the doorways and in front of the houses—three or four together, and sometimes only one, indolently. The marimbas and the marijuana were the only good things in the town, reflected Jacinto. The women were ugly and dirty, and the men were all thieves and drunkards. He remembered the three people at the station. They would be in the hotel opposite the plaza. He walked a little faster, and his eyes, bloodshot from lack of sleep and too much of the drug, opened a bit wider.

After he had eaten heartily in the market sitting by the edge of the fountain, he felt very well. By the side wall of the cathedral were all the families from the mountains, some already asleep, the others preparing for the night. Almost all the stalls in the market were dark; a few figures still stood in front of the cold fruit-juice stand. Jacinto felt in his pocket for the stub and the whole cigarette, and keeping his fingers around them, walked across to the park. The celestial fireworks were very bright, but there was no thunder. Throughout the town sounded the clink and purr of the marimbas, some near and some far away. A soft breeze stirred the branches of the few lemon trees in the park. He walked along thoughtfully until he came to a bench directly opposite the entrance of the hotel, and there he sat down and brazenly began to smoke his stub. After a few minutes it was easier for him to believe that one of the two yellow-haired women would come out. He flicked away the butt, leaned back and stared straight at the hotel. The manager had put a square loudspeaker over the entrance door, and out of it came a great crackling and hissing that covered the sound of the marimbas. Occasionally a few loud notes of band music rose above the chaos, and from time to time there seemed to be a man's voice speaking behind the noise. Jacinto was annoyed: the women would want to stay inside where they could hear the sound better.

A long time went by. The radio was silenced. The few voices in the park disappeared down the streets. By the cathedral everyone was asleep. Even the marimbas seemed to have stopped, but when the breeze occasionally grew more active, it brought with it, swelling and dying, long marimba trills from a distant part of the town.

It grew very late. There was no sound but the lemon leaves rubbing together and the jet of water splashing into the basin in the center of the market. Jacinto was used to waiting. And halfway through the night a woman stepped out of the hotel, stood for a moment looking at the sky, and walked across the street to the park. From his bench in the dark he watched her as she approached. In the lightning he saw that it was not the younger one. He was disappointed. She looked upward again before moving into the shade of the lemon trees, and in a moment she sat down on the next bench and lighted a cigarette. He waited a few minutes. Then he said: "Señorita."

The yellow-haired woman cried: "Oh!" She had not seen him. She jumped up and stood still, peering toward his bench.

He moved to the end of the seat and calmly repeated the word. "Señorita."

She walked uncertainly toward him, still peering. He knew this was a ruse. She could see him quite clearly each second or so, whenever the sky lighted up. When she was near enough to the bench, he motioned for her to sit down beside him. As he had suspected, she spoke his tongue.

"What is it?" she asked. The talk in the strange language at the station had only been for show, after all.

"Sit down, señorita."

"Why?"

"Because I tell you to."

She laughed and threw away her cigarette.

"That's not a reason," she said, sitting down at the other end of the bench. "What are you doing here so late?" She spoke carefully and correctly, like a priest. He answered this by saying: "And you, what are you looking for?"

"Nothing."

"Yes. You are looking for something," he said solemnly.

"I was not sleeping. It is very hot."

"No. It is not hot," said Jacinto. He was feeling increasingly sure of himself, and he drew out the last cigarette and began to smoke it. "What are you doing here in this town?" he asked her after a moment.

"Passing on my way south to the border," she said, and she told him how she was traveling with two friends, a husband and wife, and how she often took a walk when they had gone to bed.

Jacinto listened as he drew in the smoke and breathed it out. Suddenly he jumped up. Touching her arm, he said: "Come to the market."

She arose, asking: "Why?" and walked with him across the park. When they were in the street, he took her wrist fiercely and pressing it, said between his teeth: "Look at the sky."

She looked up wonderingly, a little fearfully. He went on in a low, intense voice: "As God is my witness, I am going into the hotel and kill the man who came here with you."

Her eyes grew large. She tried to wrest her arm away, but he would not let it go, and he thrust his face into hers. "I have a pistol in my pocket and I am going to kill that man."

"But why?" she whispered weakly, looking up and down the empty street.

"I want his wife."

The woman said: "It is not possible. She would scream."

"I know the proprietor," said Jacinto, rolling his eyes and grinning. The woman seemed to believe him. Now he felt that a great thing was about to happen.

"And you," he said, twisting her arm brutally, "you do not scream."

"No."

Again he pointed to the sky.

"God is my witness. You can save the life of your friend. Come with me."

She was trembling violently, but as they stumbled through the street and he let go of her an instant, she began to run. With one bound he had overtaken her, and he made her stop and look at the sky again as he went through his threats once more. She saw his wide, red-veined eyes in a bright flash of lightning, and his utterly empty face. Mechanically she allowed him to push her along through the streets. He did not let go of her again.

"You are saving your friend's life," he said. "God will reward you."

She was sobbing as she went along. No one passed them as they moved unsteadily on toward the station. When they were nearly there they made a great detour past the edge of town, and finally came to the cemetery.

"This is a holy place," he murmured, swiftly crossing himself. "Here you are going to save your friend's life."

He took off his shirt, laid it on the stony ground, and pushed her down. There was nothing but the insistent, silent flashing in the sky. She kept her eyes shut, but she shuddered at each flash, even with her lids closed. The wind blew harder, and the smell of the dust was in her nostrils.

He took her back as far as the park and there he let go of her. Then he said: "Good night, señorita," and walked away very quickly. He was happy because she had not asked for any money.

The next year when he came down to the town he waited at the station four afternoons to see the train come in. The last afternoon he went to the cemetery and sat near the small square building that had the stone woman on top of it. On the ground the dust blew past. The enormous clouds hung in the sky and the vultures were there high above him. As he smoked he recalled the yellow-haired woman. After a time he began to weep, and rolled over onto the earth, clutching the pebbles as he sobbed. An old woman of the town, who came every day to her son's grave, passed near to him. Seeing him, she shook her head and murmured to herself: "He has lost his mother."

Bernard Malamud

The Magic Barrel

NOT LONG AGO there lived in uptown New York, in a small, almost meager room, though crowded with books, Leo Finkle, a rabbinical student in the Yeshivah University. Finkle, after six years of study, was to be ordained in June and had been advised by an acquaintance that he might find it easier to win himself a congregation if he were married. Since he had no present prospects of marriage, after two tormented days of turning it over in his mind, he called in Pinye Salzman, a marriage broker whose two-line advertisement he had read in the *Forward*.

The matchmaker appeared one night out of the dark fourth-floor hallway of the graystone rooming house where Finkle lived, grasping a black, strapped portfolio that had been worn thin with use. Salzman, who had been long in the business, was of slight but dignified build, wearing an old hat, and an overcoat too short and tight for him. He smelled frankly of fish, which he loved to eat, and although he was missing a few teeth, his presence was not displeasing, because of an amiable manner curiously contrasted with mournful eyes. His voice, his lips, his wisp of beard, his bony fingers were animated, but give him a moment of repose and his mild blue eyes revealed a depth of sadness, a characteristic that put Leo a little at ease although the situation, for him, was inherently tense.

He at once informed Salzman why he had asked him to come, explaining that his home was in Cleveland, and that but for his parents, who had married comparatively late in life, he was alone in the world. He had for six years devoted himself almost entirely to his studies, as a result of which, understandably, he had found himself without time for a social life and the company of young women. Therefore he thought it the better part of trial and error—of embarrassing fumbling—to call in an experienced person to advise him on these matters. He remarked in passing that the function of the marriage broker was ancient and honorable, highly approved in the Jewish community, because it made practical the necessary without hindering joy. Moreover, his own parents had been brought together by a matchmaker. They had made, if not a financially profitable marriage—since neither had possessed any worldly goods to speak of—at least a successful one in the sense of their everlasting devotion to each other. Salzman listened in embarrassed surprise, sensing a sort of apology. Later, however, he experienced a glow of pride in his work, an emotion that had left him years ago, and he heartily approved of Finkle.

The two went to their business. Leo had led Salzman to the only clear place in the room, a table near a window that overlooked the lamp-lit city. He seated himself at the matchmaker's side but facing him, attempting by an act of will to suppress the unpleasant tickle in his throat. Salzman eagerly unstrapped his portfolio and removed a loose rubber band from a thin packet of much-handled cards. As he flipped through them, a gesture and sound that physically hurt Leo, the student pretended not to see and gazed steadfastly out the window. Although it was still February, winter was on its last legs, signs of which he had for the first time in years begun to notice. He now observed the round white moon, moving high in the sky through a cloud menagerie, and watched with half-open mouth as it penetrated a huge hen, and dropped out of her like an egg laying itself. Salzman, though pretending through eyeglasses he had just slipped on, to be engaged in scanning the writing on the cards, stole occasional glances at the young man's distinguished face, noting with pleasure the long, severe scholar's nose, brown eyes heavy with learning, sensitive yet ascetic lips, and a certain, almost hollow quality of the dark cheeks. He gazed around at shelves upon shelves of books and let out a soft, contented sigh.

When Leo's eyes fell upon the cards, he counted six spread out in Salzman's hand.

"So few?" he asked in disappointment.

"You wouldn't believe me how much cards I got in my office," Salzman replied. "The drawers are already filled to the top, so I keep them now in a barrel, but is every girl good for a new rabbi?"

Leo blushed at this, regretting all he had revealed of himself in a curriculum vitae he had sent to Salzman. He had thought it best to acquaint him with his strict standards and specifications, but in having done so, felt he had told the marriage broker more than was absolutely necessary.

He hesitantly inquired, "Do you keep photographs of your clients on file?"

"First comes family, amount of dowry, also what kind promises," Salzman replied, unbuttoning his tight coat and settling himself in the chair. "After comes pictures, rabbi."

"Call me Mr. Finkle. I'm not yet a rabbi."

Salzman said he would, but instead called him doctor, which he changed to rabbi when Leo was not listening too attentively.

Salzman adjusted his horn-rimmed spectacles, gently cleared his throat and read in an eager voice the contents of the top card:

"Sophie P. Twenty four years. Widow one year. No children. Educated high school and two years college. Father promises eight thousand dollars. Has wonderful wholesale business. Also real estate. On the mother's side comes teachers, also one actor. Well known on Second Avenue."

Leo gazed up in surprise. "Did you say a widow?"

"A widow don't mean spoiled, rabbi. She lived with her husband maybe four months. He was a sick boy she made a mistake to marry him."

"Marrying a widow has never entered my mind."

"This is because you have no experience. A widow, especially if she is young and healthy like this girl, is a wonderful person to marry. She will be thankful to you the rest of her life. Believe me, if I was looking now for a bride, I would marry a widow."

Leo reflected, then shook his head.

Salzman hunched his shoulders in an almost imperceptible gesture of disappointment. He placed the card down on the wooden table and began to read another:

"Lily H. High school teacher. Regular. Not a substitute. Has savings and new Dodge car. Lived in Paris one year. Father is successful dentist thirty-five years. Interested in professional man. Well Americanized family. Wonderful opportunity."

"I knew her personally," said Salzman. "I wish you could see this girl. She is a doll. Also very intelligent. All day you could talk to her about books and theater and what not. She also knows current events."

"I don't believe you mentioned her age?"

"Her age?" Salzman said, raising his brows. "Her age is thirty-two years."

Leo said after a while, "I'm afraid that seems a little too old."

Salzman let out a laugh. "So how old are you, rabbi?"

"Twenty-seven."

"So what is the difference, tell me, between twenty-seven and thirty-two? My own wife is seven years older than me. So what did I suffer?—Nothing. If Rothschild's daughter wants to marry you, would you say on account her age, no?"

"Yes," Leo said dryly.

Salzman shook off the no in the yes. "Five years don't mean a thing. I give you my word that when you will live with her for one week you will forget her age. What does it mean five years—that she lived more and knows more than somebody who is younger? On this girl, God bless her, years are not wasted. Each one that it comes makes better the bargain."

"What subject does she teach in high school?"

"Languages. If you heard the way she speaks French, you will think it is music. I am in the business twenty-five years, and I recommend her with my whole heart. Believe me, I know what I'm talking, rabbi."

"What's on the next card?" Leo said abruptly.

Salzman reluctantly turned up the third card:

"Ruth K. Nineteen years. Honor student. Father offers thirteen thousand cash to the right bridegroom. He is a medical doctor. Stomach specialist with marvelous practice. Brother-in-law owns own garment business. Particular people."

Salzman looked as if he had read his trump card.

"Did you say nineteen?" Leo asked with interest.

"On the dot."

"Is she attractive?" He blushed. "Pretty?"

Salzman kissed his finger tips. "A little doll. On this I give you my word. Let me call the father tonight and you will see what means pretty."

But Leo was troubled. "You're sure she's that young?"

"This I am positive. The father will show you the birth certificate."

"Are you positive there isn't something wrong with her?" Leo insisted.

"Who says there is wrong?"

"I don't understand why an American girl her age should go to a marriage broker."

A smile spread over Salzman's face.

"So for the same reason you went, she comes."

Leo flushed. "I am pressed for time."

Salzman, realizing he had been tactless, quickly explained. "The father came, not her. He wants she should have the best, so he looks around himself. When we will locate the right boy he will introduce him and encourage. This makes a better marriage than if a young girl without experience takes for herself. I don't have to tell you this."

"But don't you think this young girl believes in love?" Leo spoke uneasily.

Salzman was about to guffaw but caught himself and said soberly, "Love comes with the right person, not before."

Leo parted dry lips but did not speak. Noticing that Salzman had snatched a glance at the next card, he cleverly asked, "How is her health?"

"Perfect," Salzman said, breathing with difficulty. "Of course, she is a little lame on her right foot from an auto accident that it happened to her when she was twelve years, but nobody notices on account she is so brilliant and also beautiful."

Leo got up heavily and went to the window. He felt curiously bitter and upbraided himself for having called in the marriage broker. Finally, he shook his head.

"Why not?" Salzman persisted, the pitch of his voice rising.

"Because I detest stomach specialists."

"So what do you care what is his business? After you marry her do you need him? Who says he must come every Friday night in your house?"

Ashamed of the way the talk was going, Leo dismissed Salzman, who went home with heavy, melancholy eyes.

Though he had felt only relief at the marriage broker's departure, Leo was in low spirits the next day. He explained it as arising from Salzman's failure to produce a suitable bride for him. He did not care for his type of clientele. But when Leo found himself hesitating whether to seek out another matchmaker, one more polished than Pinye, he wondered if it could be—his protestations to the contrary, and although he honored his father and mother—that he did not, in essence, care for the match-making institution? This thought he quickly put out of mind yet found himself still upset. All day he ran around in the woods—missed an important appointment, forgot to give out his laundry, walked out of a Broadway cafeteria without paying and had to run back with the ticket in his hand; had even not recognized his landlady in the street when she passed with a friend and courteously called out, "A good evening to you, Doctor Finkle." By nightfall, however, he had regained sufficient calm to sink his nose into a book and there found peace from his thoughts.

Almost at once there came a knock on the door. Before Leo could say enter, Salzman, commercial cupid, was standing in the room. His face was gray and meager, his expression hungry, and he looked as if he would expire on his feet. Yet the marriage broker managed, by some trick of the muscles, to display a broad smile.

"So good evening. I am invited?"

Leo nodded, disturbed to see him again, yet unwilling to ask the man to leave.

Beaming still, Salzman laid his portfolio on the table. "Rabbi, I got for you tonight good news."

"I've asked you not to call me rabbi. I'm still a student."

"Your worries are finished. I have for you a first-class bride."

"Leave me in peace concerning this subject." Leo pretended lack of interest.

"The world will dance at your wedding."

"Please, Mr. Salzman, no more."

"But first must come back my strength," Salzman said weakly. He fumbled with the portfolio straps and took out of the leather case an oily paper bag, from which he extracted a hard, seeded roll and a small, smoked white fish. With a quick motion of his hand he stripped the fish out of its skin and began ravenously to chew. "All day in a rush," he muttered.

Leo watched him eat.

"A sliced tomato you have maybe?" Salzman hesitantly inquired.

"No."

The marriage broker shut his eyes and ate. When he had finished he carefully cleaned up the crumbs and rolled up the remains of the fish, in the paper bag. His spectacled eyes roamed the room until he discovered, amid some piles of books, a one-burner gas stove. Lifting his hat he humbly asked, "A glass tea you got, rabbi?"

Conscience-stricken, Leo rose and brewed the tea. He served it with a chunk of lemon and two cubes of lump sugar, delighting Salzman.

After he had drunk his tea, Salzman's strength and good spirits were restored.

"So tell me, rabbi," he said amiably, "you considered some more the three clients I mentioned yesterday?"

"There was no need to consider."

"Why not?"

"None of them suits me."

"What then suits you?"

Leo let it pass because he could give only a confused answer.

Without waiting for a reply, Salzman asked, "You remember this girl I talked to you—the high school teacher?"

"Age thirty-two?"

But, surprisingly, Salzman's face lit in a smile. "Age twenty-nine."

Leo shot him a look. "Reduced from thirty-two?"

"A mistake," Salzman avowed. "I talked today with the dentist. He took me to his safety deposit box and showed me the birth certificate. She was twenty-nine years last August. They made her a party in the mountains where she went for her vacation. When her father spoke to me the first time I forgot to write the age and I told you thirty-two, but now I remember this was a different client, a widow."

"The same one you told me about? I thought she was twenty-four?"

"A different. Am I responsible that the world is filled with widows?"

"No, but I'm not interested in them, nor for that matter, in school teachers."

Salzman pulled his clasped hands to his breast. Looking at the ceiling he devoutly exclaimed, "Yiddishe kinder, what can I say to somebody that he is not interested in high school teachers? So what then you are interested?"

Leo flushed but controlled himself.

"In what else will you be interested," Salzman went on, "if you not interested in this fine girl that she speaks four languages and has personally in the bank ten thousand dollars? Also her father guarantees further twelve thousand. Also she has a new car, wonderful clothes, talks on all subjects, and she will give you a first-class home and children. How near do we come in our life to paradise?"

"If she's so wonderful, why wasn't she married ten years ago?"

"Why?" said Salzman with a heavy laugh. "—Why? Because she is *partikiler*. This is why. She wants the *best*."

Leo was silent, amused at how he had entangled himself. But Salzman had aroused his interest in Lily H., and he began seriously to consider calling on her. When the marriage broker observed how intently Leo's mind was at work on the facts he had supplied, he felt certain they would soon come to an agreement.

Late Saturday afternoon, conscious of Salzman, Leo Finkle walked with Lily Hirschorn along Riverside Drive. He walked briskly and erectly, wearing with distinction the black fedora he had that morning taken with trepidation out of the dusty hat box on his closet shelf, and the heavy black Saturday coat he had thoroughly whisked clean. Leo also owned a walking stick, a present from a distant relative, but quickly put temptation aside and did not use it. Lily, petite and not unpretty, had on something signifying the approach of spring. She was au courant, animatedly, with all sorts of subjects, and he weighed her words and found her surprisingly sound—score another for Salzman, whom he uneasily sensed to be somewhere around, hiding perhaps high in a tree along the street, flashing the lady signals with a pocket mirror; or perhaps a cloven-hoofed Pan, piping nuptial ditties as he danced his invisible way before them, strewing wild buds on the walk and purple grapes in their path, symbolizing fruit of a union, though there was of course still none.

Lily startled Leo by remarking, "I was thinking of Mr. Salzman, a curious figure, wouldn't you say?"

Not certain what to answer, he nodded.

She bravely went on, blushing, "I for one am grateful for his introducing us. Aren't you?"

He courteously replied, "I am."

"I mean," she said with a little laugh—and it was all in good taste, or at least gave the effect of being not in bad—"do you mind that we came together so?"

He was not displeased with her honesty, recognizing that she meant to set the relationship aright, and understanding that it took a certain amount of experience in life, and courage, to want to do it quite that way. One had to have some sort of past to make that kind of beginning.

He said that he did not mind. Salzman's function was traditional and honorable—valuable for what it might achieve, which, he pointed out, was frequently nothing.

Lily agreed with a sigh. They walked on for a while and she said after a long silence, again with a nervous laugh, "Would you mind if I asked you something a little bit personal? Frankly, I find the subject fascinating." Although Leo shrugged, she went on half embarrassedly, "How was it that you came to your calling? I mean was it a sudden passionate inspiration?"

Leo, after a time, slowly replied, "I was always interested in the Law."

"You saw revealed in it the presence of the Highest?"

He nodded and changed the subject. "I understand that you spent a little time in Paris, Miss Hirschorn?"

"Oh, did Mr. Salzman tell you, Rabbi Finkle?" Leo winced but she went on, "It was ages ago and almost forgotten. I remember I had to return for my sister's wedding."

And Lily would not be put off. "When," she asked in a trembly voice, "did you become enamored of God?"

He stared at her. Then it came to him that she was talking not about Leo Finkle, but of a total stranger, some mystical figure, perhaps even passionate prophet that Salzman had dreamed up for her —no relation to the living or dead. Leo trembled with rage and weakness. The trickster had obviously sold her a bill of goods, just as he had him, who'd expected to become acquainted with a young lady of twenty-nine, only to behold, the moment he laid eyes upon her strained and anxious face, a woman past thirty-five and aging rapidly. Only his self control had kept him this long in her presence.

"I am not," he said gravely, " a talented religious person," and in seeking words to go on, found himself possessed by shame and fear. "I think," he said in a strained manner, "that I came to God not because I loved Him, but because I did not."

This confession he spoke harshly because its unexpectedness shook him.

Lily wilted. Leo saw a profusion of loaves of bread go flying like ducks high over his head, not unlike the winged loaves by which he had counted himself to sleep last night. Mercifully, then, it snowed, which he would not put past Salzman's machinations.

He was infuriated with the marriage broker and swore he would throw him out of the room the minute he reappeared. But Salzman did not come that night, and when Leo's anger had subsided, an unaccountable despair grew in its place. At first he thought this was caused by his disappointment in Lily, but before long it became evident that he had involved himself with Salzman without a true knowledge of his own intent. He gradually realized—with an emptiness that seized him with six hands—that he had called in the broker to find him a bride because he was incapable of doing it himself. This terrifying insight he had derived as a result of his meeting and conversation with Lily Hirschorn. Her probing questions had somehow irritated him into revealing—to himself more than her—the true nature of his relationship to God, and from that it had come upon him, with shocking force, that apart from his parents, he had never loved anyone. Or perhaps it went the other way, that he did not love God so well as he might, because he had not loved man. It seemed to Leo that his whole life stood starkly revealed and he saw himself for the first time as he truly was—unloved and loveless. This bitter but somehow not fully unexpected revelation brought him to a point of panic, controlled only by extraordinary effort. He covered his face with his hands and cried.

The week that followed was the worst of his life. He did not eat and lost weight. His beard darkened and grew ragged. He stopped attending seminars and almost never opened a book. He seriously considered leaving the Yeshivah, although he was deeply troubled at the thought of the loss of all his years of study—saw them like pages torn from a book, strewn over the city—and at the devastating effect of this decision upon his parents. But he had lived without knowledge of himself, and never in the Five Books and all the Commentaries—mea culpa—had the truth been revealed to him. He did not know where to turn, and in all this desolating loneliness there was no *to whom,* although he often thought of Lily but not once could bring himself to go downstairs and make the call. He became touchy and irritable, especially with his landlady, who asked him all manner of personal questions; on the other hand, sensing his own disagreeableness, he waylaid her on the stairs and apologized abjectly, until mortified, she ran from him. Out of this, however, he drew the consolation that he was a Jew and that a Jew suffered. But gradually, as the long and terrible week drew to a close, he regained his composure and some idea of purpose in life: to go on as planned. Although he was imperfect, the idea was not. As for his quest of a bride, the thought of continuing afflicted him with anxiety and heartburn, yet perhaps with this new knowledge of himself he would be more successful than in the past. Perhaps love would now come to him and a bride to that love. And for this sanctified seeking who needed a Salzman?

The marriage broker, a skelton with haunted eyes, returned that very night. He looked, withal, the picture of frustrated expectancy—as if he had steadfastly waited the week at Miss Lily Hirschorn's side for a telephone call that never came.

Casually coughing, Salzman came immediately to the point: "So how did you like her?"

Leo's anger rose and he could not refrain from chiding the matchmaker: "Why did you lie to me, Salzman?"

Salzman's pale face went dead white, the world had snowed on him.

"Did you not state that she was twenty-nine?" Leo insisted.

"I give you my word—"

"She was thirty-five, if a day. *At least* thirty-five."

"Of this don't be too sure. Her father told me—"

"Never mind. The worst of it was that you lied to her."

"How did I lie to her, tell me?"

"You told her things about me that weren't true. You made me out to be more, consequently less than I am. She had in mind a totally different person, a sort of semi-mystical Wonder Rabbi."

"All I said, you was a religious man."

"I can imagine."

Salzman sighed. "This is my weakness that I have," he confessed. "My wife says to me I shouldn't be a salesman, but when I have two fine people that they would be wonderful to be married, I am so happy that I talk too much." He smiled wanly. "This is why Salzman is a poor man."

Leo's anger left him. "Well, Salzman, I'm afraid that's all."

The marriage broker fastened hungry eyes on him.

"You don't want any more a bride?"

"I do," said Leo, "but I have decided to seek her in a different way. I am no longer interested in an arranged marriage. To be frank, I now admit the necessity of premarital love. That is, I want to be in love with the one I marry."

"Love?" said Salzman, astounded. After a moment he remarked, "For us, our love is our life, not for the ladies. In the ghetto they—"

"I know, I know," said Leo. "I've thought of it often. Love, I have said to myself, should be a by-product of living and worship rather than its own end. Yet for myself I find it necessary to establish the level of my need and fulfill it."

Salzman shrugged but answered, "Listen, rabbi, if you want love, this I can find for you also. I have such beautiful clients that you will love them the minute your eyes will see them."

Leo smiled unhappily. "I'm afraid you don't understand."

But Salzman hastily unstrapped his portfolio and withdrew a manila packet from it.

"Pictures," he said, quickly laying the envelope on the table.

Leo called after him to take the pictures away, but as if on the wings of the wind, Salzman had disappeared.

March came. Leo had returned to his regular routine. Although he felt not quite himself yet—lacked energy—he was making plans for a more active social life. Of course it would cost something, but he was an expert in cutting corners; and when there were no corners left he would make circles rounder. All the while Salzman's pictures had lain on the table, gathering dust. Occasionally as Leo sat studying, or enjoying a cup of tea, his eyes fell on the manila envelope, but he never opened it.

The days went by and no social life to speak of developed with a member of the opposite sex—it was difficult, given the circumstances of his situation. One morning Leo toiled up the stairs to his room and stared out the window at the city. Although the day was bright his view of it was dark. For some time he watched the people in the street below hurrying along and then turned with a heavy heart to his little room. On the table was the packet. With a sudden relentless gesture he tore it open. For a half-hour he stood by the table in a state of excitement, examining the photographs of the ladies Salzman had included. Finally, with a deep sigh he put them down. There were six, of varying degrees of attractiveness, but look at them long enough and they all became Lily Hirschorn: all past their prime, all starved behind bright smiles, not a true personality in the lot. Life, despite their frantic yoohooings, had passed them by; they were pictures in a brief case that stank of fish. After a while, however, as Leo attempted to return the photographs into the envelope, he found in it another, a snapshot of the type taken by a machine for a quarter. He gazed at it a moment and let out a cry.

Her face deeply moved him. Why, he could at first not say. It gave him the impression of youth—spring flowers, yet age—a sense of having been used to the bone, wasted; this came from the eyes, which were hauntingly familiar, yet absolutely strange. He had a vivid impression that he had met her before, but try as he might he could not place her although he could almost recall her name, as if he had read it in her own handwriting. No, this couldn't be; he would have remembered her. It was not, he affirmed, that she had an extraordinary beauty—no, though her face was attractive enough; it was that *something* about her moved him. Feature for feature, even some of the ladies of the photographs could do better; but she leaped forth to his heart—had *lived,* or wanted to—more than just wanted, perhaps regretted how she had lived—had somehow deeply suffered: it could be seen in the depths of those reluctant eyes, from the way the light enclosed and shone from her, and within her, opening realms of possiblity: this was her own. Her he desired. His head ached and eyes narrowed with the intensity of his gazing, then as if an obscure fog had blown up in the mind, he experienced fear of her and was aware that he had received an impression, somehow, of evil. He shuddered, saying softly, it is thus with us all. Leo brewed some tea in a small pot and sat sipping it without sugar, to calm himself. But before he had finished drinking, again with excitement he examined the face and found it good: good for Leo Finkle. Only such a one could understand him and help him seek whatever he was seeking. She might, perhaps, love him. How she had happened to be among the discards in Salzman's barrel he could never guess, but he knew he must urgently go find her.

Leo rushed downstairs, grabbed up the Bronx telephone book, and searched for Salzman's home address. He was not listed, nor was his office. Neither was he in the Manhattan book. But Leo remembered having written down the address on a slip of paper after he had read Salzman's advertisement in the "personals" column of the *Forward*. He ran up to his room and tore through his papers, without luck. It was exasperating. Just when he needed the matchmaker he was nowhere to be found. Fortunately Leo remembered to look in his wallet. There on a card he found his name written and a Bronx address. No phone number was listed, the reason—Leo now recalled—he had originally communicated with Salzman by letter. He got on his coat, put a hat on over his skull cap and hurried to the subway station. All the way to the far end of the Bronx he sat on the edge of his seat. He was more than once tempted to take out the picture and see if the girl's face was as he remembered it, but he refrained, allowing the snapshot to remain in his inside coat pocket, content to have her so close. When the train pulled into the station he was waiting at the door and bolted out. He quickly located the street Salzman had advertised.

The building he sought was less than a block from the subway, but it was not an office building, nor even a loft, nor a store in which one could rent office space. It was a very old tenement house. Leo found Salzman's name in pencil on a soiled tag under the bell and climbed three dark flights to his apartment. When he knocked, the door was opened by a thin, asthmatic, gray-haired woman, in felt slippers.

"Yes?" she said, expecting nothing. She listened without listening. He could have sworn he had seen her, too, before but knew it was an illusion.

"Salzman—does he live here? Pinye Salzman," he said, "the matchmaker?"

She stared at him a long minute. "Of course."

He felt embarrassed. "Is he in?"

"No." Her mouth, though left open, offered nothing more.

"The matter is urgent. Can you tell me where his office is?"

"In the air." She pointed upward.

"You mean he has no office?" Leo asked.

"In his socks."

He peered into the apartment. It was sunless and dingy, one large room divided by a half-open curtain, beyond which he could see a sagging metal bed. The near side of the room was crowded with rickety chairs, old bureaus, a three-legged table, racks of cooking utensils, and all the apparatus of a kitchen. But there was no sign of Salzman or his magic barrel, probably also a figment of the imagination. An odor of frying fish made Leo weak to the knees.

"Where is he?" he insisted. "I've got to see your husband."

At length she answered, "So who knows where he is? Every time he thinks a new thought he runs to a different place. Go home, he will find you."

"Tell him Leo Finkle."

She gave no sign she had heard.

He walked downstairs, depressed.

But Salzman, breathless, stood waiting at his door.

Leo was astounded and overjoyed. "How did you get here before me?"

"I rushed."

"Come inside."

They entered. Leo fixed tea, and a sardine sandwich for Salzman. As they were drinking he reached behind him for the packet of pictures and handed them to the marriage broker.

Salzman put down his glass and said expectantly, "You found somebody you like?"

"Not among these."

The marriage broker turned away.

"Here is the one I want." Leo held forth the snapshot.

Salzman slipped on his glasses and took the picture into his trembling hand. He turned ghastly and let out a groan.

"What's the matter?" cried Leo.

"Excuse me. Was an accident this picture. She isn't for you."

Salzman frantically shoved the manila packet into his portfolio. He thrust the snapshot into his pocket and fled down the stairs.

Leo, after momentary paralysis, gave chase and cornered the marriage broker in the vestibule. The landlady made hysterical outcries but neither of them listened.

"Give me back the picture, Salzman."

"No." The pain in his eyes was terrible.

"Tell me who she is then."

"This I can't tell you. Excuse me."

He made to depart, but Leo, forgetting himself, seized the matchmaker by his tight coat and shook him frenziedly.

"Please," sighed Salzman. *"Please."*

Leo ashamedly let him go. "Tell me who she is," he begged. "It's very important for me to know."

"She is not for you. She is a wild one—wild, without shame. This is not a bride for a rabbi."

"What do you mean wild?"

"Like an animal. Like a dog. For her to be poor was a sin. This is why to me she is dead now."

"In God's name, what do you mean?"

"Her I can't introduce to you," Salzman cried.

"Why are you so excited?"

"Why, he asks," Salzman said, bursting into tears. "This is my baby, my Stella, she should burn in hell."

Leo hurried up to bed and hid under the covers. Under the covers he thought his life through. Although he soon fell asleep he could not sleep her out of his mind. He woke, beating his breast. Though he prayed to be rid of her, his prayers went unanswered. Through days of torment he endlessly struggled not to love her; fearing success, he escaped it. He then concluded to convert her to goodness, himself to God. The idea alternately nauseated and exalted him.

He perhaps did not know that he had come to a final decision until he encountered Salzman in a Broadway cafeteria. He was sitting alone at a rear table, sucking the bony remains of a fish. The marriage broker appeared haggard, and transparent to the point of vanishing.

Salzman looked up at first without recognizing him. Leo had grown a pointed beard and his eyes were weighted with wisdom.

"Salzman," he said, "love has at last come to my heart."

"Who can love from a picture?" mocked the marriage broker.

"It is not impossible."

"If you can love her, then you can love anybody. Let me show you some new clients that they just sent me their photographs. One is a little doll."

"Just her I want," Leo murmured.

"Don't be a fool, doctor. Don't bother with her."

"Put me in touch with her, Salzman," Leo said humbly. "Perhaps I can be of service."

Salzman had stopped eating and Leo understood with emotion that it was now arranged.

Leaving the cafeteria, he was, however, afflicted by a tormenting suspicion that Salzman had planned it all to happen this way.

Leo was informed by letter that she would meet him on a certain corner, and she was there one spring night, waiting under a street lamp. He appeared, carrying a small bouquet of violets and rosebuds.

Stella stood by the lamp post, smoking. She wore white with red shoes, which fitted his expectations, although in a troubled moment he had imagined the dress red, and only the shoes white. She waited uneasily and shyly. From afar he saw that her eyes—clearly her father's—were filled with desperate innocence. He pictured, in her, his own redemption. Violins and lit candles revolved in the sky. Leo ran forward with flowers outthrust.

Around the corner, Salzman, leaning against a wall, chanted prayers for the dead.

Saul Bellow

Looking For Mr. Green

Whatsoever thy hand findeth to do, do it with thy might. . . .

HARD work? No, it wasn't really so hard. He wasn't used to walking and stair-climbing, but the physical difficulty of his new job was not what George Grebe felt most. He was delivering relief checks in the Negro district, and although he was a native Chicagoan this was not a part of the city he knew much about—it needed a depression to introduce him to it. No, it wasn't literally hard work, not as reckoned in foot-pounds, but yet he was beginning to feel the strain of it, to grow aware of its peculiar difficulty. He could find the streets and numbers, but the clients were not where they were supposed to be, and he felt like a hunter inexperienced in the camouflage of his game. It was an unfavorable day, too—fall, and cold, dark weather, windy. But, anyway, instead of shells in his deep trenchcoat pocket he had the cardboard of checks, punctured for the spindles of the file, the holes reminding him of the holes in player-piano paper. And he didn't look much like a hunter, either; his was a city figure entirely, belted up in this Irish conspirator's coat. He was slender without being tall, stiff in the back, his legs looking shabby in a pair of old tweed pants gone through and fringy at the cuffs. With this stiffness, he kept his head forward, so that his face was red from the sharpness of the weather; and it was an indoors sort of face with gray eyes that persisted in some kind of thought and yet seemed to avoid definiteness of conclusion. He wore sideburns that surprised you somewhat by the tough curl of the blond hair and the effect of assertion in their length. He was not so mild as he looked, nor so youthful; and nevertheless there was no effort on his part to seem what he was not. He was an educated man; he was a bachelor; he was in some ways simple; without lushing, he liked a drink; his luck had not been good. Nothing was deliberately hidden.

He felt that his luck was better than usual today. When he had reported for work that morning he had expected to be shut up in the relief office at a clerk's job, for he had been hired downtown as a clerk, and he was glad to have, instead, the freedom of the streets and welcomed, at least at first, the vigor of the cold and even the blowing of the hard wind. But on the other hand he was not getting on with the distribution of the checks. It was true that it was a city job; nobody expected you to push too hard at a city job. His supervisor, that young Mr. Raynor, had practically told him that. Still, he wanted to do well at it. For one thing, when he knew how quickly he could deliver a batch of checks, he would know also how much time he could expect to clip for himself. And then, too, the clients would be waiting for their money. That was not the most important consideration, though it certainly mattered to him. No, but he wanted to do well, simply for doing-well's sake, to acquit himself decently of a job because he so rarely had a job to do that required just this sort of energy. Of this peculiar energy he now had a superabundance; once it had started to flow, it flowed all too heavily. And, for the time being anyway, he was balked. He could not find Mr. Green.

So he stood in his big-skirted trenchcoat with a large envelope in his hand and papers showing from his pocket, wondering why people should be so hard to locate who were too feeble or sick to come to the station to collect their own checks. But Raynor had told him that tracking them down was not easy at first and had offered him some advice on how to proceed. "If you can see the postman, he's your first man to ask, and your best bet. If you can't connect with him, try the stores and tradespeople around. Then the janitor and the neighbors. But you'll find the closer you come to your man the less people will tell you. They don't want to tell you anything."

"Because I'm a stranger."

"Because you're white. We ought to have a Negro doing this, but we don't at the moment, and of course you've got to eat, too, and this is public employment. Jobs have to be made. Oh, that holds for me too. Mind you, I'm not letting myself out. I've got three years of seniority on you, that's all. And a law degree. Otherwise, you might be back of the desk and I might be going out into the field this cold day. The same dough pays us both and for the same, exact, identical reason. What's my law degree got to do with it? But you have to pass out these checks, Mr. Grebe, and it'll help if you're stubborn, so I hope you are."

"Yes, I'm fairly stubborn."

Raynor sketched hard with an eraser in the old dirt of his desk, left-handed, and said, "Sure, what else can you answer to such a question. Anyhow, the trouble you're going to have is that they don't like to give information about anybody. They think you're a plainclothes dick or an installment collector, or summons-server or something like that. Till you've been seen around the neighborhood for a few months and people know you're only from the relief."

It was dark, ground-freezing, pre-Thanksgiving weather; the wind played hob with the smoke, rushing it down, and Grebe missed his gloves, which he had left in Raynor's office. And no one would admit knowing Green. It was past three o'clock and the postman had made his last delivery. The nearest grocer, himself a Negro, had never heard the name Tulliver Green, or said he hadn't. Grebe was inclined to think that it was true, that he had in the end convinced the man that he wanted only to deliver a check. But he wasn't sure. He needed experience in interpreting looks and signs and, even more, the will not to be put off or denied and even the force to bully if need be. If the grocer did know, he had got rid of him easily. But since most of his trade was with reliefers, why should he prevent the delivery of a check? Maybe Green, or Mrs. Green, if there was a Mrs. Green, patronized another grocer. And was there a Mrs. Green? It was one of Grebe's great handicaps that he hadn't looked at any of the case records. Raynor should have let him read files for a few hours. But he apparently saw no need for that, probably considering the job unimportant. Why prepare systematically to deliver a few checks?

But now it was time to look for the janitor. Grebe took in the building in the wind and gloom of the late November day—trampled, frost-hardened lots on one side; on the other, an automobile junk yard and then the infinite work of Elevated frames, weak-looking, gaping with rubbish fires; two sets of leaning brick porches three stories high and a flight of cement stairs to the cellar. Descending, he entered the underground passage, where he tried the doors until one opened and he found himself in the furnace room. There someone rose toward him and approached, scraping on the coal grit and bending under the canvas-jacketed pipes.

"Are you the janitor?"

"What do you want?"

"I'm looking for a man who's supposed to be living here. Green."

"What Green?"

"Oh, you maybe have more than one Green?" said Grebe with new, pleasant hope. "This is Tulliver Green."

"I don't think I c'n help you, mister. I don't know any."

"A crippled man."

The janitor stood bent before him. Could it be that he was crippled? Oh, God! what if he was. Grebe's gray eyes sought with excited difficulty to see. But no, he was only very short and stooped. A head awakened from meditation, a strong-haired beard, low, wide shoulders. A staleness of sweat and coal rose from his black shirt and the burlap sack he wore as an apron.

"Crippled how?"

Grebe thought and then answered with the light voice of unmixed candor, "I don't know. I've never seen him." This was damaging, but his only other choice was to make a lying guess, and he was not up to it. "I'm delivering checks for the relief to shut-in cases. If he weren't crippled he'd come to collect himself. That's why I said crippled. Bedridden, chair-ridden—is there anybody like that?"

This sort of frankness was one of Grebe's oldest talents, going back to childhood. But it gained him nothing here.

"No suh. I've got four buildin's same as this that I take care of. I don' know all the tenants, leave alone the tenants' tenants. The rooms turn over so fast, people movin' in and out every day. I can't tell you."

"Then where should I ask?"

The janitor opened his grimy lips but Grebe did not hear him in the piping of the valves and the consuming pull of air to flame in the body of the furnace. He knew, however, what he had said.

"Well, all the same, thanks. Sorry I bothered you. I'll prowl around upstairs again and see if I can turn up someone who knows him."

Once more in the cold air and early darkness he made the short circle from the cellarway to the entrance crowded between the brickwork pillars and began to climb to the third floor. Pieces of plaster ground under his feet; strips of brass tape from which the carpeting had been torn away marked old boundaries at the sides. In the passage, the cold reached him worse than in the street; it touched him to the bone. The hall toilets ran like springs. He thought grimly as he heard the wind burning around the building with a sound like that of the furnace, that this was a great piece of constructed shelter. Then he struck a match in the gloom and searched for names and numbers among the writings and scribbles on the walls. He saw WHOODY-DOODY GO TO JESUS, and zigzags, caricatures, sexual scrawls, and curses. So the sealed rooms of pyramids were also decorated, and the caves of human dawn.

The information on his card was, TULLIVER GREEN—APT 3D. There were no names, however, and no numbers. His shoulders drawn up, tears of cold in his eyes, breathing vapor, he went the length of the corridor and told himself that if he had been lucky enough to have the temperament for it he would bang on one of the doors and bawl out "Tulliver Green!" until he got results. But it wasn't in him to make an uproar and he continued to burn matches, passing the light over the walls. At the rear, in a corner of the hall, he discovered a door he had not seen before and he thought it best to investigate. It sounded empty when he knocked, but a young Negress answered, hardly more than a girl. She opened only a bit, to guard the warmth of the room.

"Yes suh?"

"I'm from the district relief station on Prairie Avenue. I'm looking for a man named Tulliver Green to give him his check. Do you know him?"

No, she didn't; but he thought she had not understood anything of what he had said. She had a dream-bound, dream-blind face, very soft and black, shut off. She wore a man's jacket and pulled the ends together at her throat. Her hair was parted in three directions, at the sides and transversely, standing up at the front in a dull puff.

"Is there somebody around here who might know?"

"I jus' taken this room las' week."

He observed that she shivered, but even her shiver was somnambulistic and there was no sharp consciousness of cold in the big smooth eyes of her handsome face.

"All right, miss, thank you. Thanks," he said, and went to try another place.

Here he was admitted. He was grateful, for the room was warm. It was full of people, and they were silent as he entered—ten people, or a dozen, perhaps more, sitting on benches like a parliament. There was no light, properly speaking, but a tempered darkness that the window gave, and everyone seemed to him enormous, the men padded out in heavy work clothes and winter coats, and the women huge, too, in their sweaters, hats, and old furs. And, besides, bed and bedding, a black cooking range, a piano piled towering to the ceiling with papers, a dining-room table of the old style of prosperous Chicago. Among these people Grebe, with his cold-heightened fresh color and his smaller stature, entered like a schoolboy. Even though he was met with smiles and good will, he knew, before a single word was spoken, that all the currents ran against him and that he would make no headway. Nevertheless he began. "Does anybody here know how I can deliver a check to Mr. Tulliver Green?"

"Green?" It was the man that had let him in who answered. He was in short sleeves, in a checkered shirt, and had a queer high head, profusely overgrown and long as a shako; the veins entered it strongly from his forehead. "I never heard mention of him. Is this where he live?"

"This is the address they gave me at the station. He's a sick man, and he'll need his check. Can't anybody tell me where to find him?"

He stood his ground and waited for a reply, his crimson wool scarf wound about his neck and drooping outside his trenchcoat, pockets weighted with the block of checks and official forms. They must have realized that he was not a college boy employed afternoons by a bill collector, trying foxily to pass for a relief clerk, recognized that he was an older man who knew himself what need was, who had had more than an average seasoning in hardship. It was evident enough if you looked at the marks under his eyes and at the sides of his mouth.

"Anybody know this sick man?"

"No suh." On all sides he saw heads shaken and smiles of denial. No one knew. And maybe it was true, he considered, standing silent in the earthen, musky human gloom of the place as the rumble continued. But he could never really be sure.

"What's the matter with this man?" said shako-head.

"I've never seen him. All I can tell you is that he can't come in person for his money. It's my first day in this district."

"Maybe they given you the wrong number?"

"I don't believe so. But where else can I ask about him?" He felt that his persistence amused them deeply, and in a way he shared their amusement that he should stand up so tenaciously to them. Though smaller, though slight, he was his own man, he retracted nothing about himself, and he looked back at them, gray-eyed, with amusement and also with a sort of courage. On the bench some man spoke in his throat, the words impossible to catch, and a woman answered with a wild, shrieking laugh, which was quickly cut off.

"Well, so nobody will tell me?"

"Ain't nobody who knows."

"At least, if he lives here, he pays rent to someone. Who manages the building?"

"Greatham Company. That's on Thirty-ninth Street."

Grebe wrote it in his pad. But, in the street again, a sheet of wind-driven paper clinging to his leg while he deliberated what direction to take next, it seemed a feeble lead to follow. Probably this Green didn't rent a flat, but a room. Sometimes there were as many as twenty people living in an apartment; the real-estate agent would know only the lessee. And not even the agent could tell you who the renters were. In some places the beds were even used in shifts, watchmen or jitney drivers or short-order cooks in night joints turning out after a day's sleep and surrendering their beds to a sister, a nephew, or perhaps a stranger, just off the bus. There were large numbers of newcomers in this terrific, blight-bitten portion of the city between Cottage Grove and Ashland, wandering from house to house and room to room. When you saw them, how could you know them? They didn't carry bundles on their backs or look picturesque. You only saw a man, a Negro, walking in the street or riding in the car, like everyone else, with his thumb closed on a transfer. And therefore how were you supposed to tell? Grebe thought the Greatham agent would only laugh at his question.

But how much it would have simplified the job to be able to say that Green was old, or blind, or consumptive. An hour in the files, taking a few notes, and he needn't have been at such a disadvantage. When Raynor gave him the block of checks he had asked, "How much should I know about these people?" Then Raynor had looked as though he were preparing to accuse him of trying to make the job more important that it was. He smiled, because by then they were on fine terms, but nevertheless he had been getting ready to say something like that when the confusion began in the station over Staika and her children.

Grebe had waited a long time for this job. It came to him through the pull of an old schoolmate in the Corporation Counsel's office, never a close friend, but suddenly sympathetic and interested—pleased to show, moreover, how well he had done, how strongly he was coming on even in these miserable times. Well, he was coming through strongly, along with the Democratic administration itself. Grebe had gone to see him in City Hall, and they had had a counter lunch or beers at least once a month for a year, and finally it had been possible to swing the job. He didn't mind being assigned the lowest clerical grade, nor even being a messenger, though Raynor thought he did.

This Raynor was an original sort of guy and Grebe had taken to him immediately. As was proper on the first day, Grebe had come early, but he waited long, for Raynor was late. At last he darted into his cubicle of an office as though he had just jumped from one of those hurtling huge red Indiana Avenue cars. His thin, rough face was wind-stung and he was grinning and saying something breathlessly to himself. In his hat, a small fedora and his coat, the velvet collar a neat fit about his neck, and his silk muffler that set off the nervous twist of his chin, he swayed and turned himself in his swivel chair, feet leaving the ground; so that he pranced a little as he sat. Meanwhile he took Grebe's measure out of his eyes, eyes of an unusual vertical length and slightly sardonic. So the two men sat for a while, saying nothing, while the supervisor raised his hat from his miscombed hair and put it in his lap. His cold-darkened hands were not clean. A steel beam passed through the little make-shift room, from which machine belts once had hung. The building was an old factory.

"I'm younger than you; I hope you won't find it hard taking orders from me," said Raynor. "But I don't make them up, either. You're how old, about?"

"Thirty-five."

"And you thought you'd be inside doing paper-work. But it so happens I have to send you out."

"I don't mind."

"And it's mostly a Negro load we have in this district."

"So I thought it would be."

"Fine. You'll get along. *C'est un bon boulot.* Do you know French?"

"Some."

"I thought you'd be a university man."

"Have you been in France?" said Grebe.

"No, that's the French of the Berlitz School. I've been at it for more than a year, just as I'm sure people have been, all over the world, office boys in China and braves in Tanganyika. In fact, I damn well know it. Such is the attractive power of civilization. It's overrated, but what do you want? *Que voulez vous?* I get *Le Rire* and all the spicy papers, just like in Tanganyika. It must be mystifying, out there. But my reason is that I'm aiming at the diplomatic service. I have a cousin who's a courier, and the way he describes it is awfully attractive. He rides in the *wagon-lits* and reads books. While we— What did you do before?"

"I sold."

"Where?"

"Canned meat at Stop and Shop. In the basement."

"And before that?"

"Window shades, at Goldblatt's."

"Steady work?"

"No, Thursdays and Saturdays. I also sold shoes."

"You've been a shoe-dog, too. Well. And prior to that? Here it is in your folder." He opened the record. "St. Olaf's College, instructor in classical languages. Fellow, University of Chicago, 1926-27. I've had Latin, too. Let's trade quotations—*'Dum spiro spero.'* "

" *'Da dextram misero.'* "

" *'Alea jacta est.'* "

" *'Excelsior.'* "

Raynor shouted with laughter, and other workers came to look at him over the partition. Grebe also laughed, feeling pleased and easy. The luxury of fun on a nervous morning.

When they were done and no one was watching or listening, Raynor said rather seriously, "What made you study Latin in the first place. Was it for the priesthood?"

"No."

"Just for the hell of it? For the culture? Oh, the things people think they can pull!" He made his cry hilarious and tragic. "I ran my pants off so I could study for the bar, and I've passed the bar, so I get twelve dollars a week more than you as a bonus for having seen life straight and whole. I'll tell you, as a man of culture, that even though nothing looks to be real, and everything stands for something else, and that thing for another thing, and that thing for still further one—there ain't any comparison between twenty-five and thirty-seven dollars a week, regardless of the last reality. Don't you think that was clear to your Greeks? They were a thoughtful people, but they didn't part with their slaves."

This was a great deal more than Grebe had looked for in his first interview with his supervisor. He was too shy to show all the astonishment he felt. He laughed a little, aroused, and brushed at the sunbeam that covered his head with its dust. "Do you think my mistake was so terrible?"

"Damn right it was terrible, and you know it now that you've had the whip of hard times laid on your back. You should have been preparing yourself for trouble. Your people must have been well off to send you to the university. Stop me, if I'm stepping on your toes. Did your mother pamper you? Did your father give in to you? Were you brought up tenderly, with permission to go out and find out what were the last things that everything else stands for while everybody else labored in the fallen world of appearances?"

"Well, no, it wasn't exactly like that." Grebe smiled. *The fallen world of appearances!* no less. But now it was his turn to deliver a surprise. "We weren't rich. My father was the last genuine English butler in Chicago—"

"Are you kidding?"

"Why should I be?"

"In a livery?"

"In livery. Up on the Gold Coast."

"And he wanted you to be educated like a gentleman?"

"He did not. He sent me to the Armour Institute to study chemical engineering. But when he died I changed schools."

He stopped himself, and considered how quickly Raynor had

reached him. In no time he had your valise on the table and all your stuff unpacked. And afterward, in the streets, he was still reviewing how far he might have gone, and how much he might have been led to tell if they had not been interrupted by Mrs. Staika's great noise.

But just then a young woman, one of Raynor's workers, ran into the cubicle exclaiming, "Haven't you heard all the fuss?"

"We haven't heard anything."

"It's Staika, giving out with all her might. The reporters are coming. She said she phoned the papers, and you know she did."

"But what is she up to?" said Raynor.

"She brought her wash and she's ironing it here, with our current, because the relief won't pay her electric bill. She has her ironing board set up by the admitting desk, and her kids are with her, all six. They never are in school more than once a week. She's always dragging them around with her because of her reputation."

"I don't want to miss any of this," said Raynor, jumping up. Grebe, as he followed with the secretary, said, "Who is this Staika?"

"They call her the 'Blood Mother of Federal Street.' She's a professional donor at the hospitals. I think they pay ten dollars a pint. Of course it's no joke, but she makes a very big thing out of it and she and the kids are in the papers all the time."

A small crowd, staff and clients divided by a plywood barrier, stood in the narrow space of the entrance, and Staika was shouting in a gruff, mannish voice, plunging the iron on the board and slamming it on the metal rest.

"My father and mother came in a steerage, and I was born in our own house, Robey by Huron. I'm no dirty immigrant. I'm a US citizen. My husband is a gassed veteran from France with lungs weaker'n paper, that hardly can he go to the toilet by himself. These six children of mine, I have to buy the shoes for their feet with my own blood. Even a lousy little white communion necktie, that's a couple of drops of blood; a little piece of mosquito veil for my Vadja so she won't be ashamed in church for the other girls, they take my blood for it by Goldblatt. That's how I keep goin'. A fine thing if I had to depend on the relief. And there's plenty of people on the rolls—fakes! There's nothin' *they* can't get, that can go and wrap bacon at Swift and Armour any time. They're lookin' for them by the Yards. They never have to be out of work. Only they rather lay in their lousy beds and eat the public's money." She was not afraid, in a predominantly Negro station, to shout this way about Negroes.

Grebe and Raynor worked themselves forward to get a closer view of the woman. She was flaming with anger and with pleasure at herself, broad and huge, a golden-headed woman who wore a cotton cap laced with pink ribbon. She was barelegged and had on black gym-shoes, her hoover apron was open and her great breasts, not much restrained by a man's undershirt, hampered her arms as she worked at the kid's dress on the ironing board. And the children, silent and white, with a kind of locked obstinacy, in sheepskins and lumberjackets, stood behind her. She had captured the station, and the pleasure this gave her was enormous. Yet her grievances were true grievances. She was telling the truth. But she behaved like a liar. The look of her small eyes was hidden, and while she raged she also seemed to be spinning and planning.

"They send me out college case-workers in silk pants to talk me out of what I got comin'. Are they better'n me? Who told them? Fire them. Let 'em go and get married, and then you won't have to cut electric from people's budget."

The chief supervisor, Mr. Ewing, couldn't silence her and he stood with folded arms at the head of his staff, bald, bald-headed, saying to his subordinates like the ex-school principal he was, "Pretty soon she'll be tired and go."

"No she won't," said Raynor to Grebe. "She'll get what she wants. She knows more about the relief even than Ewing. She's been on the rolls for years and she always gets what she wants because she puts on a noisy show. Ewing knows it. He'll give in soon. He's only saving face. If he gets bad publicity, the Commissioner'll have him on the carpet, downtown. She's got him submerged; she'll submerge everybody in time, and that includes nations and governments."

Grebe replied with his characteristic smile, disagreeing completely. Who would take Staika's orders, and what changes could her yelling ever bring about?

No, what Grebe saw in her, the power that made people listen, was that her cry expressed the war of flesh and blood, perhaps turned a little crazy and certainly intensely ugly, on this place and this condition. And at first, when he went out, the spirit of Staika somehow presided over the whole district for him, and it took color from her; he saw her color, in the spotty curb-fires, and the fires under the El, the straight alley of flamey gloom. Later, too, when he went into a tavern for a shot of rye, the sweat of beer, association with West Side Polish streets, made him think of her again.

He wiped the corners of his mouth with his muffler, his handkerchief being inconvenient to reach for, and went out again to get on with the delivery of his checks. The air bit cold and hard and a few flakes of snow formed near him. A train struck by and left a quiver in the frames and a bristling icy hiss over the rails.

Crossing the street, he descended a flight of board steps into a basement grocery, setting off a little bell. It was a dark, long store and it caught you with its stinks of smoked meat, soap, dried peaches, and fish. There was a fire wrinkling and flapping in the little stove, and the proprietor was waiting, an Italian with a long, hollow face and stubborn bristles. He kept his hands warm under his apron.

No, he didn't know Green. You know people, but not names. The same man might not have the same name twice. The police didn't know, either, and mostly didn't care. When somebody was shot or knifed they took the body away and didn't look for the murderer. In the first place, nobody would tell them anything. So they made up a name for the coroner and called it quits. And in the second place, they didn't give a goddam anyhow. But they couldn't get to the bottom of a thing even if they wanted to. Nobody would get to know even a tenth of what went on among these people. They stabbed and stole, they did every crime and abomination you ever heard of, men and men, women and women, parents and children, worse than the animals. They carried on their own way, and the horrors passed off like a smoke. There was never anything like it in the history of the whole world.

It was a long speech, deepening with every word in it's fantasy and passion and becoming increasingly senseless and terrible: a swarm amassed by suggestion and invention, a huge, hugging, despairing knot, a human wheel of heads, legs, bellies, arms, rolling through his shop.

Grebe felt that he must interrupt him. He said sharply, "What are you talking about! All I asked was whether you knew this man."

"That isn't even the half of it. I been here six years. You probably don't want to believe this. But suppose it's true?"

"All the same," said Grebe, "there must be a way to find a person."

The Italian's close-spaced eyes had been queerly concentrated, as were his muscles, while he leaned across the counter trying to convince Grebe. Now he gave up the effort and sat down on his stool. "Oh—I suppose. Once in a while. But I been telling you, even the cops don't get anywhere."

"They're always after somebody. It's not the same thing."

"Well, keep trying if you want. I can't help you."

But he didn't keep trying. He had no more time to spend on Green. He slipped Green's check to the back of the block. The next name on the list was FIELD WINSTON.

He found the back-yard bungalow without the least trouble; it shared a lot with another house, a few feet of yard between. Grebe knew these two-shack arrangements. They had been built in vast numbers in the days before the swamps were filled and the streets raised, and they were all the same—a boardwalk along the fence, well under street level, three or four ball-headed posts for clotheslines, greening wood, dead shingles, and a long, long flight of stairs to the rear door.

A twelve-year-old boy let him into the kitchen, and there the old man was, sitting by the table in a wheel chair.

"Oh, it's d' government man," he said to the boy when Grebe drew out his checks. "Go bring me my box of papers." He cleared a space on the table.

"Oh, you don't have to go to all that trouble," said Grebe. But Field laid out his papers: Social Security card, relief certification, letters from the state hospital in Manteno, and a naval discharge dated San Diego, 1920.

"That's plenty," Grebe said. "Just sign."

"You got to know who I am," the old man said. "You're from the government. It's not your check, it's a government check and you got no business to hand it over till everything is proved."

He loved the ceremony of it, and Grebe made no more objections. Field emptied his box and finished out the circle of cards and letters.

"There's everything I done and been. Just the death certificate and they can close book on me." He said this with a certain happy pride and magnificence. Still he did not sign; he merely held the little pen upright on the golden-green corduroy of his thigh. Grebe did not hurry him. He felt the old man's hunger for conversation.

"I got to get better coal," he said. "I send my little gran'son to the yard with my order and they fill his wagon with screening. The stove ain't made for it. It fall through the grate. The order says Franklin County egg-size coal."

"I'll report it and see what can be done."

"Nothing can be done, I expect. You know and I know. There ain't no little ways to make things better, and the only big thing is money. That's the only sunbeams, money. Nothing is black where it shines, and the only place you see black is where it ain't shining. What we colored have to have is our own rich. There ain't no other way."

Grebe sat, his reddened forehead bridged levelly by his close-cut hair and his cheeks lowered in the wings of his collar—the caked fire shone hard within the isinglass and iron frames but the room was not comfortable—sat and listened while the old man unfolded his scheme. This was to create one Negro millionaire a month by subscription. One clever, good-hearted young fellow elected every month would sign a contract to use the money to start a business employing Negroes. This would be advertised by chain letters and word of mouth, and every Negro wage-earner would contribute a dollar a month. Within five years there would be sixty millionaires.

"That'll fetch respect," he said with a throat-stopped sound that came out like a foreign syllable. "You got to take and organize all the money that get's thrown away on the policy wheel and horse race. As long as they can take it away from you, they go no respect for you. Money, that's d' sun of human kind!" Field was a Negro of mixed blood, perhaps Cherokee, or Natchez; his skin was reddish. And he sounded, speaking about a golden sun in this dark room, and looked, shaggy and slab-headed, with the mingled blood of his face and broad lips, the little pen still upright in his hand, like one of the underground kings of mythology, old judge Minos himself.

And now he accepted the check and signed. Not to soil the slip, he held it down with his knuckles. The table budged and creaked, the center of the gloomy, heathen midden of the kitchen covered with bread, meat, and cans, and the scramble of papers.

"Don't you think my scheme'd work?"

"It's worth thinking about. Something ought to be done, I agree."

"It'll work if people will do it. That's all. That's the only thing, any time. When they understand it in the same way, all of them."

"That's true," said Grebe, rising. His glance met the old man's.

"I know you got to go," he said. "Well, God bless you, boy, you ain't been sly with me. I can tell it in a minute."

He went back through the buried yard. Someone nursed a candle in a shed, where a man unloaded kindling wood from a sprawl-wheeled baby buggy and two voices carried on a high conversation. As he came up the sheltered passage he heard the hard boost of the wind in the branches and against the house fronts, and then, reaching the sidewalk, he saw the needle-eye red of cable towers in the open icy height hundreds of feet above the river and the factories—those keen points. From here, his view was unobstructed all the way to the South Branch and its timber banks, and the cranes beside the water. Rebuilt after the Great Fire, this part of the city was, not fifty years later, in ruins again, factories boarded up, buildings deserted or fallen, gaps of prairie between. But it wasn't desolation that this made you feel, but rather a faltering of organization that set free a huge energy, an escaped, unattached, unregulated power from the giant raw place. Not only must people feel it but, it seemed to Grebe, they were compelled to match it. In their very bodies. He no less than others, he realized. Say that his parents had been servants in their time, whereas he was not supposed to be one. He thought that they had never done any service like this, which no one visible asked for, and probably flesh and blood could not even perform. Nor could anyone show why it should be performed; or see where the performance would lead. That did not mean that he wanted to be released from it, he realized with a grimly pensive face. On the contrary. He had something to do. To be compelled to feel this energy and yet have no task to do—that was horrible; that was suffering; he knew what that was. It was now quitting time. Six o'clock. He could go home if he liked, to his room, that is, to wash in hot water, to pour a drink, lie down on his quilt, read the paper, eat some liver paste on crackers before going out to dinner. But to think of this actually made him feel a little sick, as though he had swallowed hard air. He had six checks left, and he was determined to deliver at least one of these: Mr. Green's check.

So he started again. He had four or five dark blocks to go, past open lots, condemned houses, old foundations, closed schools, black churches, mounds, and he reflected that there must be many people alive who had once seen the neighborhood rebuilt and new. Now there was a second layer of ruins; centuries of history accomplished through human massing. Numbers had given the place forced growth; enormous numbers had also broken it down. Objects once so new, so concrete that it could never have occurred to anyone they stood for other things, had crumbled. Therefore, reflected Grebe, the secret of them was out. It was that they stood for themselves by agreement, and were natural and not unnatural by agreement, and when the things themselves collapsed the agreement became visible. What was it, otherwise, that kept cities from looking peculiar? Rome, that was almost permanent, did not give rise to thoughts like these. And was it abidingly real? But in Chicago, where the cycles were so fast and the familiar died out, and again rose changed, and died again in thirty years, you saw the common agreement or covenant, and you were forced to think about appearances and realities. (He remembered Raynor and he smiled. Raynor was a clever boy.) Once you had grasped this, a great many things became intelligible. For instance, why Mr. Field should conceive such a scheme. Of course, if people were to agree to create a millionaire, a real millionaire would come into existence. And if you wanted to know how Mr. Field was inspired to think of this, why, he had within sight of his kitchen window the chart, the very bones of a successful scheme—the El with its blue and green confetti of signals. People consented to pay dimes and ride the crash-box cars, and so it was a success. Yet how absurd it looked; how little reality there was to start with. And yet Yerkes, the great financier who built it, had known that he could get people to agree to do it. Viewed as itself, what a scheme of a scheme it seemed, how close to an appearance. Then why wonder at Mr. Field's idea? He had grasped a principle. And then Grebe remembered, too, that Mr. Yerkes had established the Yerkes Observatory and endowed it with millions. Now how did the notion come to him in his New York museum of a palace or his Aegean-bound yacht to give money to astronomers? Was he awed perhaps by the success of his bizarre enterprise and therefore ready to spend money to find out where in the universe being and seeming were identical? Yes, he wanted to know what abides; and whether flesh is Bible-grass; and he offered money to be burned in the fire of suns. Okay, then, Grebe thought further, these things exist because people consent to exist with them—we have got so far—and also there is a reality that doesn't depend on consent but within which consent is a game. But what about need, the need that keeps so many vast thousands in position? You tell me that, you *private* little gentlemen and *decent* soul—he used these words against himself scornfully. Why is the consent given to misery? And why so painfully ugly? Because there *is something* that is dismal and permanently ugly? Here he sighed and gave it up, and thought it was enough for the present moment that he had a real check in his pocket for a Mr. Green who must be real beyond question. If only his neighbors didn't think they had to conceal him.

This time he stopped at the second floor. He struck a match and found a door. Presently a man answered his knock and Grebe had the check ready and showed it even before he began. "Does Tulliver Green live here? I'm from the relief."

The man narrowed the opening and spoke to someone at his back.

"Does he live here?"

"Uh-uh. No."

"Or anywhere in this building? He's a sick man and he can't come for his dough." He exhibited the check in the light, which was smoky —the air smelled of charred lard—and the man held off the brim of his cap to study it.

"Uh-uh. Never seen the name."

"There's nobody around here that uses crutches?"

He seemed to think, but it was Grebe's impression that he was simply waiting for a decent interval to pass.

"No, suh. Nobody I ever see."

"I've been looking for this man all afternoon," Grebe spoke out with sudden force, "and I'm going to have to carry this check back to the station. It seems strange not to be able to find a person to *give* him something when you're looking for him for a good reason. I suppose if I had bad news for him I'd find him quick enough."

There was a responsive motion in the other man's face. "That's right, I reckon."

"It almost doesn't do any good to have a name if you can't be found by it. It doesn't stand for anything. He might as well not have any," he went on, smiling. It was as much of a concession as he could make to his desire to laugh.

"Well, now, there's a little old knot-back man I see once in a while. He might be the one you lookin' for. Downstairs."

"Where? Right side or left? Which door?"

"I don't know which. Thin face little knot-back with a stick."

But no one answered at any of the doors on the first floor. He went to the end of the corridor, searching by matchlight, and found only a stairless exit to the yard, a drop of about six feet. But there was a bungalow near the alley, an old house like Mr. Field's. To jump was unsafe. He ran from the front door, through the underground passage and into the yard. The place was occupied. There was a light through the curtains, upstairs. The name on the ticket under the broken, scoop-shaped mailbox was Green! He exultantly rang the bell and pressed against the locked door. Then the lock clicked faintly and a long staircase opened before him. Someone was slowly coming down —a woman. He had the impression in the weak light that she was shaping her hair as she came, making herself presentable, for he saw her arms raised. But it was for support that they were raised; she was feeling her way downward, down the walls, stumbling. Next he wondered about the pressure of her feet on the treads; she did not seem to be wearing shoes. And it was a freezing stairway. His ring had got her out of bed, perhaps, and she had forgotten to put them on. And then he saw that she was not only shoeless but naked; she was entirely naked, climbing down while she talked to herself, a heavy woman, naked and drunk. She blundered into him. The contact of her breasts, though they touched only his coat, made him go back against the door with a blind shock. See what he had tracked down, in his hunting game!

The woman was saying to herself, furious with insult, "So I can't ——k, huh? I'll show that son-of-a-bitch kin I, cain't I."

What should he do now? Grebe asked himself. Why, he should go. He should turn away and go. He couldn't talk to this woman. He couldn't keep her standing naked in the cold. But when he tried he found himself unable to turn away.

He said, "Is this where Mr. Green lives?"

But she was still talking to herself and did not hear him.

"Is this Mr. Green's house?"

At last she turned her furious drunken glance on him. "What do you want?"

Again her eyes wandered from him; there was a dot of blood in their enraged brilliance. He wondered why she didn't feel the cold.

"I'm from the relief."

"Awright, what?"

"I've got a check for Tulliver Green."

This time she heard him and put out her hand.

"No, no, for *Mr.* Green. He's got to sign," he said. How was he going to get Green's signature tonight!

"I'll take it. He cain't."

He desperately shook his head, thinking of Mr. Field's precautions about identification. "I can't let you have it. It's for him. Are you Mrs. Green?"

"Maybe I is, and maybe I ain't. Who want to know?"

"Is he upstairs?"

"Awright. Take it up yourself, you goddam fool."

Sure, he was a goddamned fool. Of course he could not go up because Green would probably be drunk and naked, too. And perhaps he would appear on the landing soon. He looked eagerly upward. Under the light was a high narrow brown wall. Empty! It remained empty!

"Hell with you, then!" he heard her cry. To deliver a check for coal and clothes, he was keeping her in the cold. She did not feel it, but his face was burning with frost and self-ridicule. He backed away from her.

"I'll come tomorrow, tell him."

"Ah, hell with you. Don't never come. What you doin' here in the nighttime? Don' come back." She yelled so that he saw the breadth of her tongue. She stood astride in the long cold box of the hall and held on to the banister and the wall. The bungalow itself was shaped something like a box, a clumsy, high box pointing into the freezing air with its sharp, wintry lights.

"If you are Mrs. Green, I'll give you the check," he said, changing his mind.

"Give here, then." She took it, took the pen offered with it in her left hand, and tried to sign the receipt on the wall. He looked around, almost as though to see whether his madness was being observed, and came near believing that someone was standing on a mountain of used tires in the auto-junking shop next door.

"But are you Mrs. Green?" he now thought to ask. But she was already climbing the stairs with the check, and it was too late, if he had made an error, if he was now in trouble, to undo the thing. But he wasn't going to worry about it. Though she might not be Mrs. Green, he was convinced that Mr. Green was upstairs. Whoever she was, the woman stood for Green, whom he was not to see this time. Well, you silly bastard, he said to himself, so you think you found him. So what? Maybe you really did find him—what of it? But it was important that there was a real Mr. Green whom they could not keep him from reaching because he seemed to come as an emissary from hostile appearances. And though the self-ridicule was slow to diminish, and his face still blazed with it, he had, nevertheless, a feeling of elation, too. "For after all," he said, "he *could* be found!"

Truman Capote

A Christmas Memory

IMAGINE a morning in late November. A coming of winter morning more than twenty years ago. Consider the kitchen of a spreading old house in a country town. A great black stove is its main feature; but there is also a big round table and a fireplace with two rocking chairs placed in front of it. Just today the fireplace commenced its seasonal roar.

A woman with shorn white hair is standing at the kitchen window. She is wearing tennis shoes and a shapeless gray sweater over a summery calico dress. She is small and sprightly, like a bantam hen; but, due to a long youthful illness, her shoulders are pitifully hunched. Her face is remarkable—not unlike Lincoln's, craggy like that, and tinted by sun and wind; but it is delicate too, finely boned, and her eyes are sherry-colored and timid. "Oh my," she exclaims, her breath smoking the windowpane, "it's fruitcake weather!"

The person to whom she is speaking is myself. I am seven; she is sixty-something. We are cousins, very distant ones, and we have lived together—well, as long as I can remember. Other people inhabit the house, relatives; and though they have power over us, and frequently make us cry, we are not, on the whole, too much aware of them. We are each other's best friend. She calls me Buddy, in memory of a boy who was formerly her best friend. The other Buddy died in the 1880's, when she was still a child. She is still a child.

"I knew it before I got out of bed," she says, turning away from the window with a purposeful excitement in her eyes. "The courthouse bell sounded so cold and clear. And there were no birds singing; they've gone to warmer country, yes indeed. Oh, Buddy, stop stuffing biscuit and fetch our buggy. Help me find my hat. We've thirty cakes to bake."

It's always the same: a morning arrives in November, and my friend, as though officially inaugurating the Christmas time of year that exhilarates her imagination and fuels the blaze of her heart, announces: "It's fruitcake weather! Fetch our buggy. Help me find my hat."

The hat is found, a straw cartwheel corsaged with velvet roses out-of-doors has faded: it once belonged to a more fashionable relative. Together, we guide our buggy, a delapidated baby carriage, out to the garden and into a grove of pecan trees. The buggy is mine; that is, it was bought for me when I was born. It is made of wicker, rather unraveled, and the wheels wobble like a drunkard's legs. But it is a faithful object; springtimes, we take it to the woods and fill it with flowers, herbs, wild fern for our porch pots; in the summer, we pile it with picnic paraphernalia and sugar-cane fishing poles and roll it down to the edge of a creek; it has its winter uses, too: as a truck for hauling firewood from the yard to the kitchen, as a warm bed for Queenie, our tough little orange and white rat terrier who has survived distemper and two rattlesnake bites. Queenie is trotting beside it now.

Three hours later we are back in the kitchen hulling a heaping buggyload of windfall pecans. Our backs hurt from gathering them: how hard they were to find (the main crop having been shaken off the trees and sold by the orchard's owners, who are not us) among the concealing leaves, the frosted, deceiving grass. Caarackle! A cheery crunch, scraps of miniature thunder sound as the shells collapse and the golden mound of sweet oily ivory meat mounts in the milk-glass bowl. Queenie begs to taste, and now and again my friend sneaks her a mite, though insisting we deprive ourselves. "We mustn't, Buddy. If we start, we won't stop. And there's scarcely enough as there is. For thirty cakes." The kitchen is growing dark. Dusk turns the window into a mirror: our reflections mingle with the rising moon as we work by the fireside in the firelight. At last, when the moon is quite high, we toss the final hull into the fire and, with joined sighs, watch it catch flame. The buggy is empty, the bowl is brimful.

We eat our supper (cold biscuits, bacon, blackberry jam) and discuss tomorrow. Tomorrow the kind of work I like best begins: buying. Cherries and citron, ginger and vanilla and canned Hawaiian pineapple, rinds and raisins and walnuts and whiskey and oh, so much flour, butter, so many eggs, spices, flavorings: why, we'll need a pony to pull the buggy home.

But before these purchases can be made, there is the question of money. Neither of us has any. Except for skinflint sums persons in the house occasionally provide (a dime is considered very big money); or what we earn ourselves from various activities: holding rummage sales, selling buckets of hand-picked blackberries, jars of homemade jam and apple jelly and peach preserves, rounding up flowers for funerals and weddings. Once we won seventy-ninth prize, five dollars, in a national football contest. Not that we know a fool thing about football. It's just that we enter any contest we hear about: at the moment our hopes are centered on the fifty-thousand-dollar Grand Prize being offered to name a new brand of coffee (we suggested "A.M."; and, after some hesitation, for my friend thought it perhaps sacrilegious, the slogan "A.M.! Amen!"). To tell the truth, our only *really* profitable enterprise was the Fun and Freak Museum we conducted in a back-yard woodshed two summers ago. The Fun was a stereopticon with slide views of Washington and New York lent us by a relative who had been to those places (she was furious when she discovered why we'd borrowed it); the Freak was a three-legged biddy chicken hatched by one of our own hens. Everybody hereabouts wanted to see that biddy: we charged grown-ups a nickel, kids two cents. And took in a good twenty dollars before the museum shut down due to the decease of the main attraction.

But one way and another we do each year accumulate Christmas savings, a Fruitcake Fund. These moneys we keep hidden in an ancient bead purse under a loose board under the floor under a chamber pot under my friend's bed. The purse is seldom removed from this safe location except to make a deposit, or, as happens every Saturday, a withdrawal; for on Saturdays I am allowed ten cents to go to the picture show. My friend has never been to a picture show, nor does she intend to: "I'd rather hear you tell the story, Buddy. That way I can imagine it more. Besides, a person my age shouldn't squander their eyes. When the Lord comes, let me see him clear." In addition to never having seen a movie, she has never: eaten in a restaurant, traveled more than five miles from home, received or sent a telegram, read anything except funny papers and the Bible, worn cosmetics, cursed, wished someone harm, told a lie on purpose, let a hungry dog go hungry. Here are a few things she has done, does do: killed with a hoe the biggest rattlesnake ever seen in this county (sixteen rattles), dip snuff (secretly), tame hummingbirds (just try it) till they balance on her finger, tell ghost stories (we both believe in ghosts) so tingling they chill you in July, talk to herself, take walks in the rain, grow the prettiest japonicas in town, know the recipe for every sort of old-time Indian cure, including a magical wart-remover.

Now, with supper finished, we retire to the room in a faraway part of the house where my friend sleeps in a scrap-quilt-covered iron bed painted rose pink, her favorite color. Silently, wallowing in the pleasures of conspiracy, we take the bead purse from its secret place and spill its contents on the scrap quilt. Dollar bills, tightly rolled and green as May buds. Somber fifty-cent pieces, heavy enough to weight a dead man's eyes. Lovely dimes, the liveliest coin, the one that really jingles. Nickels and quarters, worn smooth as creek pebbles. But mostly a hateful heap of bitter-odored pennies. Last summer others in the house contracted to pay us a penny for every twenty-five flies we killed. Oh, the carnage of August: the flies that flew to heaven! Yet it was not work in which we took pride. And, as we sit counting pennies, it is as though we were back tabulating dead flies. Neither of us has a head for figures; we count slowly, lose track, start again. According to her calculations, we have $12.73. According to mine, exactly $13. "I do hope you're wrong, Buddy. We can't mess around with thirteen. The cakes will fall. Or put somebody in the cemetery. Why, I wouldn't dream of getting out of bed on the thirteenth." This is true: she always spends thirteenths in bed. So, to be on the safe side, we subtract a penny and toss it out the window.

Of the ingredients that go into our fruitcakes, whiskey is the most expensive, as well as the hardest to obtain: State laws forbid its sale. But everybody knows you can buy a bottle from Mr. Haha Jones. And the next day, having completed our more prosaic shopping, we set out for Mr. Haha's business address, a "sinful" (to quote public opinion), fish-fry and dancing café down by the river. We've been there before, and on the same errand; but in previous years our dealings have been with Haha's wife, and iodine-dark Indian woman with brassy peroxided hair and a dead-tired disposition. Actually, we've never laid eyes on her husband, though we've heard that he's an Indian too. A giant with razor scars across his cheeks. They call him Haha because he's so gloomy, a man who never laughs. As we approach his café (a large log cabin festooned inside and out with chains of garish-gay naked light bulbs and standing by the river's muddy edge under the shade of river trees where moss drifts through the branches like gray mist) our steps slow down. Even Queenie stops prancing and sticks close by. People have been murdered in Haha's café. Cut to pieces. Hit on the head. There's a case coming up in court next month. Naturally these goings-on happen at night when the colored lights cast crazy patterns and the victrola wails. In the daytime Haha's is shabby and deserted. I knock at the door, Queenie barks, my friend calls: "Mrs. Haha, ma'am? Anyone to home?"

Footsteps. The door opens. Our hearts overturn. It's Mr. Haha Jones himself! And he *is* a giant; he *does* have scars; he *doesn't* smile. No, he glowers at us through Satan-tilted eyes and demands to know: "What you want with Haha?"

For a moment we are too paralyzed to tell. Presently my friend half-finds her voice, a whispery voice at best: "If you please, Mr. Haha, we'd like a quart of your finest whiskey."

His eyes tilt more. Would you believe it? Haha is smiling! Laughing, too. "Which one of you is a drinkin' man?"

"It's for making fruitcakes, Mr. Haha. Cooking."

This sobers him. He frowns. "That's no way to waste good whiskey." Nevertheless, he retreats into the shadowed café and seconds later appears carrying a bottle of daisy yellow unlabeled liquor. He demonstrates its sparkle in the sunlight and says: "Two dollars."

We pay him with nickels and dimes and pennies. Suddenly, jangling the coins in his hand like a fistful of dice, his face softens. "Tell you what," he proposes, pouring the money back into our bead purse, "just send me one of them fruitcakes instead."

"Well," my friend remarks on our way home, "there's a lovely man. We'll put an extra cup of raisins in *his* cake."

The black stove, stoked with coal and firewood, glows like a lighted pumpkin. Eggbeaters whirl, spoons spin round in bowls of butter and sugar, vanilla sweetens the air, ginger spices it; melting, nose-tingling odors saturate the kitchen, suffuse the house, drift out to the world on puffs of chimney smoke. In four days our work is done. Thirty-one cakes, dampened with whiskey, bask on window sills and shelves.

Who are they for?

Friends. Not necessarily neighbor friends: indeed, the larger share are intended for persons we've met maybe once, perhaps not at all. People who've struck our fancy. Like President Roosevelt. Like the Reverend and Mrs. J. C. Lucey, Baptist missionaries to Borneo who lectured here last winter. Or the little knife grinder who comes through town twice a year. Or Abner Packer, the driver of the six o'clock bus from Mobile, who exchanges waves with us every day as he passes in a dust-cloud whoosh. Or the young Wistons, a California couple whose car one afternoon broke down outside the house and who spent a pleasant hour chatting with us on the porch (young Mr. Wiston snapped our picture, the only one we've ever had taken). Is it because my friend is shy with everyone *except* strangers that these strangers, and merest acquaintances, seem to us our truest friends? I think yes. Also, the scrapbooks we keep of thank-you's on White House stationery, time-to-time communications from California and Borneo, the knife grinder's penny post cards, make us feel connected to eventful worlds beyond the kitchen with its view of a sky that stops.

Now a nude December fig branch grates against the window. The kitchen is empty, the cakes are gone; yesterday we carted the last of them to the post office, where the cost of stamps turned our purse inside out. We're broke. That rather depresses me, but my friend insists on celebrating—with two inches of whiskey left in Haha's bottle. Queenie has a spoonful in a bowl of coffee (she likes her coffee chicory-flavored and strong). The rest we divide between a pair of jelly glasses. We're both quite awed at the prospect of drinking straight whiskey; the taste of it brings screwed-up expressions and sour shudders. But by and by we begin to sing, the two of us singing different songs simultaneously. I don't know the words to mine, just: *Come on along, come on along, to the dark-town strutters' ball.* But I can dance: that's what I mean to be, a tap dancer in the movies. My dancing shadow rollicks on the walls; our voices rock the chinaware; we giggle: as if unseen hands were tickling us. Queenie rolls on her back, her paws plow the air, something like a grin stretches her black lips. Inside myself, I feel warm and sparky as those crumbling logs, carefree as the wind in the chimney. My friend waltzes round the stove, the hem of her poor calico skirt pinched between her fingers as though it were a party dress: *Show me the way to go home,* she sings, her tennis shoes squeaking on the floor. *Show me the way to go home.*

Enter: two relatives. Very angry. Potent with eyes that scold, tongues that scald. Listen to what they have to say, the words tumbling together into a wrathful tune: "A child of seven! whiskey on his breath! are you out of your mind? feeding a child of seven! must be loony! road to ruination! remember Cousin Kate? Uncle Charlie? Uncle Charlie's brother-in-law? shame! scandal! humiliation! kneel, pray, beg the Lord!"

Queenie sneaks under the stove. My friend gazes at her shoes, her chin quivers, she lifts her skirt and blows her nose and runs to her room. Long after the town has gone to sleep and the house is silent except for the chimings of clocks and the sputter of fading fires, she is weeping into a pillow already as wet as a widow's handkerchief.

"Don't cry," I say, sitting at the bottom of her bed and shivering despite my flannel nightgown that smells of last winter's cough syrup, "don't cry," I beg, teasing her toes, tickling her feet, "you're too old for that."

"It's because," she hiccups, "I *am* too old. Old and funny."

"Not funny. Fun. More fun than anybody. Listen. If you don't stop crying you'll be so tired tomorrow we can't go cut a tree."

She straightens up. Queenie jumps on the bed (where Queenie is not allowed) to lick her cheeks. "I know where we'll find real pretty trees, Buddy. And holly, too. With berries as big as your eyes. It's way off in the woods. Farther than we've ever been. Papa used to bring us Christmas trees from there: carry them on his shoulder. That's fifty years ago. Well, now: I can't wait for morning."

Morning. Frozen rime lusters the grass; the sun, round as an orange and orange as hot-weather moons, balances on the horizon, burnishes the silvered winter woods. A wild turkey calls. A renegade hog grunts in the undergrowth. Soon, by the edge of knee-deep, rapid-running water, we have to abandon the buggy. Queenie wades the stream first, paddles across barking complaints at the swiftness of the current, the pneumonia-making coldness of it. We follow, holding our shoes and equipment (a hatchet, a burlap sack) above our heads. A mile more: of chastising thorns, burs and briers that catch at our clothes; of rusty pine needles brilliant with gaudy fungus and molted feathers. Here, there, a flash, a flutter, an ecstasy of shrillings remind us that not all the birds have flown south. Always, the path unwinds through lemony sun pools and pitch vine tunnels. Another creek to cross: a disturbed armada of speckled trout froths the water round us, and frogs the size of plates practice belly flops; beaver workmen are building a dam. On the farther shore, Queenie shakes herself and trembles. My friend shivers, too: not with cold but enthusiasm. One of her hat's ragged roses sheds a petal as she lifts her head and inhales the pine-heavy air. "We're almost there; can you smell it, Buddy?" she says, as though we were approaching an ocean.

And, indeed, it is a kind of ocean. Scented acres of holiday trees, prickly-leafed holly. Red berries shiny as Chinese bells: black crows swoop upon them screaming. Having stuffed our burlap sacks with enough greenery and crimson to garland a dozen windows, we set about choosing a tree. "It should be," muses my friend, "twice as tall as a boy. So a boy can't steal the star." The one we pick is twice as tall as me. A brave handsome brute that survives thirty hatchet strokes before it keels with a creaking rending cry. Lugging it like a kill, we commence the long trek out. Every few yards we abandon the struggle, sit down and pant. But we have the strength of triumphant huntsmen; that and the tree's virile, icy perfume revive us, goad us on. Many compliments accompany our sunset return along the red clay road to town; but my friend is sly and noncommittal when passers-by praise the treasure perched in our buggy: what a fine tree and where did it come from? "Yonderways," she murmurs vaguely. Once a car stops and the rich mill owner's lazy wife leans out and whines: "Giveya two-bits cash for that ol tree." Ordinarily my friend is afraid of saying no; but on this occasion she promptly shakes her head: "We wouldn't take a dollar." The mill owner's wife persists. "A dollar, my foot! Fifty cents. That's my last offer. Goodness, woman, you can get another one." In answer, my friend gently reflects: "I doubt it. There's never two of anything."

Home: Queenie slumps by the fire and sleeps till tomorrow, snoring loud as a human.

A trunk in the attic contains: a shoebox of ermine tails (off the opera cape of a curious lady who once rented a room in the house), coils of frazzled tinsel gone gold with age, one silver star, a brief rope of dilapidated, undoubtedly dangerous candy-like light bulbs. Excellent decorations, as far as they go, which isn't far enough: my friend wants our tree to blaze "like a Baptist window," droop with weighty snows of ornament. But we can't afford the made-in-Japan splendors at the five-and-dime. So we do what we've always done: sit for days at the kitchen table with scissors and crayons and stacks of colored paper. I make sketches and my friend cuts them out: lots of cats, fish too (because they're easy to draw), some apples, some watermelons, a few winged angels devised from saved-up sheets of Hershey-bar tin foil. We use safety pins to attach these creations to the tree; as a final touch, we sprinkle the branches with shredded cotton (picked in August for this purpose). My friend, surveying the effect, clasps her hands together. "Now honest, Buddy. Doesn't it look good enough to eat?" Queenie tries to eat an angel.

After weaving and ribboning holly wreaths for all the front windows, our next project is the fashioning of family gifts. Tie-dye scarves for the ladies, for the men a home-brewed lemon and licorice and aspirin syrup to be taken "at the first Symptoms of a Cold and after Hunting." But when it comes time for making each other's gift, my friend and I separate to work secretly. I would like to buy her a pearl-handled knife, a radio, a whole pound of chocolate-covered cherries (we tasted some once, and she always swears: "I could live on them, Buddy, Lord yes I could—and that's not taking His name in vain"). Instead, I am building her a kite. She would like to give me a bicycle (she's said so on several million occasions: "If only I could, Buddy. It's bad enough in life to do without something *you* want; but confound it, what gets my goat is not being able to give somebody something you want *them* to have. Only one of these days I will, Buddy. Locate you a bike. Don't ask how. Steal it, maybe"). Instead, I'm fairly certain that she is building me a kite—the same as last year, and the year before: the year before that we exchanged slingshots. All of which is fine by me. For we are champion kite-fliers who study the wind like sailors; my friend, more accomplished than I, can get a kite aloft when there isn't enough breeze to carry clouds.

Christmas Eve afternoon we scrape together a nickel and go to the butcher's to buy Queenie's traditional gift, a good gnawable beef bone. The bone, wrapped in funny paper, is placed high in the tree near the silver star. Queenie knows it's there. She squats at the foot of the tree staring up in a trance of greed: when bedtime arrives she refuses to budge. Her excitement is equaled by my own. I kick the covers and turn my pillow as though it were a scorching summer's night. Somewhere a rooster crows: falsely, for the sun is still on the other side of the world.

"Buddy, are you awake?" It is my friend, calling from her room, which is next to mine; and an instant later she is sitting on my bed holding a candle. "Well, I can't sleep a hoot," she declares. "My mind's jumping like a jack rabbit. Buddy, do you think Mrs. Roosevelt will serve our cake at dinner?" We huddle in the bed, and she squeezes my hand I-love-you. "Seems like your hand used to be so much smaller. I guess I hate to see you grow up. When you're grown up, will we still be friends?" I say always. "But I feel so bad, Buddy. I wanted so bad to give you a bike. I tried to sell my cameo Papa gave me. Buddy—" she hesitates, as though embarrassed—"I made you another kite." Then I confess that I made her one, too; and we laugh. The candle burns too short to hold. Out it goes, exposing the starlight, the stars spinning at the window like a visible caroling that slowly, slowly daybreak silences. Possibly we doze; but the beginnings of dawn splash us like cold water: we're up, wide-eyed and wandering while we wait for others to waken. Quite deliberately my friend drops a kettle on the kitchen floor. I tap-dance in front of closed doors. One by one the household emerges, looking as though they'd like to kill us both; but its Christmas, so they can't. First, a gorgeous breakfast: just everything you can imagine—from flapjacks and fried squirrel to hominy grits and honey-in-the-comb. Which puts everyone in a good humor except my friend and I. Frankly, we're so impatient to get at the presents we can't eat a mouthful.

Well, I'm disappointed. Who wouldn't be? With socks, a Sunday school shirt, some handkerchiefs, a hand-me-down sweater and a year's subscription to a religious magazine for children. *The Little Shepherd*. It makes me boil. It really does.

My friend has a better haul. A sack of Satsumas, that's her best present. She is proudest, however, of a white wool shawl knitted by her married sister. But she *says* her favorite gift is the kite I built her. And it *is* very beautiful; though not as beautiful as the one she made me, which is blue and scattered with gold and green Good Conduct stars; moreover, my name is painted on it, "Buddy."

"Buddy, the wind is blowing."

The wind is blowing, and nothing will do till we've run to a pasture below the house where Queenie has scooted to bury her bone (and where, a winter hence, Queenie will be buried, too.) There, plunging through the healthy waist-high grass, we unreel our kites, feel them twitching at the string like sky fish as they swim into the wind. Satisfied, sun-warmed, we sprawl in the grass and peel Satsumas and watch our kites cavort. Soon I forget the socks and hand-me-down sweater. I'm as happy as if we'd already won the fifty-thousand-dollar Grand Prize in that coffee-naming contest.

"My, how foolish I am!" my friend cries, suddenly alert, like a woman remembering too late she has biscuits in the oven. "You know what I've always thought?" she asks in a tone of discovery, and not smiling at me but a point beyond. "I've always thought a body would have to be sick and dying before they saw the Lord. And I imagined that when He came it would be like looking at the Baptist window: pretty as colored glass with the sun pouring through, such a shine you don't know it's getting dark. And it's been a comfort: to think of that shine taking away all the spooky feeling. But I'll wager it never happens. I'll wager at the very end a body realizes the Lord has already shown Himself. That things as they are"—her hand circles in a gesture that gathers clouds and kites and grass and Queenie pawing earth over her bone—"just what they've always seen, was seeing Him. As for me, I could leave the world with today in my eyes."

This is our last Christmas together.

Life separates us. Those who Know Best decide that I belong in a military school. And so follows a miserable succession of bugle-blowing prisons, grim reveille-ridden summer camps. I have a new home too. But it doesn't count. Home is where my friend is, and there I never go.

And there she remains, puttering around the kitchen. Alone with Queenie. Then alone. ("Buddy dear," she writes in her wild hard-to-read script, "yesterday Jim Macy's horse kicked Queenie bad. Be thankful she didn't feel much. I wrapped her in a Fine Linen sheet and rode her in the buggy down to Simpson's pasture where she can be with all her Bones . . ."). For a few Novembers she continues to bake her fruitcakes single-handed; not as many, but some: and, of course, she always sends me "the best of the batch." Also, in every letter she encloses a dime wadded in toilet paper: "See a picture show and write me the story." But gradually in her letters she tends to confuse me with her other friend, the Buddy who died in the 1880's; more and more thirteenths are not the only days she stays in bed: a morning arrives in November, a leafless birdless coming of winter morning, when she cannot rouse herself to exclaim: "Oh my, it's fruitcake weather!"

And when that happens, I know it. A message saying so merely confirms a piece of news some secret vein had already received, severing from me an irreplaceable part of myself, letting it loose like a kite on a broken string. That is why, walking across a school campus on this particular December morning, I keep searching the sky. As if I expected to see, rather like hearts, a lost pair of kites hurrying toward heaven.

Appendix A

NELSON ALGREN

A BOTTLE OF MILK FOR MOTHER

I feel I am of them—
I belong to those convicts and prostitutes myself,
And henceforth I will not deny them—
For how can I deny myself?

WHITMAN

Two months after the Polish Warriors S.A.C. had had their heads shaved, Bruno Lefty Bicek got into his final difficulty with the Racine Street police. The arresting officers and a reporter from the *Dziennik Chicagoski* were grouped about the captain's desk when the boy was urged forward into the room by Sergeant Adamovitch, with two fingers wrapped about the boy's broad belt: a full-bodied boy wearing a worn and sleeveless blue work shirt grown too tight across the shoulders; and the shoulders themselves with a loose swing to them. His skull and face were shining from a recent scrubbing, so that the little bridgeless nose glistened between the protective points of the cheekbones. Behind the desk sat Kozak, eleven years on the force and brother to an alderman. The reporter stuck a cigarette behind one ear like a pencil.

"We spotted him followin' the drunk down Chicago——" Sergeant Comiskey began.

Captain Kozak interrupted. "Let the jackroller tell us how he done it hisself."

"I ain't no jackroller."

"What you doin' here, then?"

Bicek folded his naked arms.

"Answer me. If you ain't here for jackrollin' it must be for strong-arm robb'ry—'r you one of them Chicago Av'noo mollbuzzers?"

"I ain't that neither."

"C'mon, c'mon, I seen you in here before—what were you up to, followin' that poor old man?"

"I ain't been in here before."

Neither Sergeant Milano, Comiskey, nor old Adamovitch moved an inch; yet the boy felt the semicircle about him drawing closer. Out of the corner of his eye he watched the reporter undoing the top button of his mangy raccoon coat, as though the barren little query room were already growing too warm for him.

"What were you doin' on Chicago Av'noo in the first place when you live up around Division? Ain't your own ward big enough you have to come down here to get in trouble? What do you *think* you're here for?"

"Well, I was just walkin' down Chicago like I said, to get a bottle of milk for Mother, when the officers jumped me. I didn't even see 'em drive up, they wouldn't let me say a word, I got no idea what I'm here for. I was just doin' a errand for Mother 'n——"

"All right, son, you want us to book you as a pickup 'n hold you overnight, is that it?"

"Yes sir."

"What about this, then?"

Kozak flipped a spring-blade knife with a five-inch blade onto the police blotter; the boy resisted an impulse to lean forward and take it. His own double-edged double-jointed spring-blade cuts-all genuine Filipino twisty-handled all-American gut-ripper.

"Is it yours or ain't it?"

"Never see it before, Captain."

Kozak pulled a billy out of his belt, spread the blade across the bend of the blotter before him, and with one blow clubbed the blade off two inches from the handle. The boy winced as though he himself had received the blow. Kozak threw the broken blade into a basket and the knife into a drawer.

"Know why I did that, son?"

"Yes sir."

"Tell me."

" 'Cause it's three inches to the heart."

"No. 'Cause it's against the law to carry more than three inches of knife. C'mon, Lefty, tell us about it. 'N it better be good."

The boy began slowly, secretly gratified that Kozak appeared to know he was the Warriors' first-string left-hander: maybe he'd been out at that game against the Knothole Wonders the Sunday he'd finished his own game and then had relieved Dropkick Kodadek in the sixth in the second. Why hadn't anyone called him "Iron-Man Bicek" or "Fireball Bruno" for that one?

"Everythin' you say can be used against you," Kozak warned him earnestly. "Don't talk unless you want to." His lips formed each syllable precisely.

Then he added absently, as though talking to someone unseen. "We'll just hold you on an open charge till you do."

And his lips hadn't moved at all.

The boy licked his own lips, feeling a dryness coming into his throat and a tighening in his stomach. "We seen this boobatch with his collar turned inside out cash'n his check by Konstanty Stachula's Tonsorial Palace of Art on Division. So I followed him a way, that was all. Just break'n the old monotony was all. Just a notion, you might say, that come over me. I'm just a neighborhood kid, Captain."

He stopped as though he had finished the story. Kozak glanced over the boy's shoulder at the arresting officers and Lefty began again hurriedly.

"Ever' once in a while he'd pull a little single-shot of scotch out of his pocket, stop a second t' toss it down, 'n toss the bottle at the car tracks. I picked up a bottle that didn't bust but there wasn't a spider left in 'er, the boobatch'd drunk her dry. 'N do you know, he had his pockets *full* of them little bottles? 'Stead of buyin' hisself a fifth in the first place. Can't understand a man who'll buy liquor that way. Right before the corner of Walton 'n Noble he popped into a hallway. That was Chiney-Eye-the-Princinct-Captain's hallway, so I popped right in after him. Me'n Chiney-Eye 'er just like that." The boy crossed two fingers of his left hand and asked innocently, "Has the alderman been in to straighten this out, Captain?"

"What time was all this, Lefty?"

"Well, some of the street lamps was lit awready 'n I didn't see nobody either way down Noble. It'd just started spitt'n a little snow 'n I couldn't see clear down Walton account of Wojciechowski's Tavern bein' in the way. He was a old guy, a dino you. He couldn't speak a word of English. But he started in cryin' about how every time he gets a little drunk the same old thing happens to him 'n he's gettin' fed up, he lost his last three checks in the very same hallway 'n it's gettin' so his family don't believe him no more . . ."

Lefty paused, realizing that his tongue was going faster than his brain. He unfolded his arms and shoved them down his pants pockets; the pants were turned up at the cuffs and the cuffs were frayed. He drew a colorless cap off his hip pocket and stood clutching it in his left hand.

"I didn't take him them other times, Captain," he anticipated Kozak.

"Who did?"

Silence.

"What's Benkowski doin' for a living these days, Lefty?"

"Just nutsin' around."

"What's Nowogrodski up to?"

"Goes wolfin' on roller skates by Riverview. The rink's open all year round."

"Does he have much luck?"

"Never turns up a hair. They go by too fast."

"What's that evil-eye up to?"

Silence.

"You know who I mean. Idzikowski."

"The Finger?"

"You know who I mean. Don't stall."

"He's hexin' fights, I heard."

"Seen Kodadek lately?"

"I guess. A week'r two'r a month ago."

"What was he up to?"

"Sir?"

"What was Kodadek doin' the last time you seen him?"

"You mean Dropkick? He was nutsin' around."

"Does he nuts around drunks in hallways?"

Somewhere in the room a small clock or wrist watch began ticking distinctly.

"Nutsin' around ain't jackrollin'."

"You mean Dropkick ain't a jackroller but you are."

The boy's blond lashes shuttered his eyes.

"All right, get ahead with your lyin' a little faster."

Kozak's head came down almost neckless onto his shoulders, and his face was molded like a flatiron, the temples narrow and the jaws rounded. Between the jaws and the open collar, against the graying hair of the chest, hung a tiny crucifix, slender and golden, a shade lighter than his tunic's golden buttons.

"I told him I wasn't gonna take his check, I just needed a little change, I'd pay it back someday. But maybe he didn't understand. He kept hollerin' how he lost his last check, please to let him keep this one. 'Why you drink'n it all up, then,' I put it to him, 'if you're that anxious to hold onto it?' He gimme a foxy grin then 'n pulls out four of them little bottles from four different pockets, 'n each one was a different kind of liquor. I could have one, he tells me in Polish, which do I want, 'n I slapped all four out of his hands. All four. I don't like to see no full-grown man drinkin' that way. A Polak hillbilly he was, 'n certain'y no citizen.

" 'Now let me have that change,' I asked him, 'n that wasn't so much t'ask. I don't go around just lookin' fer trouble, Captain. 'N my feet was slop-full of water 'n snow. I'm just a neighborhood fella. But he acted like I was gonna kill him 'r something'. I got one hand over his mouth 'n a half nelson behind him 'n talked polite-like in Polish in his ear, 'n he begun sweatin' 'n tryin' t' wrench away on me. 'Take it easy,' I asked him. 'Be reas'nable, we're both in this up to our necks now.' 'N he wasn't drunk no more then, 'n he was plenty t' hold onto. You wouldn't think a old boobatch like that'd have so much stren'th left in him, boozin' down Division night after night, year after year, like he didn't have no home to go to. He pulled my hand off his mouth 'n started hollerin', *'Mlody bandyta! Mlody bandyta!'* 'n I could feel him slippin'. He was just too strong fer a kid like me to hold——"

"Because you were reach'n for his wallet with the other hand?"

"Oh, no. The reason I couldn't hold him was my right hand had the nelson 'n I'm not so strong there like in my left 'n even my left ain't what it was before I thrun it out pitchin' that double-header."

"So you kept the rod in your left hand?"

The boy hesitated. Then: "Yes sir." And felt a single drop of sweat slide down his side from under his armpit. Stop and slide again down to the belt.

"What did you get off him?"

"I tell you, I had my hands too full to get *anythin'*—that's just what I been tryin' to tell you. I didn't get so much as one of them little single-shots for all my trouble."

"How many slugs did you fire?"

"Just one, Captain. That was all there was in 'er. I didn't really fire, though. Just at his feet. T' scare him so's he wouldn't jump me. I fired in self-defense. I just wanted to get out of there." He glanced helplessly around at Comiskey and Adamovitch. "You do crazy thing sometimes, fellas—well, that's all I was doin'."

The boy caught his tongue and stood mute. In the silence of the query room there was only the scraping of the reporter's pencil and the unseen wrist watch. "I'll ask Chiney-Eye if it's legal, a reporter takin' down a confession, that's my out," the boy thought desperately and added aloud, before he could stop himself: "'N beside I had to show him——"

"Show him what, son?"

Silence.

"Show him what, Left-hander?"

"That I wasn't just another greenhorn sprout like he thought."

"Did he say you were just a sprout?"

"No. But I c'd tell. Lots of people think I'm just a green kid. I show 'em. I guess I showed 'em now all right." He felt he should be apologizing for something and couldn't tell whether it was for strong-arming a man or for failing to strong-arm him.

"I'm just a neighborhood kid. I belonged to the Keep-Our-City-Clean Club at St. John Cant'us. I told him polite-like, like a Polish-American citizen, this was Chiney-Eye-a-Friend-of-Mine's hallway. 'No more after this one,' I told him. 'This is your last time gettin' rolled, old man. After this I'm pertectin' you, I'm seein' to it nobody touches you—but the people who live here don't like this sort of thing goin' on any more'n you 'r I do. There's gotta be a stop to it, old man—'n we all gotta live, don't we?' That's what I told him in Polish."

Kozak exchanged glances with the prim-faced reporter from the *Chicagoski*, who began cleaning his black tortoise-shell spectacles hurriedly yet delicately, with the fringed tip of his cravat. They depended from a black ribbon; he snapped them back onto his beak.

"You shot him in the groin, Lefty. He's dead."

The reporter leaned slightly forward, but perceived no special reaction and so relaxed. A pretty comfy old chair for a dirty old police station, he thought lifelessly. Kozak shaded his eyes with his gloved hand and looked down at his charge sheet. The night lamp on the desk was still lit, as though he had been working all night; as the morning grew lighter behind him lines came out below his eyes, black as though packed with soot, and a curious droop came to the St. Bernard mouth.

"You shot him through the groin—zip." Kozak's voice came, flat and unemphatic, reading from the charge sheet as though without understanding. "Five children. Stella, Mary, Grosha, Wanda, Vincent. Thirteen, ten, six, six, and one two months. Mother invalided since last birth, name of Rose. WPA fifty-five dollars. You told the truth about *that,* at least."

Lefty's voice came in a shout: "You know *what?* That bullet must of bounced, that's what!"

"Who was along?"

"I was singlin'. Lone-wolf stuff." His voice possessed the first faint touch of fear.

"You said, 'We seen the man.' Was he a big man? How big a man was he?"

"I'd judge two hunerd twenty pounds," Comiskey offered, "at least. Fifty pounds heavier'n this boy, just about. 'N half a head taller."

"Who's 'we,' Left-hander?"

"Captain, I said, 'We seen.' Lots of people, fellas, seen him is all I meant, cashin' his check by Stachula's when the place was crowded Konstanty cashes checks if he knows you. Say, I even know the project that old man was on, far as that goes, because my old lady wanted we should give up the store so's I c'd get on it. But it was just me done it, Captain."

The raccoon coat readjusted his glasses. He would say something under a by-line like "This correspondent has never seen a colder gray than that in the eye of the wanton killer who arrogantly styles himself the *lone wolf of Potomac Street.*" He shifted uncomfortably, wanting to get farther from the wall radiator but disliking to rise and push the heavy chair.

"Where was that bald-headed pal of yours all this time?"

"Don't know the fella, Captain. Nobody got hair any more around the neighborhood, it seems. The whole damn Triangle went 'n got army haircuts by Stachula's."

"Just you'n Benkowski, I mean. Don't be afraid, son—we're not tryin' to ring in anythin' you done afore this. Just this one you were out cowboyin' with Benkowski on; were you help'n him'r was he help'n you? Did you'r him have the rod?"

Lefty heard a Ford V-8 pull into the rear of the station, and a moment later the splash of the gas as the officers refueled. Behind him he could hear Milano's heavy breathing. He looked down at his shoes, carefully buttoned all the way up and tied with a double bowknot. He'd have to have new laces mighty soon or else start tying them with a single bow.

"That Benkowski's sort of a toothless monkey used to go on at the City Garden at around a hundred an' eighteen pounds, ain't he?"

"Don't know the fella well enough t' say."

"Just from seein' him fight once 'r twice is all. 'N he wore a mouthpiece, I couldn't tell about his teeth. Seems to me he came in about one thirty-three, if he's the same fella you're thinkin' of, Captain."

"I guess you fought at the City Garden once 'r twice yourself, ain't you?"

"Oh, once 'r twice."

"How'd you make out, Left'?"

"Won 'em both on K.O.s. Stopped both fights in the first. One was against that boogie from the Savoy. If he woulda got up I woulda killed him fer life. Fer Christ I would. I didn't know I could hit like I can."

"With Benkowski in your corner both times?"

"Oh no, sir."

"That's a bloodsuck'n lie. I seen him in your corner with my own eyes the time you won off Cooney from the C.Y.O. He's your manager, jackroller."

"I didn't say he wasn't."

"You said he wasn't secondin' you."

"He don't."

"Who does?"

"The Finger."

"You told me the Finger was your hex-man. Make up your mind."

"He does both, Captain. He handles the bucket 'n sponge 'n in between he fingers the guy I'm fightin', 'n if it's close he fingers the ref 'n judges. Finger, he never losed a fight. He waited for the boogie outside the dressing room 'n pointed him clear to the ring. He win that one for me awright." The boy spun the frayed greenish cap in his hand in a concentric circle about his index finger, remembering a time when the cap was new and had earlaps. The bright checks were all faded now, to the color of worn pavement, and the earlaps were tatters.

"What possessed your mob to get their heads shaved, Lefty?"

"I strong-armed him myself, I'm rugged as a bull." The boy began to swell his chest imperceptibly; when his lungs were quite full he shut his eyes, like swimming under water at the Oak Street beach, and let his breath out slowly, ounce by ounce.

"I didn't ask you that. I asked you what happened to your hair."

Lefty's capricious mind returned abruptly to the word "possessed" that Kozak had employed. That had a randy ring, sort of: "What possessed you boys?"

"I forgot what you just asked me."

"I asked you why you didn't realize it'd be easier for us to catch up with your mob when all of you had your heads shaved."

"I guess we figured there'd be so many guys with heads shaved it'd be harder to catch a finger than if we all had hair. But that was some accident all the same. A fella was gonna lend Ma a barber chair 'n go fifty-fifty with her shavin' all the Polaks on P'tom'c Street right back of the store, for relief tickets. So she started on me, just to show the fellas, but the hair made her sicker 'n ever 'n back of the store's the only place she got to lie down 'n I hadda finish the job myself.

"The fellas begun giv'n me a Christ-awful razzin' then, ever' day. God oh God, wherever I went around the Triangle, all the neighborhood fellas 'n little niducks 'n old-time hoods by the Broken Knuckle, whenever they see me they was pointin' 'n laughin' 'n sayin', 'Hi, Baldy Bicek!' So I went home 'n got the clippers 'n the first guy I seen was Bibleback Watrobinski, you wouldn't know him. I jumps him 'n pushes the clip right through the middle of his hair—he ain't had a haircut since the alderman got indicted you—'n then he took one look at what I done in the drugstore window 'n we both bust out laughin' 'n laughin', 'n fin'lly Bible says I better finish what I started. So he set down on the curb 'n I finished him. When I go all I could off that way I took him back to the store 'n heated water 'n shaved him close 'n Ma couldn't see the point at all.

"Me 'n Bible prowled around a couple days 'n here come Catfoot Nowogrodski from Fry Street you, out of Stachula's with a spanty-new sideburner haircut 'n a green tie. I grabbed his arms 'n let Bible run it through the middle just like I done him. Then it was Catfoot's turn, 'n we caught Chester Chekhovka fer *him,* 'n fer Chester we got Cowboy Okulanis from by the Nort'western Viaduct you, 'n fer him we got Mustang, 'n fer Mustang we got John from the Joint, 'n fer John we got Snake Baranowski, 'n we kep' right on goin' that way till we was doin' guys we never seen before even, Wallios 'n Greeks 'n a Flip from Clark Street he musta been, walkin' with a white girl we done it to. 'N fin'lly all the sprouts in the Triangle start comin' around with their heads shaved, they want to join up with the Baldheads A.C., they called it. They thought it was a club you.

"It got so a kid with his head shaved could beat up on a bigger kid because the big one'd be a-scared to fight back hard, he thought the Baldheads'd get him. So that's why we changed our name then, that's why we're not the Warriors any more, we're the Baldhead True American Social 'n Athletic Club.

"I played first for the Warriors when I wasn't on the mound," he added cautiously, " 'n I'm enterin' the Gold'n Gloves next year 'less I go to collitch instead. I went to St. John Cant'us all the way through. Eight' grade, that is. If I keep on gainin' weight I'll be a hunerd ninety-eight this time next year 'n be five-foot-ten—I'm a fair-size light-heavy right this minute. That's what in England they call a cruiser weight you."

He shuffled a step and made as though to unbotton his shirt to show his proportions. But Adamovitch put one hand on his shoulders and slapped the boy's hand down. He didn't like this kid. This was a low-class Polak. He himself was a high-class Polak because his name was Adamovitch and not Adamowski. This sort of kid kept spoiling things for the high-class Polaks by always showing off instead of just being good citizens like the Irish. That was why the Irish ran the City Hall and Police Department and the Board of Education and the Post Office while the Polaks stayed on relief and got drunk and never got anywhere and had everybody down on them. All they could do like the Irish, old Adamovitch reflected bitterly, was to fight under Irish names to get their ears knocked off at the City Garden.

"That's why I want to get out of this jam," this one was saying beside him. "So's it don't ruin my career in the rope' arena. I'm goin' straight. This has sure been one good lesson fer me. Now I'll go to a big-ten collitch 'n make good you."

Now, if the college-coat asked him, "What big-ten college?" he'd answer something screwy like "The Boozological Stoodent-Collitch." That ought to set Kozak back awhile, they might even send him to a bug doc. He'd have to be careful—not *too* screwy. Just screwy enough to get by without involving Benkowski.

He scuffed his shoes and there was no sound in the close little room save his uneasy scuffling; square-toed boy's shoes, laced with a buttonhook. He wanted to look more closely at the reporter but every time he caught the glint of the fellow's glasses he felt awed and would have to drop his eyes; he'd never seen glasses on a string like that before and would have given a great deal to wear them a moment. He took to looking steadily out of the barred window behind Kozak's head, where the January sun was glowing sullenly, like a flame held steadily in a fog. Heard an empty truck clattering east on Chicago, sounding like either a '38 Chevvie or a '37 Ford dragging its safety chain against the car tracks; closed his eyes and imagined sparks flashing from the tracks as the iron struck, bounced, and struck again. The bullet had bounced too. Wow.

"What do you think we ought to do with a man like you, Bicek?"

The boy heard the change from the familiar "Lefty" to "Bicek" with a pang; and the dryness began in his throat again.

"One to fourteen is all I can catch fer manslaughter." He appraised Kozak as coolly as he could.

"You like farm work the next fourteen years? Is that okay with you?"

"I said that's all I could get, at the most. This is a first offense 'n self-defense too. I'll plead the unwritten law."

"Who give you *that* idea?"

"Thought of it myself. Just now. You ain't got a chance to send me over the road 'n you know it."

"We can send you to St. Charles, Bicek. 'N transfer you when you come of age. Unless we can make it first-degree murder."

The boy ignored the latter possibility.

"Why, a few years on a farm'd true me up fine. I planned t' cut out cigarettes 'n whisky anyhow before I turn pro—a farm'd be just the place to do that."

"By the time you're released you'll be thirty-two, Bicek—too late to turn pro then, ain't it?"

"I wouldn't wait that long. Hungry Piontek-from-by-the-Warehouse you, he lammed twice from that St. Charles farm. 'N Hungry don't have all his marbles even. He ain't even a citizen."

"Then let's talk about somethin' you couldn't lam out of so fast 'n easy. Like the chair. Did you know that Bogatski from Noble Street, Bicek? The boy that burned last summer, I mean."

A plain-clothes man stuck his head in the door and called confidently: "That's the man, Captain. That's the man."

Bicek forced himself to grin good-naturedly. He was getting pretty good, these last couple days, at grinning under pressure. When a fellow got sore he couldn't think straight, he reflected anxiously. And so he yawned in Kozak's face with deliberateness, stretching himself as effortlessly as a cat.

"Captain, I ain't been in serious trouble like this before . . ." he acknowledged, and paused dramatically. He'd let them have it straight from the shoulder now: "So I'm mighty glad to be so close to the alderman. Even if he is indicted."

There. Now they knew. He'd told them.

"You talkin' about my brother, Bicek?"

The boy nodded solemnly. Now they knew who they had hold of at last.

The reporter took the cigarette off his ear and hung it on his lower lip. And Adamovitch guffawed.

The boy jerked toward the officer: Adamovitch was laughing openly at him. Then they were all laughing openly at him. He heard their derision, and a red rain danced one moment before his eyes; when the red rain was past, Kozak was sitting back easily, regarding him with the expression of a man who has just been swung at and missed and plans to use the provocation without undue haste. The captain didn't look like the sort who'd swing back wildly or hurriedly. He didn't look like the sort who missed. His complacency for a moment was as unbearable to the boy as Adamovitch's guffaw had been. He heard his tongue going, trying to regain his lost composure by provoking them all.

"Hey, Stingywhiskers!" He turned on the reporter. "Get your Eversharp goin' there, write down I plugged the old rumpot, write down Bicek carries a rod night 'n day 'n don't care where he points it. You, I go around slappin' the crap out of whoever I feel like——"

But they all remained mild, calm, and unmoved: for a moment he feared Adamovitch was going to pat him on the head and say something fatherly in Polish.

"Take it easy, lad," Adamovitch suggested. "You're in the query room. We're here to help you, boy. We want to see you through this thing so's you can get back to pugging. You just ain't letting us help you, son."

Kozak blew his nose as though that were an achievement in itself, and spoke with the false friendliness of the insurance man urging a fleeced customer toward the door.

"Want to tell us where you got that rod now, Lefty?"

"I don't want to tell you anything." His mind was setting hard now, against them all. Against them all in here and all like them outside. And the harder it set, the more things seemed to be all right with Kozak: he dropped his eyes to his charge sheet now and everything was all right with everybody. The reporter shoved his notebook into his pocket and buttoned the top button of his coat as though the questioning were over.

It was all too easy. They weren't going to ask him anything more, and he stood wanting them to. He stood wishing them to threaten, to shake their heads ominously, wheedle and cajole and promise him mercy if he'd just talk about the rod.

"I ain't mad, Captain. I don't blame you men either. It's your job, it's your bread 'n butter to talk tough to us neighborhood fellas—ever'body got to have a racket, 'n yours is talkin' tough." He directed this last at the captain, for Comiskey and Milano had left quietly. But

Kozak was studying the charge sheet as though Bruno Lefty Bicek were no longer in the room. Nor anywhere at all.

"I'm still here," the boy said wryly, his lip twisting into a dry and bitter grin.

Kozak looked up, his big, wind-beaten, impassive face looking suddenly to the boy like an autographed pitcher's mitt he had once owned. His glance went past the boy and no light of recognition came into his eyes. Lefty Bicek felt a panic rising in him: a desperate fear that they weren't going to press him about the rod, about the old man, about his feelings. "Don't look at me like I ain't nowheres," he asked. And his voice was struck flat by fear.

Something else! The time he and Dropkick had broken into a slot machine! The time he and Casey had played the attention racket and made four dollars! Something! Anything else!

The reporter lit his cigarette.

"Your case is well disposed of," Kozak said, and his eyes dropped to the charge sheet forever.

"I'm born in this country, I'm educated here——"

But no one was listening to Bruno Lefty Bicek any more.

He watched the reporter leaving with regret—at least the guy could have offered him a drag—and stood waiting for someone to tell him to go somewhere now, shifting uneasily from one foot to the other. Then he started slowly, backward, toward the door: he'd make Kozak tell Adamovitch to grab him. Halfway to the door he turned his back on Kozak.

There was no voice behind him. Was this what "well disposed of" meant? He turned the knob and stepped confidently into the corridor; at the end of the corridor he saw the door that opened into the courtroom, and his heart began shaking his whole body with the impulse to make a run for it. He glanced back and Adamovitch was five yards behind, coming up catfooted like only an old man who has been a citizen-dress man can come up catfooted, just far enough behind and just casual enough to make it appear unimportant whether the boy made a run for it or not.

The Lone Wolf of Potomac Street waited miserably, in the long unlovely corridor, for the sergeant to thrust two fingers through the back of his belt. Didn't they realize that he might have Dropkick and Catfoot and Benkowski with a sub-machine gun in a streamlined cream-colored roadster right down front, that he'd zigzag through the courtroom onto the courtroom fire escape and—swish—down off the courtroom roof three stories with the chopper still under his arm and through the car's roof and into the driver's seat? Like that George Raft did that time he was innocent at the Chopin, and cops like Adamovitch had better start ducking when Lefty Bicek began making a run for it. He felt the fingers thrust overfamiliarly between his shirt and his belt.

A cold draft came down the corridor when the door at the far end opened; with the opening of the door came the smell of disinfectant from the basement cells. Outside, far overhead, the bells of St. John Cantius were beginning. The boy felt the winding steel of the staircase to the basement beneath his feet and heard the whining screech of a Chicago Avenue streetcar as it paused on Ogden for the traffic lights and then screeched on again, as though a cat were caught beneath its back wheels. Would it be snowing out there still? he wondered, seeing the whitewashed basement walls.

"Feel all right, son?" Adamovitch asked in his most fatherly voice, closing the cell door while thinking to himself: "The kid don't *feel* guilty is the whole trouble. You got to make them *feel* guilty or they'll never go to church at all. A man who goes to church without feeling guilty for *something* is wasting his time, I say." Inside the cell he saw the boy pause and go down on his knees in the cell's gray light. The boy's head turned slowly toward him, a pious oval in the dimness. Old Adamovitch took off his hat.

"This place'll rot down 'n mold over before Lefty Bicek starts prayin', boobatch. Prays, squeals, 'r bawls. So run along 'n I'll see you in hell with yer back broke. I'm lookin' for my cap I dropped is all."

Adamovitch watched him crawling forward on all fours, groping for the pavement-colored cap; when he saw Bicek find it he put his own hat back on and left feeling vaguely dissatisfied.

He did not stay to see the boy, still on his knees, put his hands across his mouth and stare at the shadowed wall.

Shadows were there within shadows.

"I knew I'd never get to be twenty-one anyhow," Lefty told himself softly at last.

A Commentary on Algren's "A Bottle of Milk for Mother"

In "A Bottle of Milk for Mother," Bruno Lefty Bicek, the young pitcher of the Polish Warriors S.A.C., and an aspiring boxer, makes his descent, step by step, into hell. At the beginning of the story he stands, a shorn Samson (the Warriors have all had their heads shaved), in the query room of the Racine Street police station before his accusers—Milano and Comiskey, the arresting officers; Sergeant Adamovitch, the fatherly turnkey; and Captain Kozak, "eleven years on the force and brother to an alderman." A prim-faced reporter in a raccoon coat from the *Dziennik Chicagoski* is also present. Lefty has been caught robbing a drunk of his pay in a precinct captain's hallway. The bullet he fired into the floor to scare the "boobatch" accidentally hit the old man in the groin, and he is dead; but at the beginning of the story Lefty doesn't know this. It is only revealed to him in the course of the interrogation, which takes the form of an impersonally cruel cancelling out of every one of the boy's hopes and dreams, his defenses.

Algren's story is built around several related conflicts which only gradually emerge in the course of the action. On the simplest level, perhaps, is the conflict between Lefty Bicek and Captain Kozak. In the course of the interrogation the Captain tries to make the boy confess his role in the robbery of the old man and also to implicate various members of the Polish Warriors S.A.C. We watch the Captain persist until he has enough to convict the boy, if not the others.

On a more complex level, and partly revealed by the lines from

Whitman which Algren has chosen as an epigraph for his story, is the conflict between the author and his society. It is clear that the indictment returned by Nelson Algren in "A Bottle of Milk for Mother" is not against Lefty Bicek but against a society which, failing to realize and accept the full measure of its responsibility, has turned its back on the boy and others like him. This is relatively easy to see from even a casual reading of the story, but to gather the full implication of what Algren is saying, and the full force of his art, we have to pay attention to his use of detail, character, and symbolic devices—as well as to the larger pattern of his fable.

As the interrogation of Lefty proceeds, and as it becomes more and more difficult for the youth to smile, the symbolic configuration of Algren's world emerges. For all the story's seeming realism, Algren uses reality as Dante did, and in some ways his effects are as startling as Dante's. Like Dante, Algren possesses an infernal vision.

Algren's figures, one should point out, are largely Roman Catholics, and the author uses Christian imagery to articulate the pattern of guilt which he sees behind the corruption of society. Social commentary and Christian motif are so interwoven in Algren's fiction as to be almost inseparable. This can be seen in the basic pattern which underlies "A Bottle of Milk for Mother," the symbolic reenactment of a portion of the Christ story, his denial and descent into hell. It is made explicit by the story's ending. His confession elicited and the questioning over, Lefty Bicek remains standing before the Captain's desk. The arresting officers have slipped out. The reporter, his notebook put away, is buttoning his coat. Captain Kozak is "studying the charge sheet as though Bruno Lefty Bicek were no longer in the room. Nor anywhere at all."

> "I'm still here," the boy said wryly, his lip twisting into a dry and bitter grin.
>
> Kozak looked up, his big, wind-beaten, impassive face looking suddenly to the boy like an autographed pitcher's mitt he had once owned. His glance went past the boy and no light of recognition came into his eyes. Lefty Bicek felt a panic rising in him: a desperate fear that they weren't going to press him about the rod, about the old man, about his feelings. "Don't look at me like I ain't nowheres," he asked. And his voice was struck flat by fear.

" 'Your case is well disposed of,' Kozak said, and his eyes dropped to the charge sheet forever." Lefty Bicek's earthly life is over. He will be led out of the interrogation room, into the corridor, and through the open door to the winding steel staircase and the cells below. Algren's Christ-figure begins his spiral descent down into the tiers of hell.

Algren's hero is a figure of adolescent mind and limited emotional experience. His mind is a hodge podge of dreams, schemes, plans: a cluster of tawdry hopes and aspirations pulled from the rag bag of American culture. Even the possibility of escape is conceived by him in terms of a crude B-grade movie, with his friends appearing in front of the police station with a sub-machine gun in a cream-colored roadster, while he makes a melodramatic run for it, zigzagging through the building and down a fire escape three stories into the roadster below. "Like that George Raft did that time he was innocent at the Chopin. . . ." Throughout "A Bottle of Milk for Mother" Lefty's thoughts are cast in a similar vernacular, revealing the fantasy world in which he privately lives, particularly his yearnings for recognition as ball player and boxer. He is secretly gratified that Captain Kozak seems to know that he is the Warrior's first-string pitcher, and he wonders if the Captain saw him play the Sunday he finished his own game and then relieved Dropkick Kodadek in the sixth inning of the second game. "Why hadn't anyone called him 'Iron-Man Bicek' or 'Fireball Bruno' for that one?" If Lefty is reluctant to discuss his occasional boxing career, it is only because he is aware that Captain Kozak is trying to link his handler, Benkowski, with the hold-up. At various times in the course of the story he goes into a boxer's shuffle. Once he is on the verge of unbuttoning his shirt to show off his chest; Adamovitch puts one hand on his shoulder and slaps the boy's hand down. But Lefty's irrepressible ego cannot really be beaten down. At once boyish and inoffensive, it keeps breaking in upon the awareness of the officers and the Captain, who would much rather dismiss the boy out of mind than have to acknowledge his humanity. In a profoundly moving way Lefty is Algren's symbolic reminder of the sanctity of the individual; he represents Algren's affirmation of the inviolable human spirit.

Like Fitzgerald's Jay Gatsby, Algren's Bruno "Lefty" Bicek is an essential innocent (it is surely the deliberate author who makes George Raft an innocent figure in the gangster film at the Chopin

Theater), and like Gatsby he is caught up in the national dream, though in "A Bottle of Milk for Mother" its form is somewhat cruder and its underlying realities are given more explicit statement than in *The Great Gatsby*. Lefty dreams of success by the traditional routes open to the newly arrived and the poor and the ill-educated, the fight ring and the ball park. In Algren's version of the story there is no fetching symbol, no Daisy Buchanan, to embody the Dream; there is no green light at the end of the dock to beckon romantically in the dark, no cascade of expensive and "beautiful shirts" for a Daisy to sob over. The overriding symbol is Lefty's shriven head, ready to receive its crown of thorns, while the symbolic objects of Lefty's world are a worn and sleeveless blue work shirt too tight across the shoulders, a pair of square-toed boy's shoes laced with a buttonhook, a pair of trousers with ragged, turn-up cuffs, and a frayed greenish cap which once had bright checks and earlaps (the crown of thorns).

In the course of Algren's story Lefty Bicek seems only dimly aware of the difference between right and wrong; he seemingly has no sense of guilt. (At the end of the story Sergeant Adamovitch—the name is symbolic—locks the boy in his cell. He asks him in his most fatherly voice, "Feel all right, son?" In his mind he is thinking: "The kid don't *feel* guilty is the whole trouble. You got to make them *feel* guilty or they'll never go to church at all. A man who goes to church without feeling guilty for *something* is wasting his time, I say.") Lefty makes no overt comment, either to the men in the police station or in his mind, to indicate that he understands such distinctions. Like Gatsby, he seems lacking in rudimentary moral knowledge. But Lefty does have an essential if limited understanding of how society operates in his world. One catches a reflection of this in his account of what he told his victim in Polish when he strong-armed him in the precinct captain's hallway. "I told him polite-like, like a Polish-American citizen, this was Chiney-Eye-a-Friend-of-Mine's hallway. 'No more after this one,' I told him. 'This is your last time gettin' rolled, old man. After this I'm pertectin' you, I'm seein' to it nobody touches you. . . .' " The Captain exchanges glances with the reporter from the *Chicagoski*, who nervously turns to cleaning his glasses, which depend from a black ribbon (and which impress the naïve Lefty). Both Kozak and the reporter understand what lies behind the boy's imitation of his elders.

The reporter is an important figure in Algren's world, not in himself, but for what he represents. A bored observer of the scene, he is the representative of the outside world, of all clean-living, right-thinking Poles. In the query room his major concern is his own comfort, particularly the chair he is sitting in, which he finds "a pretty comfy old chair for a dirty old police station." But the chair is too close to the wall radiator, the reporter is uncomfortably warm. He simply doesn't have the energy to move the heavy chair. Just how close he is to seeing the brinks of hell, he never realizes, and the true meaning of the events which transpire in the police station passes him by. He fails to appreciate the innocent nature of the bluff behind Lefty's refusal to involve his buddies. "I was singlin'. Lone-wolf stuff," the boy tells the Captain. At which the reporter, thinking out his news story in advance, writes in his mind: "This correspondent has never seen a colder gray than that in the eyes of the wanton killer who arrogantly styles himself *the lone wolf of Potomac Street.*" The reporter's disavowal of Lefty, his dismissal of the boy as a human being, is all the more obvious for being implied rather than stated. It is this evasion of responsibility, the denial of the boy's humanity, that lies at the root of Algren's indictment of society.

Ultimately Lefty Bicek's defiance, his tough but faked exterior, his opposition to authority, is based on Algren's profound awareness of the complicity of society in the criminal act. It is also based on his radical vision of the nature of authority. Like Dante, who placed his simonists in the reaches of hell, he is aware of the corruption at the heart of authority. In the climactic scene in "A Bottle of Milk for Mother" this becomes increasingly clear. Lefty makes his final appeal.

> "Captain, I ain't been in serious trouble like this before . . ." he acknowledged, and paused dramatically. He'd let them have it straight from the shoulder now: "So I'm mighty glad to be so close to the alderman. Even if he is indicted."
>
> There. Now they knew. He'd told them.
>
> "You talkin' about my brother, Bicek?"
>
> The boy nodded solemnly. Now they knew who they had hold of at last.

Lefty's appeal, of course, is greeted with derision. Significantly it is Sergeant Adamovitch who leads in the mockery of the boy. (He has already denied him in his mind: "He didn't like this kid. This was a low-class Polak. He himself was a high-class Polak because his name was Adamovitch and not Adamowski.") Adamovitch guffaws.

> The boy jerked toward the officer: Adamovitch was laughing openly at him. Then they were all laughing openly at him. He heard their derision, and a red rain danced one moment before his eyes; when the red rain was past, Kozak was sitting back easily, regarding him with the expression of a man who has just been swung at and missed and plans to use the provocation without undue haste.

Lefty then loses his composure, turns to the reporter ("Hey, Stingy-whiskers!") and yells: "Write down I plugged the old rumpot, write down Bicek carries a rod night 'n day 'n don't care where he points it. You, I go around slappin' the crap out of whoever I feel like—." He fails to provoke them, they all remain unmoved. The Captain resumes his questioning, but Lefty's mind has set against them all.

"A Bottle of Milk for Mother" ends with Lefty Bicek in his cell on his knees, his head a pious oval in the cell's gray light. Adamovitch thinks the boy is praying and he takes off his hat. Lefty responds: "This place'll rot down 'n mold over before Lefty Bicek starts prayin', boobatch. Prays, squeals, 'r bawls. So run along 'n I'll see you in hell with your back broke. I'm lookin' for my cap I dropped is all." Adamovitch watches Lefty grope for his cap, then leaves.

> He did not stay to see the boy, still on his knees, put his hand across his mouth and stare at the shadowed wall.
>
> Shadows were there within shadows.
>
> "I knew I'd never get to be twenty-one anyhow," Lefty told himself softly at last.

In achieving something like tragic eloquence for his now muted hero, Algren suggests a knowledge of good and evil, of guilt and punishment, which transcends the complacent proscriptions of society.

It could be said that Algren writes in what he has called "the antilegalistic tradition toward society which . . . distinguished Chicago writers since the early years of the century." Both *The American Tragedy* and *Native Son,* Algren points out in *Who Lost an American?*, were written in that tradition.

> Dreiser's method of challenging the legal apparatus and Wright's method were different, but the purpose of both was to demand that

> those economically empowered disprove their complicity in the crimes for which Clyde Griffiths and Bigger Thomas stood accused. Both writers made literature by demanding that the prosecuting attorney show his hands.

Yet neither this tradition, nor the broader one of American naturalism, in which his writing is usually placed, explains Algren's originality or the powerful effects he achieves with the sparsest of materials. The major source of his power lies elsewhere, as I have already suggested: in Algren's infernal vision and its radical use of the resources of Christian tradition. The epigraph to "A Bottle of Milk for Mother" is the lines from Whitman that run

I feel I am of them—
I belong to those convicts and prostitutes myself—
And henceforth I will not deny them—
For how can I deny myself?

If the idiom is highly personal (as is Algren's), the thoughts are nevertheless those of basic Christianity. They echo the New Testament and the words of Barabbas's and Mary Magdalene's Christ —just as Algren's stories and novels embody Christian themes and rework in various patterns fragments of the Christ story. In the closing scene of "A Bottle of Milk for Mother," Algren's universal man-child, his suffering god, overtly suggests Christ in Gethsemane. I am not maintaining for a minute that Algren writes systematic allegory, but I am suggesting that the symmetry of pattern in Algren's fiction has its roots in a deeper cultural source than the traditional underdog bias of social realism.

Finally, there is the form of "A Bottle of Milk for Mother": a spiralling form, an intense tiering downward. This Dantesque spiralling is symbolically mirrored at the end of the story in Lefty Bicek's descent down the winding steel staircase to the cells below; but throughout the story something like this spiral has operated in the narrative, providing pattern and depth to the seemingly random interrogation in the police station query room. The questioning circles and circles around the circumstances of the shooting of the old man, driving the boy inward and downward, alienating him from those in the room, placing him solely on his own limited resources.

We watch Lefty as he first reacts to the prodding of Captain

Kozak, who, his lips barely moving, remarks that Lefty will be held on open charge until he talks. "The boy licked his own lips, feeling a dryness coming into his throat and a tightening in his stomach." He begins to talk about seeing the old man cash his paycheck, stops as if he has finished his story, then resumes hurriedly as Kozak glances over the boy's shoulder at the arresting officer. Soon he realizes that his tongue is going faster than his brain, and he pauses. The Captain begins to question him about his friends, Benkowski and Nowogrodski and Idzikowski, with the obvious intention of making Lefty admit that one or more of them was in with him on the stickup. We become conscious of a small clock or a wrist watch somewhere in the room ticking away distinctly. Kozak tells the boy "to get ahead with your lyin' a little faster." Lefty then describes the scene in the hallway. The Captain asks him about the gun and Lefty feels "a single drop of sweat slide down his side from under his armpit. Stop and glide again down to the belt." A minute later and he is told that the old man is dead. Then the Captain returns relentlessly to the question of who was with him. Lefty replies that he was alone. But his voice has taken on "the first faint touch of fear." The questioning goes on, the Captain again probing for a way to make the boy admit that others were with him: Lefty feints and dodges, deflecting the questions as best he can, pretending he barely knows Benkowski, bluffing that he's not afraid of prison, yawning in their faces: each time more desperate, more naked, more empty inside—until the men in the query room are no longer interested in him. They have what they need to convict him, if not the others.

The questioning has swiftly carried the boy toward the pit from which there is no hope of deliverance. Lefty will never see his twenty-first birthday.

Questions

1. **Scene, setting, and situation all contribute to establishing the initial conflict between Lefty and the law. Why are Milano and Comiskey, the arresting officers, present? At what point do they disappear from the room? Why do they?**
2. **What is the meaning of the title? Is it in any way ironic? Does**

Lefty expect his explanation for being on the street near the scene of the crime to be accepted? If not, why does he offer it? What does it reveal about the character of the boy? Why isn't Lefty told immediately that the old man is dead? How else is suspense achieved? What, besides the ticking of a timepiece somewhere in the query room, makes us aware that time is running out on Lefty?

3. How does Algren describe the reporter from the *Dziennik Chicagoski*? What is the effect of such statements as: "the raccoon coat readjusted his glasses"?
4. What is significant about the name of the turnkey, old Adamovitch? More than once he is described as "fatherly." How is this related to his name? Is he fatherly? In what ways is Adamovitch like the reporter? How do both men reflect the conflict in the story?
5. What does "S.A.C." mean in "Polish Warriors S.A.C."? What other ethnic elements play a role in the story? Why is the movie house called the *Chopin*?
6. The commentary calls Lefty "an essential innocent." What precisely is meant by the term?
7. The commentary speaks of Algren's art as in the broad tradition of "American naturalism." What is meant by this?

Appendix B

A Student Discussion

IN THE pages which follow you will find a short story, Ernest Hemingway's "Old Man at the Bridge," together with the transcript of an actual discussion of the story by a small group of students and myself. The discussion is set down as it occurred, except for minor editing.

No discussion of fiction, including the one you are about to read, takes place in a vacuum, in a room sealed-off in time and space. For one thing, you bring to the discussion what you are—what your background is and what your training has been. You contribute your notions of the nature of fiction and also your understanding of the story, of the sequence of fact and the total meaning. And you respond to the group, as well as to the instructor. A discussion works because you make it work—and its success is revealed in the mesh of fact, comment, and opinion. A discussion has its own form.

In the case of Hemingway's "Old Man at the Bridge," the number and range of questions that can be raised about what is seemingly a very simple story may surprise you; yet none is irrelevant, and most lead to still other questions about the story. A good many deal with what could be called the technical side of fiction, its formal aspects, yet these questions, you will see, always turn back toward the meaning of the story. We are never very far removed from the central questions of what Hemingway is trying to say and how well he has said it.

The group was limited in size so that a student's voice could readily be identified on the recording tape, and also to insure the same degree of informality and freedom which a class, used to meeting regularly as a discussion group, usually achieves. All the participants were upper-division college students, though not all were English majors. Our discussion of "Old Man at the Bridge" illustrates in detail something like the process that goes on, often unconsciously, within the intelligent reader of fiction every time he reads a short story.

ERNEST HEMINGWAY

OLD MAN AT THE BRIDGE

An old man with steel rimmed spectacles and very dusty clothes sat by the side of the road. There was a pontoon bridge across the river and carts, trucks, and men, women and children were crossing it. The mule-drawn carts staggered up the steep bank from the bridge with soldiers helping push against the spokes of the wheels. The trucks ground up and away heading out of it all and the peasants plodded along in the ankle deep dust. But the old man sat there without moving. He was too tired to go any farther.

It was my business to cross the bridge, explore the bridgehead beyond and find out to what point the enemy had advanced. I did this and returned over the bridge. There were not so many carts now and very few people on foot, but the old man was still there.

"Where do you come from?" I asked him.

"From San Carlos," he said, and smiled.

That was his native town and so it gave him pleasure to mention it and he smiled.

"I was taking care of animals," he explained.

"Oh," I said, not quite understanding.

"Yes," he said, "I stayed, you see, taking care of animals. I was the last one to leave the town of San Carlos."

He did not look like a shepherd nor a herdsman and I looked at his black dusty clothes and his gray dusty face and his steel rimmed spectacles and said, "What animals were they?"

"Various animals," he said, and shook his head. "I had to leave them."

I was watching the bridge and the African looking country of the Ebro Delta and wondering how long now it would be before we would see the enemy, and listening all the while for the first noises that would signal that ever mysterious event called contact, and the old man still sat there.

"What animals were they?" I asked.

"There were three animals altogether," he explained. "There were two goats and a cat and then there were four pairs of pigeons."

"And you had to leave them?" I asked.

"Yes. Because of the artillery. The captain told me to go because of the artillery."

"And you have no family?" I asked, watching the far end of the bridge where a few last carts were hurrying down the slope of the bank.

"No," he said, "only the animals I stated. The cat, of course, will be all right. A cat can look out for itself, but I cannot think what will become of the others."

"What politics have you?" I asked.

"I am without politics," he said. "I am seventy-six years old. I have come twelve kilometers now and I think now I can go no further."

"This is not a good place to stop," I said. "If you can make it, there are trucks up the road where it forks for Tortosa."

"I will wait a while," he said, "and then I will go. Where do the trucks go?"

"Towards Barcelona," I told him.

"I know no one in that direction," he said, "but thank you very much. Thank you again very much."

He looked at me very blankly and tiredly, then said, having to share his worry with some one, "The cat will be all right, I am sure. There is no need to be unquiet about the cat. But the others. Now what do you think about the others?"

"Why they'll probably come through it all right."

"You think so?"

"Why not," I said, watching the far bank where now there were no carts.

"But what will they do under the artillery when I was told to leave because of the artillery?"

"Did you leave the dove cage unlocked?" I asked.

"Yes."

"Then they'll fly."

"Yes, certainly they'll fly. But the others. It's better not to think about the others," he said.

"If you are rested I would go," I urged. "Get up and try to walk now."

"Thank you," he said and got to his feet, swayed from side to side and then sat down backwards in the dust.

"I was taking care of animals," he said dully, but no longer to me. "I was only taking care of animals."

There was nothing to do about him. It was Easter Sunday and the Fascists were advancing toward the Ebro. It was a gray overcast day with a low ceiling so their planes were not up. That and the fact that cats know how to look after themselves was all the good luck that old man would ever have.

A Student Discussion of Hemingway's "Old Man at the Bridge"

Speakers: Tom—Thomas Fuchs
Jerry—Gerald Haggerty
Allan—Allan Hendrix
Linda—Linda Stein
Bonnie—Bonnie Gaines

Instructor: R. W. Lid

R. W. Lid *This is a discussion of Hemingway's "Old Man at the Bridge." The first question I want to ask is: Is this a story? Is this what you normally expect a story to look like? It is very short, some 750 words. So the question I raise right off is whether it is really a story or not.*

Allan *Well, it doesn't look like the normal story, it doesn't look like what you would expect, but I think it is a story.*

R. W. Lid *What do you normally expect a short story to look like?*

Allan *Oh, you expect a lot of action or at least a good amount of action, a plot that is fairly easy to follow—one in which you start at a point and end at a point.*

Tom *Is there a plot here?*

Allan *I think there is a plot here.*

Tom *Do we have to define "plot" or can we just discuss what this particular plot is and then maybe we'll have an idea of what "plot" is.*

Allan *That might be a good tack.*

Tom *I'm sorry I brought it up. /laughter/*

Linda *Allan means an action that reaches a conclusion. Makes a point.*

Jerry *Marks a change of character, perhaps.*

Tom *Yes, though that is not happening here. That is not in the particular effect in this story.*

Jerry *The story here, it seems, is one of the conflict that is going on within the old man's mind. Is he going to stay or is he going to leave as the enemy approaches? So in that sense, there is plot. There is this element of tension.*

R. W. Lid *Well, you are defining plot, then, to mean conflict. Am I right?*

Jerry *Well, that is one aspect of it.*

Linda *Resolution, also.*

R. W. Lid *A solution? Resolution?*

Linda *Well, if there has to be conflict for it to really be a plot, doesn't there have to be resolution?*

R. W. Lid *I don't know. Is there resolution here?*

Linda *Couldn't you say that nothing happens in this story? He is left right where he was found—the old man.*

R. W. Lid *Well, we have a story told by a young army scout whose job it is to locate the Fascist forces which are advancing toward the Ebro. He meets an old man who, too tired to walk farther, is sitting in the dust by a pontoon bridge. They talk awhile, our soldier-narrator interrogating the old man. Then the story comes to an end. But don't you feel that something has happened to the old man's life by the time the story is over? In other words, is he really in the same position as when the story started?*

Linda *Well, now he is there for good.*

R. W. Lid *You mean his life is over somehow?*

Linda *Somehow.*

R. W. Lid *The title of the story is "Old Man at the Bridge," and I suppose . . .*

Bonnie *"Bridge," I'm sure, is symbolic.*

R. W. Lid *Is symbolic? The easiest symbol to identify, I suppose. It's one indication that something decisive happens to the old man in the course of the story.*

Tom *He seems to have been jammed in this business. He speaks of the animals and he says the same thing over and over about the animals. And you can't really get a coherent statement out of him and yet perhaps. . . . You have the feeling after the story that this meeting has made him aware of his situation. But I think also the purpose of the story is to make us aware of the situation, which is a very important part of it. This is a pretty simple-minded thing to say, but that is the point of the story—to make us aware of his situation.*

R. W. Lid *Or predicament, I suppose.*

Tom *Right.*

R. W. Lid *Well, let's try to determine what his predicament is, then, more precisely.*

Jerry *It seems that is established in the first paragraph. It is the kind of thing another author would perhaps dwell on at some length. In the first sentence you learn his clothes are very dusty. This indicates that he has been on the road a long time. It is funny in a story this short that words like "dust" and "dusty" are repeated so often. They have at least overtones of the idea of "ashes to ashes" and "dust to dust." The emphasis seems to be on death. Of course the more literal meaning is that the old man has come a long way.*

Tom *The detail of the steel-rimmed spectacles is also important. The "dusty" tells what his immediate past has been. Perhaps the steel-rimmed spectacles say something of his earlier life.*

R. W. Lid *He is not a peasant, then?*

Bonnie *Probably not.*

Jerry *That is established later in the story, I think. He says that he did not look like a shepherd nor a herdsman.*

R. W. Lid *And he has been taking care of animals in his immediate village until thrust out of it. Are the animals his? Do you think that he owns them?*

Tom *You have the feeling the animals sort of wandered in and he began to take care of them. They are not his. They are his in the sense that no one else is taking care of them but—when he leaves they'll manage. They are not his property.*

Jerry *Some of them will manage and some of them won't.*

Tom *Right.*

R. W. Lid *One question we have to answer is: Why is he taking care of the animals?*

Linda *Because somebody has to take care of them. You are never told exactly why, at least not in so many words.*

Tom *Also he has no family, apparently.*

Linda *Well, also that seems to be sort of his reason for being. He is the "animal taker carer of." /laughter/*

R. W. Lid *There are three kinds of animals—pigeons, cats, and goats. He is more concerned with the pigeons, I guess, and the goats, isn't he, than the cats? What I'm wondering is whether these animals are in any way symbolic animals. How do they figure in the story? I noticed that when the narrator talks about the birds' escape—their cage has been left unlocked and they will fly away under the noise of the artillery—they are called "doves," which deliber-*

	ately brings in the idea of the "doves of peace." I was wondering about the other animals.
Linda	*Could the goats be domestic animals that need people to survive and the cat could be more of a wild animal?*
R. W. Lid	*Of course you think of goats as hardy animals.*
Jerry	*You think of them also, however, in the terms of scapegoat.*
R. W. Lid	*Scapegoat? Maybe that is the sense here, then.*
Jerry	*This parallels the way Hemingway uses the pigeons. The fact that he calls them pigeons in the beginning and then refers to a dove cage tends to emphasize the shift in meaning. In a story this short, with a craftsman like Hemingway, I don't think he would violate point of view for no reason.*
R. W. Lid	*So you can assume, from this kind of evidence, that the animals function on another level than merely being animals? I suppose this brings us back to the question of why the old man is taking care of them.*
Tom	*Well, I think it is partly because he has nothing else to do. He has no family. This gives him something to do. It is a duty, a way of life.*
Allan	*The interrogator says, "And you have no family," and he says, "No. Only the animals, I have stated." There is a sort of suggestion that this might be his family, these animals. This is a feeling.*
Tom	*I think that is part of it.*
R. W. Lid	*Well, if they are kind of a substitute family, it does say something about the old man, then, about why he is taking care of them?*
Linda	*He needs them as much as they need him.*
Allan	*Actually they are almost more important to him than he is to them because the cat can get away, the birds will fly away. The goats are left all alone but . . .*

Bonnie *Did we establish whether there was a meaning behind "cat"?*

R. W. Lid *No, we really didn't.*

Linda *He says the cat can take care of itself at the end.*

Bonnie *Well, there is the old saying that a cat has nine lives.*

R. W. Lid *That is true, too.*

Bonnie *Which echoes the ability to survive.*

Jerry *Well, if the cat has nine lives, certainly the old man doesn't. I don't think there is any question that, after the story is over, he is going to die.*

Allan *He seems almost equated with the goats.*

Linda *More than with the other animals?*

Allan *Yes, because as he said the cat can get away. He's not worried about the cat. The pigeons, he says, will certainly fly. The only ones left are the others, and he says it is better not to think about the others. He is in sort of the same situation.*

R. W. Lid *It is better not to think about old men such as this one, caught in the war?*

Tom *Stuck in the war!*

R. W. Lid *Earlier we talked briefly about the action in the story. Most of the story is simply an interrogation, isn't it, between the old man and the young scout, in other words a verbal action. Is there any other action that we can find in the story?*

Bonnie *Well, there is the background action of the trucks which are mentioned at the beginning and which are gone, which have continued over the bridge and disappeared, I believe, at the end.*

R. W. Lid *So that by the end of the story you simply have no trucks at all on the landscape.*

Tom *There is one detail which fascinates me about the descrip-*

tion of the trucks. "The trucks ground up and away," Hemingway says, "heading out of it all," as though this is an area to be gotten away from. That is something—heading out of it all, clearing out.

Jerry *There is no way for the old man to get away at the end.*

R. W. Lid *What do you think the equivalent of this background action would be if this story, or say a similar story, one with the same theme, had been written by another author?*

Allan *Well, it would be longer. There would be much more of it.*

R. W. Lid *That's true, though I had something else in mind here. In most stories we usually get complication and rising action, often in considerable detail. I wonder if the background action here is in any way the equivalent of what another, more traditional writer might provide by spinning his story out and drawing you up. Here you know that by the time the entire landscape has thinned, and contact is made with the enemy, the old man's life will be over. (Pause) What about foreground action? Is there any?*

Allan *Well, in the second paragraph. "It was my business to cross the bridge, explore the bridge head beyond and find out to what point the enemy advanced. I did this and returned to the bridge." That is foreground action or preliminary action, anyway, indicating a great amount of time really.*

R. W. Lid *Yet it is all condensed in two sentences.*

Allan *Yes, in two sentences, two fairly short sentences. And even in the next sentence, he develops the foreground action in a way by describing the scene at the bridge. "There were not so many carts now and very few people on foot, but the old man was still there." I think that Hemingway is laying out the foreground action for the whole story. From then on we don't hear about it until the very end but we have to realize it is going on.*

Bonnie *By "don't hear about it" do you mean that it is not echoed again? Because later the movement is echoed when he says that a few carts were hurrying over the slope of the bank at the end of the bridge. And then, later still, the narrator says that there are no carts visible at all.*

Allan *Yes, this would sort of reinforce the notion. Keep it in our mind, I suppose. I hadn't noticed that.*

Jerry *As a matter of fact, that seems the most important action in the story in a way. Each time the carts are mentioned, time is emphasized. It keeps being brought up to the reader.*

R. W. Lid *Is there any other physical action that we could focus on?*

Bonnie *There is where he sits back down again.*

R. W. Lid *All right. At the end of the story the old man tries to rise, stands up, wavers a minute, and then sits back down in the dust.*

Bonnie *Why?*

R. W. Lid *All right, why? Why does he flop back down?*

Tom *Well, I think that signals his realization that he is not going anywhere.*

Bonnie *Or is it because he is tired?*

Allan *This is the climax of the conventional story, I think. Everything beyond this is denouement, letdown, to make a bad pun. This is the point where his mind is made up.*

R. W. Lid *Could it be that this is the complete action of many stories in a particular way? In its own terms, I'm suggesting, the old man's dumb show of rising and flopping back down in the dust is the equivalent of four acts of a Shakespearean tragedy. Of course this is only a "fragment of an* agon.*" But there is a reversal of situation, isn't there?*

Linda *There is a moment of indecision, I think, when he sways from side to side.*

R. W. Lid *Well, if this is true, then the crucial question becomes one of why the old man sat back down, doesn't it? We still haven't really answered that question.*

Linda *He just couldn't stand up any more.*

Jerry *It says in the story that he was too tired to go any farther.*

Linda *But that means he is too tired to stay alive any more.*

Jerry *Yes, I wonder what the author means to imply by "too tired."*

Linda *Too tired to try to keep on living, perhaps.*

Jerry *Is he too tired physically?*

Linda *That depends on what Hemingway means.*

Jerry *I realize that. That is what I meant.*

R. W. Lid *In other words, is he too tired physically or mentally? Well, perhaps "point of view" will help us with our question. The story is told from the narrator's point of view.*

Bonnie *This is part of the reason, I think, we're having trouble with the question. Because the narrator does not have the ability to look into the old man's mind. So you never learn.*

R. W. Lid *So you never know whether it's mental or physical fatigue. What would you just guess if you were given a choice?*

Tom *Well, do you have to decide between one or the other? I think what happens happens because the man is an old man. I suppose what generally happens is that physical tiredness and mental tiredness come at the same time, acting upon each other. Mainly, when a man gets old and finds it hard to do things, he also gets tired mentally when he is in a situation which requires physical strength. He can't do it and he starts getting tired.*

Jerry *Well, there is also the suggestion in the story that he is tired of living. He is tired of seeing events like war. He is without politics and he is still the victim of the war, just like the animals are.*

R. W. Lid *We've said that the writer never lets you inside the old man's mind. Well, why doesn't he? If he wanted to, and you must assume that the writer has a range of possibilities, he could let you in.*

Bonnie *Well, the old man is a symbol and if the writer desired to let the reader see what is in his mind, this might destroy his value as a symbol.*

R. W. Lid *Why would it do that?*

Linda *Because if you explain everything it is not a symbol anymore. /laughter/*

Jerry *Also, by not letting you directly inside the old man's mind, he, in effect, allows you to think the old man's thoughts for him.*

Bonnie *I don't know whether this is significant or not but everything the old man says is condensed. He doesn't seem to want to say very much. Everything he says is short and abrupt.*

R. W. Lid *Well, how articulate is he? How used to talking like this is he?*

Tom *Apparently he is in a state of shock, a shell-shocked state, and is reduced to this.*

Linda *He hasn't been talking to people very much lately. Just animals.*

R. W. Lid *Could you say that part of Hemingway's achievement here is that for once one of the inarticulate mass of humanity, the goats, gets a chance to talk, even if he is only minimally articulate?* (*Pause*) *This brings us to a central question: What is it Hemingway is trying to do in this story?*

Tom *Well, it is a real problem with this story. It is certainly effective on the literal level. That is to say, if you just saw this happen in the order it does here, you would be impressed with the man's condition, but now we have been talking about sort of the symbolic level. Now does that reinforce the literal level? Or does the literal level reinforce . . . ? What is happening? What is the relationship between those two?*

R. W. Lid *Are there really other levels here?*

Tom *Well, certainly Hemingway wants us to think so at the end. Either that or he is just being cutely ironic. But I think there is more, definitely.*

Jerry *It would seem a pretty pointless story if there wasn't.*

Tom *Well, no. It would still work. It would still be interesting if you just told a little sketch of something the narrator had seen from war. That would be interesting.*

Jerry *But then it wouldn't be a story. It would be a sketch.*

Tom *All right, is there some kind of very general inference that we can draw from this story?*

Linda *Is he trying to suggest something perhaps about the human condition? Not just this old man but that this is what everybody comes down to. The people up on the plains, the advancing army. The people with all the machinery and everything. They are going to come down to being in just this kind of situation eventually.*

Allan *The war context had something to do with this, I think.*

R. W. Lid *The futility of all of it?*

Allan *The fact that the man is caught. He has nothing to do with the war. It is none of his business at all and yet it affects him, you have to assume, rather profoundly. It ends his life. He has nothing to say about it at all.*

Linda *Well, could Hemingway be considering the pathos of*

people who are involved in things they don't want to be involved in? Or is he commenting on everyone who is involved in the war, saying that they are in some way involved in futility like the old man?

Allan *I think that maybe both are operating in a strange sort of way. You can draw both out. Because of Easter Sunday. Wouldn't he be bringing that in to sort of reflect on all humanity, to make it more universal?*

R. W. Lid *The ironic condition that almost 2,000 years after Christ's death people are still killing each other? (Pause) Well, do we have two war stories going here and one is related to that background and one is related to the foreground? I wonder, or is that too neat?*

Linda *You mean the wars between the two armies and then the war between the armies and the people they have to trample? Their own people. You can't consider people like that!*

Jerry *The narrator sees the results of somebody who has no politics, the most generalized human figure being crossed by both sides. He has no opportunity . . .*

R. W. Lid *That is a good phrase. He is a generalized human figure, isn't he?*

Linda *That is why the narrator has to forget about the old man, people like that.*

R. W. Lid *So the narrator isn't really indifferent or cold, but it is a case of what he has to do?*

Linda *He is fighting for humanity, not for separate people.*

Tom *Well, the narrator says there was nothing to do about the old man.*

R. W. Lid *Yes. And we assume from the fact that he is telling the story that he is not indifferent but he is not an engaged narrator in any sense of the word, is he?*

Tom	*He is very much engaged in this big big movement. He has got something that he has to do.*
Jerry	*He has to go back and report what he has seen, too, if he is a scout.*
Tom	*Right.*
Jerry	*The rest of whatever Army he is working with depends, at least in part, on his information. He can't really take a lot of time to talk with the old man or to carry him to a truck or anything like that.*
R. W. Lid	*How good a story do you think this is?*
Tom	*Well, what is your standard?*
Jerry	*Well, whatever it is, it has certainly brought up a lot of discussion for something so short.*
R. W. Lid	*Well, I just wonder. How do we go about evaluating a story like this?*
Tom	*Well, I think the first thing is, you read it as intelligently and as fair-eyed as you can. If it moves you, if it has an effect on you, then you know that something has happened in the story, and to find out how it happened, you go back and look. And if something really did happen, then it is a good story.*
Allan	*Isn't it a good story if it is successful in bringing out what Hemingway wants it to bring out?*
Tom	*I don't know about that. That is part of it. I would say that what he wanted to do was to move you. Because if he just wanted to make a statement, he could have said "war is hell." And he could have summed up the basic events of the story perhaps in two or three lines, but he wanted to have all the harmonics of it. He wanted you to really feel it.*
Allan	*But it isn't simply a tear-jerker, Tom.*
Tom	*Oh, no. No! No!*

R. W. Lid *By the way, it is the only tear-jerker Hemingway ever wrote, though.*

Allan *Well, it is close to a tear-jerker, but there is more to it than that, I think.*

R. W. Lid *Yes, there is; and the story can only be called a "tear-jerker" in comparison with Hemingway's other stories.*

Jerry *If he had the old man burst into tears and say "war has done this to me," and the narrator make some kind of comment at the end like, "I had to go back to my outfit but I felt sorry for the old man," well, it certainly wouldn't have done the story any good.*

R. W. Lid *No, it wouldn't have. It says something about Hemingway's art, the restraint he practised.*

Tom *This is a very deceptive story in the sense that you can just start it and read it right through. It is short, you read it very quickly. But a lot of things have happened to you if you have actually read each line. And that is part of the art.*

R. W. Lid *Does the fact that the story is largely dialogue affect you at all?*

Tom *It may be more dialogue than description in terms of inches but that description is extremely important.*

R. W. Lid *Yes, it is.*

Tom *And he sets that up first. He gets the trucks, he gets the old man, placed; he gets the narrator placed; he gets the trucks moving; and then you can talk.*

R. W. Lid *Does the dialogue slow the story down or speed it up?*

Tom *I think if anything the dialogue, in terms of pace or speed, slows it up.*

R. W. Lid *It slows things down a great deal, doesn't it?*

Allan *He does a funny thing with language that tends to slow it down even further. He's got this strange construction, strange language.*

Linda *It sounds like he is translating from Spanish.*

Jerry *I think that is just what he is doing. He wrote this way in a great many stories.*

Linda *Yes, I know.*

R. W. Lid *Then he wants you to feel you are listening to Spanish being spoken?*

Linda *I think that he succeeds. For me, anyway.*

Jerry *Well, I've never taken a course in Spanish, and as far as I'm concerned it merely sounds strange to me.*

Allan *Well, that is enough, though.*

Linda *It sounds formal. It sounds strangely formal. I don't know Spanish that well, but I have a feeling that Spanish is like that. That even the peasants speak very formally although the things they say are simple. They have a certain dignity.*

R. W. Lid *The old man's language, then, has a kind of dignified air to it. Perhaps this helps give the old man the stature that Hemingway wants him to have.*

Jerry *This dialogue doesn't function like a lot of dialogues that I have read. It doesn't reveal a lot about the speakers, about their personality.*

Tom *Well, there is a lot of short sentences and also repetition. The word "animal" must come up fifteen times—I haven't counted them. In that respect I think the dialogue very much represents the man's condition.*

Jerry *Well, it represents his condition but it doesn't represent a lot about his personality.*

R. W. Lid *You have the generalized old man again with a few generic traits?*

Jerry	*All the dialogue reveals is his condition, not his personality.*
Tom	*Well, wait a minute. I don't think there is much personality left, because if you get tired enough, there isn't much personality left, and this man is very, very tired.*
Jerry	*I'm sure the old man would feel he had a personality.*
R. W. Lid	*Well, I don't know. I don't think the writer gave him very much.*
Tom	*Well, that is true, too. Because it probably would have been distracting from the main part of the story.*
R. W. Lid	*Or would have complicated things beyond what a story this short can handle? We are back again, aren't we, with the question of how good a story this is?*
Allan	*It is a very short story, but it is also very well done. We get the meat of what Hemingway is trying to say. And the extraneous is completely cut out.*
Tom	*This story has nothing in it which strikes me as being wrong. There is nothing here which I can't believe. Hemingway succeeded for me. He set up this little world, right down by the bridge, and nothing happens in the story which violates the situation.*
R. W. Lid	*So that it is believable, or carries an air of authenticity with it which you don't dispute?*
Tom	*And none of the details destroy that authenticity.*
Jerry	*And there is no detail which seems extraneous to the author's purpose, either. I think that is really important.*
R. W. Lid	*I don't know if I should dwell on this question of how good a story this is, since it is proving to be a difficult question for us to handle, and I don't know if there is any way to get at it easily here.*
Jerry	*Well, you might ask whether the story is flawed or unflawed. It is easier to find fault with a story.*

R. W. Lid *All right. Let's try the reverse. Is this story flawed?*

Linda *In the last paragraph I think he could have been less heavy-handed. I think he deviated from his method. He could have suggested Easter, somehow, in a more integral way.*

R. W. Lid *It occurs that Easter isn't really integral at all, then?*

Linda *No, it is sort of an after-thought, and so is the business about cats in the last sentence.*

R. W. Lid *In the last paragraph the narrator, or perhaps the author, gets in very directly, doesn't he? "There was nothing to do about him. It was Easter Sunday and the Fascists were advancing toward the Ebro. It was a gray overcast day with a low ceiling so their planes were not up. That and the fact that cats know how to look after themselves was all the good luck that the old man would ever have."*

Tom *Why is it Easter Sunday?*

R. W. Lid *That is a good question.*

Tom *I think it is more than just locking the matter in as an historical fact that on that day of the year the Fascists reached the Ebro. Probably there is something more to it than just that. Is there something about goats and Christian symbolism, or is this getting out of hand?*

Linda *Scapegoat, but that is as much . . .*

R. W. Lid *Well, the Christian scapegoat, too.*

Linda *That is Christ.*

Jerry *The doves are certainly very obvious Christian symbols.*

Tom *But what do we do with the cat?*

R. W. Lid *It won't fit in. So you are faced with what happens when you try to make everything fit too neatly.*

Linda *I don't think the old man is a Christ symbol, really, because he seems to be dying like the animals for no reason.*

Tom *Of course, that could be a suggestion that that is what happens to Christ figures.*

Jerry *It seems important that the old man is not dying for a cause. He isn't a hero. He is . . .*

Tom *He is getting smashed. That is what is happening. He is getting bowled over.*

R. W. Lid *Do you think the writer is worried that the reader might have missed his point?*

Linda *And that is why he put in the last paragraph?*

Jerry *It reiterates what a lot of readers have probably suspected from reading. It comes out right and states that the old man will have no more life. His time is, in effect, up.*

R. W. Lid *Is it necessary, do you think? Or is this a worried writer?*

Jerry *It depends upon how closely someone reads the story.*

Linda *You mean, is it necessary because the rest of the story is insufficient?*

R. W. Lid *"Does it add anything?" is what I think I'm asking.*

Linda *It seems like he is deviating from his method in the rest of his story.*

Bonnie *I don't think it really adds anything. I think it reinforces what he has already said.*

R. W. Lid *Is it ironic?*

Linda *It is trying to be ironic, I think.*

Jerry *I think that in writing the story it might have been perhaps more effective if Hemingway had ended with the trucks leaving in the distance. That would have then framed the rest between the opening description of the trucks, there and waiting, with the possibility of hope, and their leaving, the last hope that he could have taken advantage of.*

Tom — *Let's see now. The last line of dialogue says, " 'I was taking care of animals,' he said dully, but no longer to me. 'I was only taking care of animals.' " Hemingway could end the story there but perhaps he doesn't want to.*

Jerry — *He could have used that sentence and then said, "In the distance he could see the dust rising from the wheels of the trucks."*

Tom — *The real problem, I'm suggesting, is that any ending tends to be kind of a sledge hammer. No matter where he leaves it, it just might be too gross.*

Linda — *Or too sentimental.*

Tom — *I suggest that you could not have the last line of the story be, "There was nothing to do about him." You could not have that as the last line. A certain kind of energy has been built up, immediate energy has been built up, and I suggest that it has to be tapered off slightly for the story to end.*

R. W. Lid — *So there are reasons for that ending even if it is not the best ending then?*

Tom — *Something had to be there, I think.*

R. W. Lid — *The attempt is to be ironic and hence not allow the tears to flow. And yet to us it seems so heavy-handed?*

Linda — *With the story this short, also, I think it would have to end with some kind or narration, not dialogue, because it started with narration.*

Jerry — *Well, perhaps he could have done what he did in several other stories. In the last couple of lines the narrator simply would tell what happened to himself. "I rode off and we engaged the enemy two days later."*

Linda *I think that would be a better way to end it than has been suggested so far.*

Tom *And, yet, we've thought of something we think is a better ending, but Hemingway knew an awfully lot more about it than we do, even though sometimes, as they say, a writer can't see his work as clearly as someone else.*

Linda *We would have to talk to him for a better ending, Tom.*

Tom *Nevertheless Hemingway knew an awfully lot more about it than I do. Why did he make this mistake, then, if you are going to call it a mistake?*

Linda *Maybe he couldn't prevent it somehow.*[1]

R. W. Lid *Let me raise one last question about Hemingway's art in "Old Man at the Bridge." Is the story perhaps as short as it is because Hemingway is relying on a literary convention to help him? Is there any parallel with, say, the sonnet form, for example?*

Tom *The sonnet draws on tremendous convention. One word, one phrase, draws on an enormous amount of literature.*

Jerry *You can have a poem like Ezra Pound's "In a Station of the Metro" that is one line, two lines, I guess.*

Allan *Three lines.*

Tom *Well, American Indians used to write poems that were half lines because their poetry drew on well-defined conventions.*

Linda *Well, doesn't this, too?*

[1] Our trouble in deciding whether the last paragraph was good or bad, necessary or unnecessary, stemmed in part from our failure to see that it made the story unique. To put it another way, the ending gives the story its form. This becomes rather a subtle matter because, until this point in the story, the form—the narrator's growth of awareness about the old man, his movement toward understanding—has been implied, not stated. Hemingway has not explicitly traced its course through the story. It is only the last paragraph which makes explicit the depth to which the old man's predicament has penetrated the narrator's consciousness.

Tom	*What conventions does this draw on?*
Linda	*As a poem uses imagery, this uses recurrent words, and of course, symbols.*
Tom	*But we mentioned the sonnet. A sonnet is only fourteen lines long, and yet a lot can be done. A phrase in a sonnet can refer to a whole set of feelings. Sonnets of the Elizabethan period drew on tremendous literature. You knew what to think about a phrase. You knew what to think, and that was as far as the poet took it. Or sometimes he would turn it on you, and you would start out thinking, I'm supposed to think this, and by the end he had turned it around. But here I'm wondering what convention Hemingway is drawing on.*
Jerry	*The convention of the short story.*
Tom	*Wait a minute. He is not drawing. I'm trying to say it is possible that Hemingway has invented a convention.*
Allan	*I don't think he has invented one, but he is drawing on a different sort of convention. It is not literary, it's . . .*
R. W. Lid	*You mean you conjure up certain things when someone says "old man"?*
Allan	*Yes, certain things, a whole set of feelings.*
Jerry	*Well, I wonder in reading the story if you don't have to write a lot of it yourself to make it fit the traditional notion of a short story, really. You aid the author.*
R. W. Lid	*And you've read enough stories to do a lot of aiding actually.*
Tom	*Lots of things are aiding—the movies, for example, but a lot of that stuff is because of Hemingway. What do you know about the Spanish Civil War except what you've learned through Hemingway?*
Jerry	*To turn back to the short story form, Joyce wrote his stories almost thirty years, I guess, before this story was written.*

Tom *At least. This is a very late Hemingway story.*

Jerry *Certainly he is drawing on the short story convention which goes even beyond Joyce.*

Tom *I think a lot of it goes right back to Hemingway, is my point.*

R. W. Lid *It's an interesting theory.*

Tom *It is the world of Hemingway, you know.*

R. W. Lid *Well, on that note, I think we should close our discussion.*[1]

[1] Let me point out that the convention on which Hemingway's art depends in "Old Man at the Bridge" is the traditional story he chose not to write. He simply left out, omitted, everything that wasn't essential. But the real art of "Old Man at the Bridge" lies not so much in omission as in the selection of detail and the uses to which that detail is put. The story bears certain broad resemblances to a news dispatch, particularly in its seemingly factual nature. It might conceivably be taken by some readers to be simply a piece of good reporting—except that behind the reporting lies the calculation of art. The objective quality of the story, in other words, is deceiving; for Hemingway employs the Flaubertian art of illuminated detail, of exterior landscape used to reveal the interior of the mind. The old man's worry about the cat and the goats and the pigeons seems an apparently trivial concern in the face of his own dilemma—until we realize why he is so concerned about them. Let me also suggest one point about our conception of the old man as a "generalized human figure" and his involvement in the war. Much of Hemingway's astonishing originality derives from his creation of his own symbolic patterns out of the raw stuff of contemporary experience. Finally, a word about "the world of Hemingway." Some aspects of it are represented by our story of course, but to explore that world in any depth we would need to discuss other Hemingway stories, and perhaps his novels as well. As it is, we have explored one dimension of that world in considerable detail in "Old Man at the Bridge." One aspect of the story has escaped us, however, and this is one which none of my students was equipped to discuss. Indeed, this aspect of fiction in general has caused professional critics a good deal of trouble. This is the question of the subtle and complex relationship between a work of fiction and the dual figures of the author-as-man and the author-as-writer. I would only suggest here, without offering any evidence to support my view, that ultimately Hemingway saw himself as the old man in the story we have just discussed.—Think about it, at least. If it leads you to ask further questions, then you are on the way to understanding the art of the short story.